S0-ATR-804

THE ILLUSTRATED ENCYCLOPEDIA OF SCIENCE AND TECHNOLOGY

HOW IT WORKS

Volume 11

**LOCK —
MINE**

Editor	Ralph Hancock	Artwork Researcher	Karen Gunnell
Art Editor	Gillian Allan	Chief Picture Researchers'	Clive Andrews
Deputy Editor	Vanessa Galvin		Zilda Tandy
Editors	Mike Bisacre	Picture Researchers	Warwick Clarke
	Donald Clarke		Leo Cronin
	Rob Gough		William Fisher
	Jinty Lentier		John McGilley
	Robin Scargell	Picture Clerks	Heather Peter
	Ian Wood		Jackie Rustin
Designers	Clive Dorman	Editorial Secretaries	Loraine Beckford
	Lesley Munday		Julia Bye

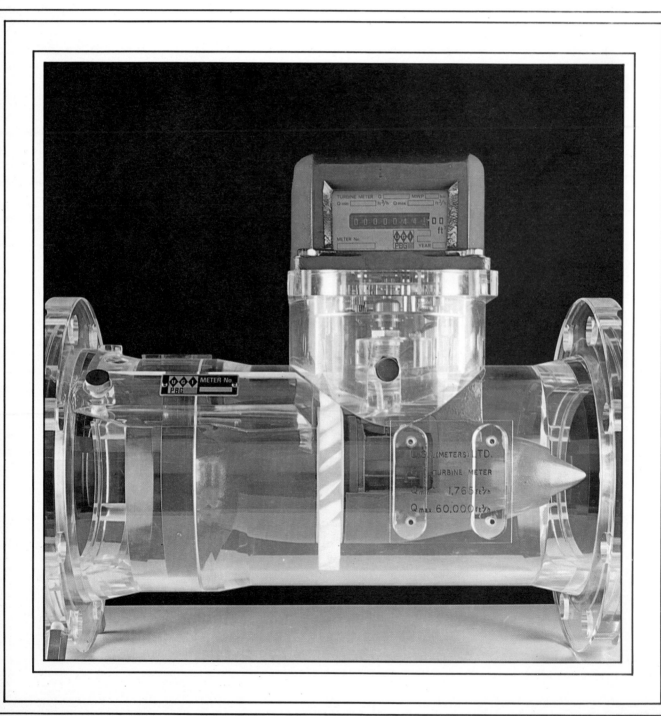

THE ILLUSTRATED ENCYCLOPEDIA OF SCIENCE AND TECHNOLOGY

HOW IT WORKS

New Caxton Library Service

Volume 11
Contents

LOCK, door	1389
LOCK, water	1392
LOCOMOTIVE	1394
LOGARITHM	1401
LOGIC CIRCUITS	1402
LONGBOW	1406
LONG RANGE GUN	1408
LOOM	1410
LOUDSPEAKER	1414
LUBRICATION	1417
LUBRICATION SYSTEM, car	1419
LUMIERE, L & A	1421
LUMINESCENCE	1422
MACHINE GUN	1424
MACHINE TOOLS	1426
MAGNETIC TAPE	1431
MAGNETISM	1432
MAGNETO	1438
MAGNETOHYDRODYNAMICS	1439
MAGNETOMETER	1442
MANOMETER	1443
MANUFACTURED BOARD	1445
MAP MAKING TECHNIQUES	1447
MARCONI, Guglielmo	1450
MAREY, Etienne Jules	1451
MARGARINE PRODUCTION	1452
MARINE PROPULSION	1454
MARSHALLING YARDS	1457
MASS and WEIGHT	1461
MASS-ENERGY EQUIVALENCE	1463
MASS SPECTROSCOPY	1464
MATCH manufacture	1466
MATHEMATICS	1469
MATTER, properties of	1473
MAUDSLAY, Henry	1476
MAXIM, Sir Hiram	1477
MAXWELL, James Clerk	1478
MEMORY DEVICES	1479
MENDELEEV, Dmitrii	1482
MERCURY	1483
METAL	1485
METAL DETECTORS	1488
METEOROLOGY	1491
METER, electricity	1497
METER, gas	1499
METER, parking	1501
METRONOME	1502
MICROENCAPSULATION	1503
MICROFILM	1504
MICROMETER	1507
MICROPHONE	1508
MICROPHOTOGRAPHY	1512
MICROSCOPE	1513
MICROTOME	1517
MICROWAVES	1519
MILKING MACHINE	1523
MINCER, meat grinder	1525
MINE, explosive	1526

This edition published 1977

© Marshall Cavendish Limited 1974, 1977
58 Old Compton Street
London W1V 5PA

Printed in Great Britain by
Colorgraphic Limited, Leicester

SBN 903322 17 x

LOCK, door

The earliest known mechanical fastening for doors is the wooden Egyptian lock, in use four thousand years ago. Specimens have been found in the pyramids, and this type of lock is depicted in ancient bas-relief sculptures. It is a pin-tumbler type in which the bolt is hollowed out; the key is a curved, flattened wooden stick with pins projecting from the end. When the key is inserted into the lock and levered upwards, the pins push upward on pins projecting down into the bolt from a fixed staple, allowing the bolt to be withdrawn. These locks were made up to two feet (60 cm) long.

A variation on this type of lock, in which the key reaches the pins through a hole in the staple rather than in the bolt, was used until the twentieth century in Scandinavia, the remoter parts of Scotland and other countries. In this version the bolt is withdrawn separately rather than with the key.

Another prevalent type of ancient lock, found in China and other parts of the world, is a padlock which works on a *spring barb* principle. The bolt has an indentation (sometimes a reverse projection) into which a *leaf spring* snaps and is held fast. The key, a plain strip of metal, is slid in, depressing the spring, drawing the barbs together and releasing them from the indentation so that the bolt can be withdrawn.

Yet another primitive lock is a *screw action* padlock. Here the key is an ordinary male screw, and as it is turned the barrel is withdrawn and the shackle released. This was used throughout Europe, and is still made in Persia.

From these descriptions it is easy to see that the early locks were no more than an inconvenience to the burglar. The first locks made of metal which attempted to provide security by requiring a key of peculiar configuration were the *warded* locks, first made by the Romans and common in Europe by the thirteenth century. The wards are obstructions inside the lock; the *bit* of the key must be made to bypass the wards of the particular lock. The sliding or pushing motion of the key now gave way to the familiar modern turning motion. Sometimes the keys were made pipe-shaped to fit over a fixed pin, in which case the lock could be operated from one side only, or else they were made solid with a projecting bit which could enter the lock from either side. The Romans made keys small enough to be worn as finger rings.

Lock making now became a skilled trade, and an extraordinary range of ward designs were produced. Sometimes they were combined with springs to hold the bolt shut, against which the key was turned. A *back-spring* lock was produced in which a key, passing the wards, pushed the spring off the bolt with a clicking sound; this lock was actually less secure than the ancient Egyptian lock because the bolt could be forced back by any pressure applied to its end. *Skeleton keys* could be made which would open a variety of warded locks. Wards and keys became more fancy and elaborate, and additional

Right: diagrams of several types of locks. At the top is the ancient Egyptian wooden lock. When the 'key' is levered upwards, the pins in the staple are raised, allowing the bolt (with the key in it) to be withdrawn. Second from top: a warded lock mechanism. The bit of the key must be machined to match the wards, allowing the key to be turned. Third from top: the familiar Yale lock, invented in 1848 by Linus Yale and in wide use all over the world today. The serrations in the edge of the key must match the length of the lower halves of the spring-loaded pins; the pins act as wards. Fourth from top: a combination lock. The numbers must be correctly lined up before the bolt can be withdrawn.

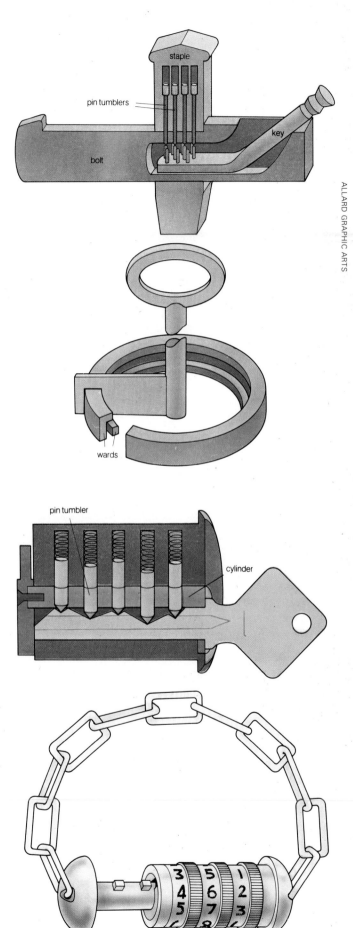

security was provided by hiding the keyhole behind secret panels, sometimes with the provision of a dummy keyhole to sidetrack the lock-picker. There were also warded locks with many bolts, operated by levers moved by the main bolt; these are sometimes found on old trunks, but do not offer extra security since only one bolt need be picked.

Modern locks The security provided by modern locks began in the eighteenth century, when the *tumbler* lock was invented. Basically, the tumbler is a latch or pawl which fits into a slot on the bolt; the key lifts the latch. In its simplest form, the tumbler can be raised by a skeleton key, but in 1778 the Englishman Robert Barron invented the *double-action tumbler*, in which two (later, more than two) tumblers must be raised, each to exactly the right height to clear its slot. (If any tumbler is raised too high, it catches in another slot above, so that the bolt still cannot be drawn.) This was the great modern advance in lock security, and the multiple tumbler is still the basis of most locks made today. An interesting variant on the Barron tumbler lock was the detector device, patented by Jeremiah Chubb in 1818, also still in use today. If this type of lock is tampered with, a tumbler stays in the raised position, so that the bolt cannot be withdrawn until the correct key is turned backwards. This gives notice to the keyholder that someone has been trying to open the lock with the wrong key.

The *Bramah lock*, like the Barron double-tumbler lock, was invented in the eighteenth century. This lock is operated by a pipe-shaped key with notches of varying lengths. The lock

Below: an Egyptian wooden lock of the type in use four thousand years ago. The long horizontal part is the hollowed-out bolt. When the key is levered upwards, the pins push up the fixed pins in the staple, allowing the bolt to be drawn.

Top right: a bronze lock-plate and hasp, from the Roman period in France.

Lower right: an illustration from the first encyclopedia, the eighteenth century compilation of Diderot. The ironwork of the period is very impressive; the lock in the lid of this box operates no fewer than twelve bolts against spring pressure. Since only one lock need be picked, however, the number of bolts adds little in the way of security, except that the lid would be difficult to pry open with a lever.

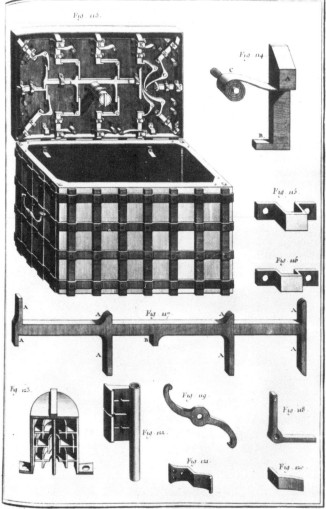

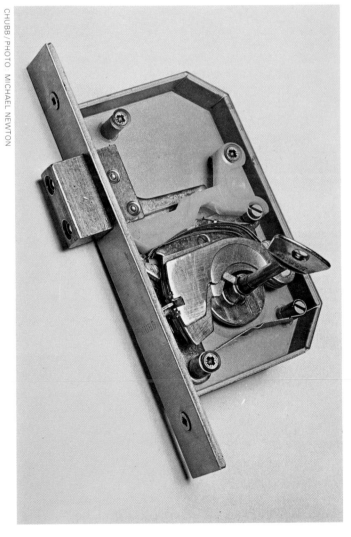

includes a notched diaphragm plate and a number of spring-loaded radial slides. The notched key pushes the slides down until they match with the notches on the diaphragm, allowing the cylindrical barrel of the lock to be turned.

Nowadays the most common lock used to fasten the front doors of houses is the *Yale lock*, a cylindrical pin-tumbler design which combines the best features of many locks, including the ancient Egyptian wooden one. It was invented in 1848 by Linus Yale, an American from Connecticut, and improved by his son. The rotation of the *plug* in the cylinder is prevented by five pins which extend down into the plug, the same way the pins extend into the hollowed-out bolt of the Egyptian lock. The pins are divided into upper and lower halves; the lower half of each is called the tumbler and the upper half is called the *driver*. Each tumbler is a different length from the others, and the same is true of the driver halves. Only a key with the correct serrations can lift all five tumblers to the correct height to allow the plug to turn, thus operating the bolt. The pin-tumblers are spring-loaded so that they are always in the locking position except when the proper key is inserted. The Yale lock is fairly difficult to pick and offers reasonable security under ordinary circumstances.

Combination locks The bolt or shackle in a combination lock has slots in it. A number of rings [tumblers] are provided with numbers or letters around the outside, and projections on the inside, which fit the slots. The rings must be lined up correctly in order for the shackle to be withdrawn. If the lock has three rings with one hundred numbers on each, there are a million possible combinations, only one of which will open the lock. The combination lock has been known in Europe since at least the sixteenth century, and its origins are lost; the modern variety has a dial on the front which is turned back and forth until the rings inside are lined up. Most combination locks are designed so that the combination can be changed occasionally for security.

Safes Safes usually have combination locks because these have no keyhole into which explosives can be inserted to 'blow' the safe. Sometimes they also have time-lock devices, so that they cannot be opened during certain hours even by someone who has the combination. The most secure safes today depend on alloy steel cladding which can only be burned through by electric arc cutting torches after many hours of work.

Electronic lock In the 1970s, some buildings in the United States were being made secure during closing hours by an electronic lock which works on the same principle as the push-button ('touch-tone') telephone. Telephone company properties in particular are using this type of lock. It has several spring-loaded buttons on the outside, each of which sounds a different electronic tone when it is pushed. The right sequence of tones operates the lock. The advantages of this type of lock for properties which must allow access to repair and maintenance personnel at odd hours are that no keys are required, the lock is as tamper-proof as a combination lock, and the 'combination' sequence can be easily and frequently changed for greater security.

Top left: a modern mortise lock. This type can be operated by a key from the outside or by a spring-operated lever from the inside, and double-locked by a pin on the inside.

Lower left: an electronic apartment-house security device. When a caller is identified, the person in the flat pushes a button, and an electromagnet operates the bolt.

LOCK, water

A boat on a canal or river, or entering a dock, may have to be passed from one level to another. The simplest device which can do this is a *pound* (or *chamber*) lock. The general form of the modern lock is that of an open-topped chamber, with water-tight gates at each end. Once the boat is inside, the gates are shut and the water level in the lock then rises or falls (depending on whether the boat is ascending or descending). When the water in the chamber has reached the right level, the appropriate gate is opened to allow the boat to leave the lock.

Locks have a history of at least two thousand years, although the earliest were not pound locks. One factor limiting the navigability of rivers is the depth of water and to increase this, dams were often built. Part of each dam was removable, permitting boats to be winched upstream through the gap, or swirled downstream by the current. The removable part is called a *flash lock*; the entire structure, a *navigation weir*. Its use was two-fold: the impounded water not only increased upstream depths, but could also be released in a surge to assist vessels in shallow water downstream. Locks of this type existed in China in 70 AD, and their use later spread as they were built into water-mill weirs as well. Although this reduced disputes between millers and boatmen, these could not be settled until the adoption of the pound lock, whose closed chamber minimizes the water loss from the higher level. In 984, the first known example of a pound lock was built in China, and was operated by raising or lowering gates at each end (now called *guillotine gates*). Europe's earliest pound lock which can be dated precisely was built in 1373 at Vreeswijk,

Holland, and also had guillotine gates.

Most modern locks have an improved type of gate invented by Leonardo da Vinci in the fifteenth century for a canal in Milan, Italy. These gates turn on hinges, like doors, and each end of the lock has two such gates which meet to form a vee pointing upstream, giving them the name *mitre gates*. England's first pound locks with mitre gates were built in 1567 on the Exeter Canal.

One advantage of mitre gates is that since the vee shape points upstream, they are self sealing. When there is a difference in water level between one side and the other, the pressure holding the gates together is at its greatest.

Ancient locks were often built entirely of wood, but stone or brick chambers later became standard. Gates were usually of wood, lasting up to 50 years. To fill and empty the lock, hand-operated sluices were fitted to the gates, but it was later found that mounting these in conduits bypassing the gates gave a smoother water flow.

Where steep rises have to be negotiated, locks are built contiguously, with the upper gates of one acting as the lower gates of the next. The resulting structure is called a *staircase* and many examples exist from 'two-steps' (three sets of gates) to the mighty 'Neptune's Staircase' on the Caledonian Canal, Scotland, which consists of eight locks condensed into one structure with nine sets of gates.

Construction Modern lock construction can readily be seen to represent a refinement of older types, with concrete usually used for the chamber and welded steel for the gates. Hydraulic power or electricity is used to operate the gates and

ALLARD GRAPHIC ARTS

balance beam

coping stones

sluice control

lock chamber

upper level

lower gate

lower level

sluice inlet

upper gates

sluice outlet

sill

brick lined bottom

sluices. As locks have grown in size to admit larger vessels, so, on canals, the problem of the water lost from higher to lower levels has increased. To overcome this, pumping may be employed, or *economizer locks* built. These have small reservoirs alongside the chamber to store some of the water emptied from it. This water is later used to refill the lock. The outstanding examples of this type are on the Rhine-Main-Danube Canal which will link Germany's waterways to those of southeastern Europe. Here, multiple side-reservoirs allow savings of up to 60% of the lock water. The locks are 623 ft (190 m) long, 39 ft (12 m) wide and have rises up to 81 ft (25 m).

In the mid-nineteenth century, locks rarely had rises above 30 ft (9 m), but today's largest has a rise of 138 ft (42 m). This is at Ust-Kamenogorskiy, USSR, and lifts 1600 ton vessels past a hydroelectric dam on the River Irtish. The chamber, 328 ft (100 m) long and 56 ft (17 m) wide, takes about half an hour to fill or empty. The lower gate does not extend for the full height; it moves vertically to seal a 'tunnel' through which ascending vessels pass to enter the lock.

The Panama Canal also has large locks, especially remarkable as it was opened in 1914. These have mitre gates up to 82 ft (25 m) high and can accommodate vessels 1000 ft (305 m) long

Above right: this flight or 'staircase' of locks is on the Rideau Canal near Ottawa, Canada. The mitre gates are operated by winches, which can be seen at one side, rather than by hand, but even so the time involved in passing through the flight is considerable.

Below: most locks on small canals need muscle power to operate gates, such as this one on the Canal d'Ille et Rance at Tinteniac in Brittany, France.

Below right: an early drawing, dating from 1438, of a guillotine gate. This is a simple sluice, for raising and controlling the water level, and boats had to be manhandled overland around it.

Left: cross section of a canal lock. To fill the lock chamber the upper paddles are opened and those in the lower gates closed. Water can now flow in from the upper canal level. When the chamber is full the upper gates open and a boat can move inside. To reach the lower level the upper paddles and gates are closed and lower paddles opened, the excess water flowing out to the lower part of the canal. When the lower gates open the boat can pass on down the canal.

ROBERT ESTALL

STAATSBIBLIOTHEK BERLIN

JOHN WATNEY

and 110 ft (34 m) wide, taking only eight minutes to fill or empty.

Gates Early dock entrance locks closely resemble eighteenth century canal locks, having brick or masonry chambers, timber mitre gates and manual operation. A dock entrance lock rarely needs a rise exceeding 20 ft (6 m), but the draught of ocean going vessels requires that the gates be very deep. Modern gates are of several types: many are mitre gates but others are hinged along their lower edge (flap gates), moved sideways on rails (traversing caissons), or are floated into place (floating caissons). All are of hollow welded steel construction, permanently ballasted with concrete. Operating ballast may also be required: this is provided by pumping water in or out of the interior of the gate to sink or float it.

Although deep water terminals are replacing enclosed docks for the largest ships, many massive dock entrances exist. Enclosed docks are unnecessary if the tidal range is less than about 12 ft (4 m), so there are many major ports without entrance locks. Typical ports where locks are necessary are Bremerhaven, Germany, which has a lock 1220 ft (372 m) long and 148 ft (45 m) wide, and Antwerp, Belgium, which has one 1180 ft (360 m) by 148 ft (45 m). The time taken to operate these is more dependent on manœuvring the large ships than on actually filling the lock and can be up to 90 minutes. Unless a suitable natural water supply exists at a higher level, water must be pumped back up into the dock to compensate for that lost in locking, seepage and evaporation.

Below: an aerial view of an 'economizer' lock on the Rhine-Main-Danube Canal, to the north of Nuremburg in Germany. Instead of the water in the lock being discharged downstream when the water level is lowered, it is pumped into the side reservoirs.

LOCOMOTIVE

Few machines in the machine age have inspired so much affection as railway locomotives in their 170 years of operation. RAILWAYS were constructed in the sixteenth century, but the wagons were drawn by muscle power until 1804. In that year an engine built by Richard TREVITHICK worked on the Penydarren Tramroad in South Wales. It broke some cast iron tramplates, but it demonstrated that steam could be used for haulage, that steam generation could be stimulated by turning the exhaust steam up the chimney to draw up the fire, and that smooth wheels on smooth rails could transmit motive power.

Steam locomotives The steam locomotive is a robust and simple machine. Steam is admitted to a cylinder and by expanding pushes the piston to the other end; on the return stroke a port opens to clear the cylinder of the now expanded steam. By means of mechanical coupling, the travel of the piston turns the drive wheels of the locomotive.

History Trevithick's engine was put to work as a stationary engine at Penydarren. During the following twenty-five years, a limited number of steam locomotives enjoyed success on colliery railways, fostered by the soaring cost of horse fodder towards the end of the Napoleonic wars. The cast iron *plateways*, which were L-shaped to guide the wagon wheels, were not strong enough to withstand the weight of steam locomotives, and were soon replaced by smooth rails and flanged wheels on the rolling stock.

John Blenkinsop built several locomotives for collieries, which ran on smooth rails but transmitted power from a toothed wheel to a RACK which ran alongside the running rails. William Hedley was building smooth-wheeled locomotives which ran on plateways, including the first to have the popular nickname *Puffing Billy*.

The **ROCKET** *of Mr Robt Stephenson*
Which drawing a load equivalent to three times its wei
of 12½ miles an hour, & with a carriage & passengers
Cost per mile for fuel about three halfpe

In 1814 George STEPHENSON began building for smooth rails at Killingworth, synthesizing the experience of the earlier designers. Until this time nearly all machines had the cylinders partly immersed in the boiler and usually vertical. In 1815 Stephenson and Losh patented the idea of direct drive from the cylinders by means of cranks on the drive wheels instead of through gear wheels, which imparted a jerky motion, especially when wear occurred on the coarse gears. Direct drive allowed a simplified layout and gave greater freedom to designers.

In 1825 only 18 steam locomotives were doing useful work. One of the first commercial railways, the Liverpool & Manchester, was being built, and the directors had still not decided between locomotives and cable haulage, with railside steam engines pulling the cables. They organized a competition which was won by Stephenson in 1829, with his famous engine, the *Rocket*, now in London's Science Museum.

Locomotive boilers had already evolved from a simple flue to a return flue type, and then to a *tubular* design, in which a nest of fire tubes, giving more heating surface, ran from the firebox tube plate to a similar tube plate at the smokebox end. In the smokebox the exhaust steam from the cylinders created a blast on its way to the chimney which kept the fire up when the engine was moving. When the locomotive was stationary a *blower* was used, creating a blast from a ring of perforated pipe into which steam was directed. A further development, the *multitubular* boiler, was patented by Henry Booth, treasurer of the Liverpool & Manchester, in 1827. It was incorporated by

Stephenson in the *Rocket*, after much trial and error in making the ferrules of the copper tubes to give water-tight joints in the tube plates.

After 1830 the steam locomotive assumed its familiar form, with the cylinders level or slightly inclined at the smokebox end and the fireman's stand at the firebox end.

As soon as the cylinders and axles were no longer fixed in or under the boiler itself, it became necessary to provide a frame to hold the various components together. The *bar frame* was used on the early British locomotives and exported to America; the Americans kept to the bar frame design, which evolved from wrought iron to cast steel construction, with the cylinders mounted outside the frame. The bar frame was superseded in Britain by the *plate frame*, with cylinders inside the frame, spring suspension (coil or laminated) for the frames and *axleboxes* (lubricated bearings) to hold the axles.

As British railways nearly all produced their own designs, a great many characteristic types developed. Some designs with cylinders inside the frame transmitted the motion to crank-shaped axles rather than to eccentric pivots on the outsides of the drive wheels; there were also *compound* locomotives, with the steam passing from a first cylinder or cylinders to another set of larger ones.

When steel came into use for building boilers after 1860, higher operating pressures became possible. By the end of the nineteenth century 175 psi (12 bar) was common, with 200 psi (13.8 bar) for compound locomotives. This rose to 250 psi

Below: two early steam locomotives. On the left is the 'Rocket', built by Stephenson in 1829. On the right is 'Puffing Billy', built by William Hedley in 1813. Hedley and Richard Trevithick were builders whose experiences were useful to Stephenson.

Note the differences in the drive linkage: Hedley's goes to the axles underneath; Stephenson's is more direct and less complicated. The Rocket pulled a weight three times its own at 12½ miles per hour; fuel cost per mile was about three halfpence.

castle.
velled at the rate
ate of 24 miles.

smoke box door

chimney

steam chest

steampipes

exhaust steampipe

steampipe

valve gear

buffers

bogie pivot

four wheel bogie

Below: a 120 ton steam locomotive of the Castle class which was in service on the Great Western Railway. Coal burning in the firebox heats the boiler water and the superheated steam passes through the steam pipes to the cylinders, driving the pistons and thus the wheels via the driving rods. Exhaust smoke and steam pass out through the chimney.

(17.2 bar) later in the steam era. (By contrast, Stephenson's *Rocket* only developed 50 psi, 3.4 bar.) In the 1890s express engines had cylinders up to 20 inches (51 cm) in diameter with a 26 inch (66 cm) stroke. Later diameters increased to 32 inches (81 cm) in places like the USA, where there was more room, and locomotives and rolling stock in general were built larger.

Supplies of fuel and water were carried on a separate *tender*, pulled behind the locomotive. The first *tank engine*, carrying its own supplies, appeared in the 1830s; on the continent of Europe they were confusingly called *tender engines*. Separate tenders continued to be common because they made possible much longer runs. While the fireman stoked the firebox, the boiler had to be replenished with water by some means under his control; early engines had pumps running off the axle, but there was always the difficulty that the engine had to be running. The *injector* was invented in 1859. Steam from the boiler (or latterly, exhaust steam) went through a cone-shaped jet and lifted the water into the boiler against the greater pressure there through energy imparted in condensation. A *clack* (non-return valve) retained the steam in the boiler.

Early locomotives burned wood in America, but coal in Britain. As British railway Acts began to include penalties for emission of dirty black smoke, many engines were built after 1829 to burn coke. Under Matthew Kirtley on the Midland Railway the *brick arch* in the firebox and deflector plates were developed to direct the hot gases from the coal to pass over the flames, so that a relatively clean blast came out of the chimney and the cheaper fuel could be burnt. After 1860 this simple expedient was universally adopted. Fireboxes were protected by being surrounded with a water jacket; *stays* about four inches (10 cm) apart supported the inner firebox from the outer.

Valve gear

Steam was distributed to the pistons by means of valves. The valve gear provided for the valves to uncover the ports at different parts of the stroke, so varying the *cut-off* to provide for expansion of steam already admitted to the cylinders and to give *lead* or *cushioning* by letting the steam in about ⅛ inch (3 mm) from the end of the stroke to begin the reciprocating motion again. The valve gear also provided for reversing by admitting steam to the opposite side of the piston.

Long lap or *long travel* valves gave wide open ports for the exhaust even when early cut-off was used, whereas with short travel at early cut-off, exhaust and emission openings became smaller so that at speeds of over 60 mph (96 kph) one third of the energy of the steam was expended just getting in and out of the cylinder. This elementary fact was not universally accepted until about 1925 because it was felt that too much extra wear would occur with long travel valve layouts.

Valve operation on most early British locomotives was by *Stephenson link motion*, dependent on two eccentrics on the driving axle connected by rods to the top and bottom of an expansion link. A *block* in the link, connected to the reversing lever under the control of the driver, imparted the reciprocating motion to the valve spindle. With the block at the top of the link, the engine would be in full forward gear and steam would be admitted to the cylinder for perhaps 75% of the stroke. As the engine was *notched up* by moving the lever back over its serrations (like the handbrake lever of a car), the cut-off was shortened; in mid-gear there was no steam admission to the cylinder and with the block at the bottom of the link the engine was in full reverse.

Walschaert's valve gear, invented in 1844 and in general use after 1890, allowed more precise adjustment and easier operation for the driver. An eccentric rod worked from a return crank by the driving axle operated the expansion link; the block imparted the movement to the valve spindle, but the movement was modified by a combination lever from a crosshead on the piston rod.

Superheating

Steam was collected as dry as possible along the top of the boiler in a perforated pipe, or from a point above the boiler in a *dome*, and passed to a *regulator* which controlled its distribution. The most spectacular development of steam locomotives for heavy haulage and high speed runs was the introduction of *superheating*. A return tube, taking the steam back towards the firebox and forward again to a header at the front end of the boiler through an enlarged flue tube, was invented by Wilhelm Schmidt of Cassel, and modified by other designers. The first such equipment was used in Britain in 1906 and immediately the savings in fuel and especially water were remarkable. Steam at 175 psi, for example, was

generated 'saturated' at 371°F (188°C); by adding 200°F (93°C) of superheat, the steam expanded much more readily in the cylinders, so that twentieth-century locomotives were able to work at high speeds at cut-offs as short as 15%. Steel tyres, glass fibre boiler lagging, long lap piston valves, direct steam passage and superheating all contributed to the last phase of steam locomotive performance.

Steam from the boiler was also used for other purposes. Steam sanding was introduced for traction in 1887 on the Midland Railway, to improve adhesion better than gravity sanding, which often blew away. Continuous brakes were operated by a vacuum created on the engine or by compressed air supplied by a steam pump. Steam heat was piped to the carriages, and steam dynamos [generators] provided electric light.

Classification

Steam locomotives are classified according to the number of wheels. Except for small engines used in MARSHALLING YARDS, all modern steam locomotives had leading wheels on a pivoted bogie or truck to help guide them around curves. The trailing wheels helped carry the weight of the firebox. For many years the 'American standard' locomotive was a 4-4-0, having four leading wheels, four driving wheels and no trailing wheels. The famous Civil War locomotive, the *General*, was a 4-4-0, as was the New York Central *Engine No 999*, which set a speed record of 112.5 mph (181 kph) in 1893. Later, a common freight locomotive configuration was the *Mikado* type, a 2-8-2.

A Continental classification counts axles instead of wheels, and another modification gives drive wheels a letter of the alphabet, so the 2-8-2 would be 1-4-1 in France and 1D1 in Germany.

The largest steam locomotives were *articulated*, with two sets of drive wheels and cylinders using a common boiler. The sets of drive wheels were separated by a pivot; otherwise such a large engine could not have negotiated curves. The largest ever built was the Union Pacific *Big Boy*, a 4-8-8-4, used to haul freight in the mountains of the western United States. Even though it was articulated it could not run on sharp curves. It weighed nearly 600 tons, compared to less than five tons for Stephenson's *Rocket*.

Steam engines could take a lot of hard use, but they are now obsolete, replaced by electric and especially diesel-electric locomotives. Because of heat losses and incomplete combustion of fuel, their thermal efficiency was rarely more than 6%.

Diesel locomotives

Diesel locomotives are most commonly *diesel-electric* (see DIESEL-ELECTRIC PROPULSION). A DIESEL ENGINE drives a DYNAMO which provides power for electric motors which turn the drive wheels, usually through a pinion gear driving a ring gear on the axle. The first diesel-electric propelled rail car was built in 1913, and after World War 2 they replaced steam engines completely, except where electrification of railways is economical.

Diesel locomotives have several advantages over steam engines. They are instantly ready for service, and can be shut down completely for short periods, whereas it takes some time to heat the water in the steam engine, especially in cold weather, and the fire must be kept up while the steam engine is on standby. The diesel can go further without servicing, as it consumes no water; its thermal efficiency is four times as high, which means further savings of fuel. Acceleration and high speed running are smoother with a diesel, which means less wear on rails and roadbed. The economic reasons for turning to diesels were overwhelming after the war, especially in North America, where the railways were in direct competition with road haulage over very long distances.

Since the diesel-electric locomotive generates its own electricity, the generator and traction motors are usually DC rather than AC. A large locomotive may have a sixteen cylinder diesel engine weighing more than fifteen tons. A British Rail locomotive holds the world speed record for diesel-electric propulsion of 143 mph (231 kph).

Electric traction

The first electric-powered rail car was built in 1834, but early electric cars were battery powered, and the batteries were heavy and required frequent recharging. Today electric trains are not self-contained, which means that

Below: an articulated locomotive allowed a larger boiler on a single machine. The British-built Beyer-Garratt 4-8-2-2-8-4 was built for South Africa; it carried 7000 gallons of water, 12 tons of coal and had a mechanical stoking system.

BRITISH RAILWAYS BOARD

TOM BROWNE

they get their power from overhead wires or from a third rail. The power for the traction motors is collected from the third rail by means of a *shoe* or from the overhead wires by a PANTOGRAPH.

Electric trains are the most economical to operate, provided that traffic is heavy enough to repay electrification of the railway. Where trains run less frequently over long distances the cost of electrification is prohibitive. DC systems have been used as opposed to AC because lighter traction motors can be used, but this requires power substations with RECTIFIERS to convert the power to DC from the AC of the commercial mains. (High voltage DC power is difficult to transmit over long distances.) The latest development of electric trains has been the installation of rectifiers on the cars themselves and the use of the same AC frequency as the commercial mains (50 Hz in Europe, 60 Hz in North America) which means that fewer substations are necessary.

Underground [subway] and other RAPID TRANSIT systems are always electrified; this is not only economical but keeps down air pollution in cities. Outside cities, railways are electrified in small countries and on commuter lines where usage justifies it, as in southern England and some east coast commuter lines in the USA. Electric inter-urban lines reached a peak of development in the USA around World War 1, but have since been largely abandoned in favour of diesel-electric power. Urban congestion, air pollution and the increasing shortage of fossil fuels mean that electric railway development will probably receive new impetus in the future. The Japanese have built the most modern electric railways in the world, designed to accommodate top speeds of 150 mph (241 kph), because their population density and pollution problems are the greatest in the industrialized world. (See also MONORAILS.)

Other types *Steam turbine, electric turbine* and *gas turbine* locomotives have been built, and a few gas turbine locomotives are in service in the USA, but they are not yet competitive with diesel-electric propulsion because their thermal efficiency is not high (see JET ENGINE & GAS TURBINE).

LODESTONE (see magnetism)

LOG (SHIPS AUTOMATIC) (see distance recorder)

Above top: in a British Rail maintenance shop, a view of bogies with frame mounted traction motors as fitted to the British Rail class 87, 500 horsepower, 25 Kv AC locomotives. The locomotive takes its power from overhead wires; the suburban third rail systems can have more frequent power substations and have 600 V DC motors. The third rail is cheaper to install than the wires.

Above: a 4-6-2- steam locomotive at a watering station.

Right: the driver's desk on the class 87 locomotive. The AC traction system is built by GEC Traction Limited and works on 50 Hz. Top speed of the locomotive is 176 km/h, or 110 miles per hour. A British Rail diesel-electric engine holds the speed record for that type of locomotive, which is 143 mph (231 km/h). Japanese electric locomotives reach 150 mph (241 km/h). The record for steam locomotives is about 126 mph (203 km/h).

Far right: by contrast, the cab of a steam locomotive which operates in the Khyber Pass. Driving a steam locomotive was more work and dirtier, requiring a fireman.

GEC TRACTION LTD

MACQUITTY COLLECTION

LOGARITHM

A logarithm is a different way of representing a number but integrally linked with the nature of numbers in general. An enormous range of numbers, from the minutest fractions to the largest figures, can be encompassed by a range of logarithms that can be easily handled. They are used extensively in science, engineering and MATHEMATICS. Logarithmic tables have been devised to enable quick conversions between a number and its logarithm and a SLIDE RULE has logarithmic scales.

Numbers   We are accustomed to counting numbers to the *base* of ten. We have ten fingers and ten numerical symbols—zero (o), one (1) and so on up to nine (9). With these ten characters we can represent any number of any size by stringing them together. For any integer number (that is, a whole number) greater than 9 but less than 100, two characters placed side by side are required. With three characters it is possible to specify any integer number between 100 and 999.

This system of numbers is easy to understand and simple to use. It is one of the first things taught at school and essential to all transactions especially involving money—maybe a child's first practical experience with numbers.

Such a system, however, becomes extremely cumbersome with large numbers—not only do they become incomprehensible but also unwieldy. It is easy to envisage 10 people but 1000 people is more difficult to grasp. The population of the world is over two thousand five hundred million and is baffling even when written as 2,500,000,000. One ampere of electrical current is the passage of slightly more than six million million million electrons per second. Numerically, 6,000,000,000,000,000,000 is incomprehensible.

The same difficulty is encountered with extremely small numbers. One tenth can be written as 0.1, one hundredth as 0.01, but one millionth, which is 0.000001, is already unwieldy.

Powers and logarithms   There is a simple way to represent very large and very small numbers—using powers. 100 is equal to 10 multiplied by 10 and can be more easily written as 10^2. This is pronounced 'ten squared' and means ten *to the power* two. Similarly, one million is ten repeatedly multiplied by ten six times. Therefore one million is ten to the power six and written as 10^6.

This system greatly shortens the space required to describe large numbers and can be extended down to the smallest fraction. As one hundred is 10^2, ten is 10^1 (ten to the power one) and one is 10^0 (that is, ten to the power zero—in fact, any number to the power zero is one). Proceeding to still smaller numbers (less than one) the power becomes negative. For example, one tenth (0.1) is 10^{-1} (ten to the power minus one), one hundredth (0.01) is 10^{-2} and one millionth is 10^{-6}.

It is not necessary, however, to keep on writing the base number if it is understood. The power alone is then sufficient to describe the original number and this power is called the *logarithm* of that number (to the base 10). Thus 6 is the logarithm to the base ten of one million and -2 is the *logarithm* of one hundredth (0.01). The logarithm of ten is one and the logarithm of one is zero. The brevity of this system can be demonstrated by the fact that logarithms between $+6$ and -6 represent numbers between one million and one millionth.

Logarithmic tables   We do not always handle numbers so convenient as 10, 100 or 0.001, but every number, integer or not, has a logarithm. For example, the logarithm of 554.6 to the base ten will lie between 2 (which is 100) and 3 (which is 1000) and must therefore include decimal places. Such a logarithm is not easily determined using pen and paper and so logarithmic

Above: John Napier (1550–1617) was the inventor of logarithms and logarithmic tables. Natural logarithms have been named after him.

tables (or log tables for short) have been devised to make the task easier. The logarithm of 554.6 from log tables is 2.744 to three decimal places.

To convert a logarithm back into a number, the log tables can be used in reverse. *Antilog* tables have, however, been devised to make these conversions easier.

Applications of logarithms   Logarithms enable complicated multiplications and divisions to be performed by simple addition and subtraction. For example, $100 \times 10,000$ equals 1,000,000. Put another way, $10^2 \times 10^4 = 10^6$. From this it can be seen that the two powers to the left of the equals sign add up to the power on the right. In other words, two numbers can be multiplied by adding their logarithms and finding the antilog of this. Division is accomplished by subtracting one log from the other.

A slide rule operates on this principle. It consists of two logarithmic scales one of which can be moved against the other. Multiplications and divisions are rapidly determined by adding and subtracting along the two scales.

Logarithms to other bases   Once the logarithm of a number has been established in principle, it is possible to use any base. For example, 64 is two multiplied by two six times—that is, 2^6 (two to the power six). Thus, the logarithm of 64 to the base two is 6. Similarly, the logarithm of $\frac{1}{2}$ to the base two is -1 and $\frac{1}{4}$ is -2. Because 2^0 equals one the logarithm of 1 to the base two is 0.

Natural or Naperian logarithms   In the realm of science and mathematics there is one number so important that it is even given its own symbol—**e**—this is the *exponential number* and **e** = 2.71828 to five decimal places. The exponential number **e** is important in calculations concerning natural growths; this is, growth which is *continuous* rather than in stages. For example, the compound interest on a sum of money, say £1, is calculated in yearly stages knowing the *annual* interest rate. In one year the sum has grown to £$(1+r/100)$ where r is yearly interest rate as a percentage. This sum is then the new sum for the next year's calculation; therefore, after two years the initial sum has grown to £$(1+r/100)^2$.

After n years, it has grown to £$(1+r/100)^n$—this is growth in stages. If the interest rate is 100% per year, then at the end of the first year, the £1 has increased to £2, after 2 years £4, 3 years £8 and so on.

Now, consider reviewing the interest on the sum twice yearly —thus reducing the gaps between updating the accumulated sum. The interest rate *per half year* is 50% (still 100% per year) and the sum accumulated at the end of one year is £ $(1+50/100)^2$ which is £ $(1.5)^2$ or £2.25. Consequently, with interest reviews more frequent than once yearly the sum accumulated is larger. Increasing the reviews per year will not, however, lead to ever increasing accumulations over the yearly period. As the number of reviews per year become infinitely frequent (continuous growth) the accumulated sum over the year rises more slowly and tends towards £2.71828, that is £e.

To demonstrate this fact, with four reviews per year with an interest rate of 25% per quarter year, the accumulated sum at the end of one year is £ $(1+25/100)^4$ which is £ $(1.25)^4$ or £2.44. With 8 reviews per year it is £ $(1.125)^8$ which is £2.565, 16 reviews is £2.64 and 32 reviews £2.675. This figure is approaching e.

Natural or Naperian logarithms are logarithms to the base e and are used wherever natural growth functions are encountered. For example, the voltage across the plates of a CAPACITOR being charged through a RESISTOR increases in a certain exponential way which when represented mathematically will include powers of e.

Below: polonium is radioactive with half-life of 140 days—this means whatever activity it shows one day it will be half this 140 days later. An ordinary graph of activity versus time is curved, but when activity is plotted logarithmically a straight line is produced.

LOGIC CIRCUITS

Logic as a subject was originally a branch of philosophy and was developed to improve the validity of reasoning. The history of formal logic in the western world is generally thought tô have begun with the Greek philosopher Aristotle (384–322 BC), although logical thinking and clear reasoning certainly existed as far back as 2000 BC. Development of logic was slow until the seventeenth century, when such men as Francis Bacon, Leibniz and Descartes contributed their thoughts and ideas.

In 1847 two mathematicians, George Boole and Augustus de Morgan, independently proposed forms of algebra (see MATHEMATICAL PRINCIPLES) to represent logical expressions. Seven years later Boole published *The Laws of Thought*, which was the first practical way of expressing logic in algebraic form. *Boolean algebra*, as it is now called, has only two values, '0' and '1', and as such lends itself ideally to COMPUTER logic applications.

Logic can be applied to a very broad spectrum of problems, and is used almost subconsciously in a large variety of everyday situations. Applying the principles of logic to problem analysis provides a powerful tool with which to solve the problems. In the same way the use of logic circuits, which operate according to the principles of logic, provides an automated method of solving problems. Such circuits are found not only in computers but also in many other places like telephone systems and household items such as central heating controls and automatic washing machine controls.

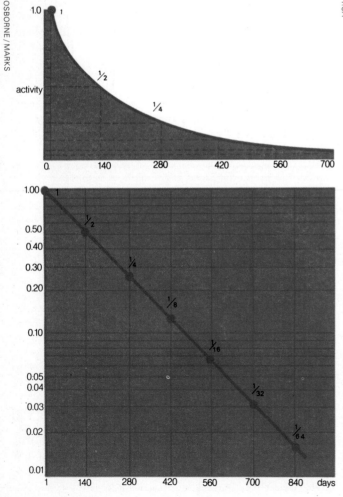

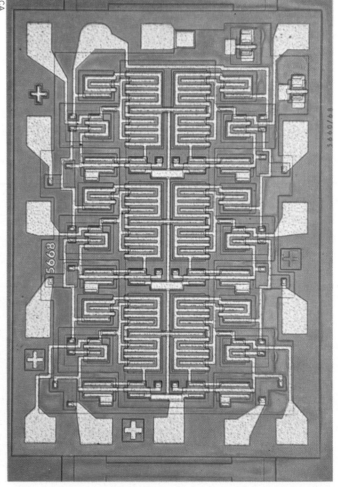

Hardware Electronic circuits, based on components such as DIODES, TRANSISTORS, CAPACITORS, RESISTORS and INTEGRATED CIRCUITS, are used for the majority of logic applications, but the design of logic circuits is not restricted to electronic devices. Early CALCULATING MACHINES were purely mechanical; the first computers used RELAY logic, as do many office machines, LIFT [elevator] control systems and industrial control systems. In addition there is a separate branch of logic, FLUIDICS or *fluid logic,* which uses fluid flows instead of electrical or electronic signals.

The most important characteristic of logic circuits is the fact that they are made up of large collections of basically

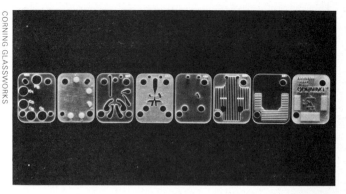

Below left: an integrated circuit logic element, a hexadecimal non-inverting buffer. Hexadecimal, or 'hex', is a numerical system to base 16, using the numericals 0 to 9 and the letters A,B,C,D,E, and F so that the numbers 0 to 15 can be reproduced by single characters. This gives a more economical use of the registers and data storage space within a computer.

Top right: the component parts of a fluidic AND/NAND module.

Right: a relay logic panel used for controlling the operating sequences of a lift [elevator] installation.

Below: this resistor-transistor logic (RTL) element, introduced in 1961, was the computer industry's first monolithic chip integrated circuit. It is a set/reset latch or 'flip-flop'.

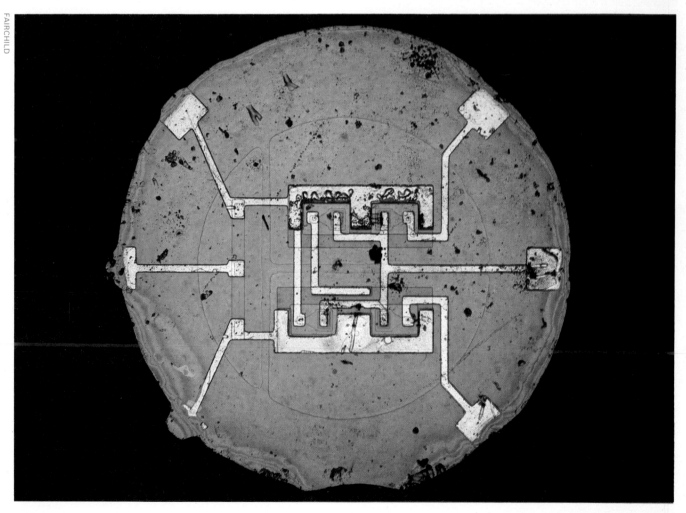

similar devices, each of which is relatively simple. A large computer will have literally millions of these simple devices. By interconnecting these devices and controlling the timing of the signals which operate them, extremely complex systems can be built up.

To maintain the simplicity of the devices each circuit usually operates with only two signal values. These two *states* are called by different names. One state can be called 'active' and the signal is said to be 'up'; conversely the other state is 'inactive' and the signal is 'down'. There are a variety of names for many features of logic devices. For instance a relay coil can be 'energized' or 'picked', and its contacts said to be 'closed' or 'made', or 'opened' or 'broken'.

All that is needed for correct operation of the device is for the two signal values to be different. In terms of actual voltages within a machine, it is up to the designers to decide what constitutes an active or inactive signal for any given device. For example, one device may require an active level of $+12$ volts and an inactive level of o volts, another an active level of -5 volts and an inactive level of $+5$ volts.

Logic functions

There are only three basic logic devices needed to perform the logical functions in a computer. These are the AND, OR and NOT functions, and all other more complex devices are built up from these. Block diagrams, rather than circuit diagrams, are used to represent these functions, and are called *logic blocks*. Different manufacturers use different symbols and diagrams, although it is usual to indicate the inputs going into the left of the block, and the output leaving from the right.

The AND function

An AND function is a logic device comprising two or more inputs and one output. If all inputs to an AND function are at an active level, then the output will be active, and the AND block is said to be 'satisfied'. If any one input to an AND function is at an inactive level, then its output will also be inactive. A good analogy of an AND function is an electric light controlled by two switches wired in series. In order to turn the light on (active output) both switches must be on (active). If either of the two switches is turned off (inactive), the light will go off (inactive output).

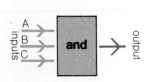

inputs			out put
A	B	C	
0	0	0	0
0	0	1	0
0	1	0	0
0	1	1	0
1	0	0	0
1	0	1	0
1	1	0	0
1	1	1	1

The logic block shows an AND function with three inputs. In addition to the logic block it is often useful to have a 'truth table', showing the levels of the input signals and the resulting output. It is usual to show the inactive level as a o, and the active level as a 1.

OR and NOT functions

An OR function comprises two or more inputs and one output. If any of the inputs to an OR function are active then the output will be active. A similar analogy to the AND function will illustrate the OR function. In this case the two switches (inputs) to the light are wired in parallel. Turning on either one switch or the other will turn on the light.

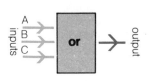

inputs			output	
A	B	C	or	ex or
0	0	0	0	0
0	0	1	1	1
0	1	0	1	1
0	1	1	1	0
1	0	0	1	1
1	0	1	1	0
1	1	0	1	0
1	1	1	1	0

The diagram shows the logic block and truth table for a three input OR function. As indicated this type of OR function has an active output if any of the inputs are active. There is, however, a second type of OR function called EXCLUSIVE OR, which will have an active output if any one (but only one) input is active. The output for a three input EXCLUSIVE OR is also shown on the truth table.

A NOT function is a logic device with one input and one output. Its operation changes the state of the signal; if the input is active, the output is inactive, and conversely if the input is inactive the output is active. This function may also be called an *inverter* or a *negater*.

input	output
0	1
1	0

NAND and NOR functions

From the three basic logic functions AND, OR and NOT it is possible to build complex logic devices. If a logic element is made up of an AND function followed by a NOT function, the result is a NAND function (NOT-AND) whose output is active when any or all of its inputs are inactive.

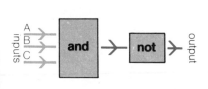

inputs			out put
A	B	C	
0	0	0	1
1	0	0	1
0	1	0	1
0	0	1	1
1	1	0	1
0	1	1	1
1	0	1	1
1	1	1	0

When an OR function is followed by a NOT function a NOR element (NOT-OR) is created, which has an active output only when none of its inputs are active.

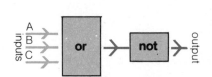

inputs			out put
A	B	C	
0	0	0	1
1	0	0	0
0	1	0	0
0	0	1	0
1	1	0	0
0	1	1	0
1	0	1	0
1	1	1	0

Latches

One of the commonest complex logic devices is the *latch*, which has the very useful property of being able to 'remember' a signal. It has a 'set' input which will cause the latch to turn on, and the output to become active. It will remain active even after the set input goes inactive. To turn the latch off (output inactive) a 'reset' line is made active. The latch is made up of AND, OR and NOR functions which are interconnected.

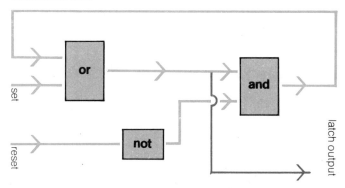

The logic functions operate in the following manner. If both the set and reset lines are inactive, the OR block is not 'satisfied' and the NOT function converts its inactive output into an active output which will satisfy one input to the AND block. The latch output is inactive. When the set line becomes active the OR block is satisfied, and this in turn gives an active latch output and also satisfies the other input to the AND block.

The active AND output is used to satisfy the OR block so that it will 'hold' the circuit, even when the set line goes inactive. If the reset line is now made active, the NOT function will give an inactive output which will no longer satisfy the AND block. The output from the AND block is now inactive again and consequently so are both inputs to the OR block, which results in an inactive latch output again.

This type of circuit was first described in 1919 by W H Eccles and F W Jordan, whose circuit used triode VALVES [tubes] as the NOT elements. Latches are also known as *triggers, bistable multivibrators, flip-flops* and *toggles,* and have many uses including their application in computer processor registers and stores (see also MEMORY DEVICES).

Boolean algebra

The two distinct values that are used in logic circuits represent the choice between two alternatives. Any variable which can be expressed as one of two alternatives is known as a *logical variable* or *Boolean element,* and it is usual in computer technology, which is based on binary arithmetic, to assign the symbols '0' and '1' to the two variables.

Boolean algebra using two variables

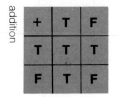

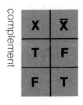

T = true (1) F = true (2)

In Boolean algebra the sign for addition is '+', the sign for multiplication is '.' and the *complement* (opposite) is represented by a bar over the symbol, for example '$\overline{X}$'. The complement can also be called 'NOT', that is the complement of 'X' is 'NOT X'. It can be seen from the tables that the addition, multiplication and complement are identical to the respective logic functions OR, AND and NOT.

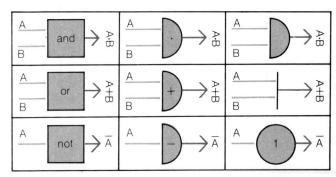

One application of Boolean algebra is in the analysis of switching circuits. The following common switching problem can be solved using Boolean algebra.

A light, X, for a flight of stairs, is to be controlled by two switches. One switch, A, is upstairs, the other, B, is downstairs. It is required to be able to switch the light on or off using either switch.

Each switch has two states designated by the symbols 0 and 1. Assuming that the light is on, then X = 1, with each switch in state 1. Changing the state of either switch must cause the light to go out. Hence X = 0 when A = 1 and B = 0, or when A = 0 and B = 1. A further change of state of a single switch must turn the light on again, hence X is also equal to 1 when A = 0 and B = 0.

A truth table for A, B and X will therefore be as follows.

A	B	X
1	1	1
1	0	0
0	1	0
0	0	1

The procedure for finding the expression in Boolean algebra is to take the sum of the forms where X = 1, in this case the first and last lines of the table which gives the result as $X = A.B + \overline{A}.\overline{B}$.

To put this expression into a usable form made up of the more familiar AND and OR functions, we substitute the OR function for the addition, and the multiplications (A.B and $\overline{A}.\overline{B}$) are replaced by AND functions. As shown in the equivalent circuit diagram, the light will come on when the switches A AND B are both on, OR when they are both off ($\overline{A}$ AND $\overline{B}$).

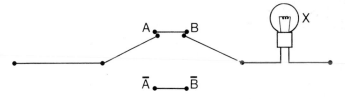

After a circuit has been represented symbolically by an algebraic expression, the rules of Boolean algebra can be used to find equivalent expressions. Each equivalent expression represents a switching circuit which could replace the original one. Thus very complicated switching arrangements can be analyzed to find the simplest circuit arrangement that will perform the desired functions.

LONGBOW

The earliest records of the bow, the first form of stored energy, date from the Upper Palaeolithic period (30,000 to 15,000 BC) and come from arrowheads found in north Africa and cave paintings in Spain, which clearly depict hunters using bows. The development of the bow has been governed mainly by the materials available for its construction and the way that it was used in warfare or hunting. Short, sometimes recurved, bows have predominated where timber was scarce or stunted in growth, or horn or bone were used as bow materials. In addition, shorter bows were also easier to use on horseback, both for hunting and warfare. In countries with access to long straight timber, the longbow became the weapon of the foot archer. It was about 5 to 6 feet (1.5 to 1.8 m) long and provided useful long range accuracy at about 300 to 400 paces. Although not as powerful in terms of penetration as the crossbow, it could be loosed five to six times more rapidly and was simpler and cheaper to make, costing from three to five times less than a crossbow of the same period.

Development   As a military weapon the bow was probably introduced into Britain by the Romans, and it was certainly used both in battle and hunting by the Angles and Danes. But it was under the Normans that archery was improved, organized and diffused throughout the country. The English longbow, which appears to have originated in south Wales, began to be accepted as a national weapon in the mid-13th century.

It was not long after this that laws, rigorously enforced, governed the manufacture, distribution and proficiency with the longbow. In addition, great care was taken to ensure ample importation of bow staves of carefully defined qualities and sizes, and to ensure that bowyers (bow makers) were present in sufficient numbers in all parts of the country. During the reign of Edward III, the price of bows was regulated by statute, and Sundays and holidays were directed to be spent practising with the bow at targets, in lieu of other pastimes. This rigid regulation of production and use continued through the reign of Elizabeth I and was reinforced at frequent intervals. Despite the improvements made in firearms, the longbow continued to be used in Britain until the sixteenth century, when its military applications began to decline. As a pastime, however, it retained its popularity until late in the seventeenth century, when it fell into neglect until its revival as a sport a century later.

Materials used   The wood most favoured for the English longbow was Spanish yew, with hazel, ash and elm as secondary choices. The value placed upon the yew bow was such that a law was passed instructing bowyers to make four hazel, ash or

Below left: the longbow, after a 15th century French painting.

Below: commencing the draw. The cedar arrow is nocked and the bowman will now raise the bow, pushing out his right hand and pulling the left hand under his chin. (This is a left handed draw.) He wears a shooting tab to protect his fingers from the bowstring.

Right: a modern self (meaning all) yew longbow. It is actually made in two halves and spliced together in the handle. It has a dacron bowstring and is used at a range of 100 yd for target shooting.

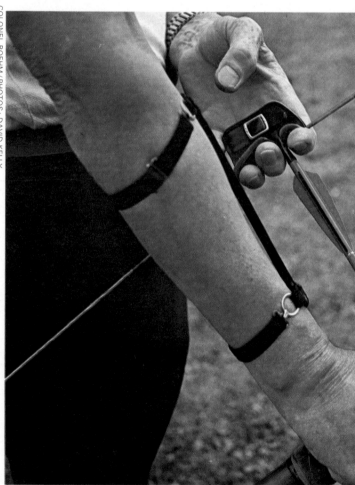

elm bows to every one made of yew, and fines were imposed upon people who did not meet the age and property qualifications, and used yew bows. Despite price-fixing, the cost of imported yew became one of the causes for the decline in the production of the English longbow.

Bowstrings were made of flax, spun and twisted and greased with beeswax: each end was woven into itself and strengthened with stitching and sometimes leather. Arrows were made of 'good dry timber' with as many as 15 varieties of wood listed as suitable in the middle of the sixteenth century. By the nineteenth century red pine was the wood most frequently used. Arrowheads used with the longbow were mainly of iron or steel and fell into three categories: broad head, fork head (with the barbs facing forwards), and blunt head, this type being of wood. The broad head came closest to being an all-purpose type, while the fork heads were used against large game and flying birds and the blunt heads, small game and birds. The feathers, which stabilize and guide the flight of the arrow, were generally of goose or turkey. Arrows were formerly as long as 3 feet (91 cm) but by the nineteenth century had been reduced in size to about 28 inches (71 cm), a length that remains in common use today.

Using the longbow

The bow must first be strung so that the upper end of the bowstring (which is released from tension when the bow is not in use) is engaged in notches at the upper end of the bow, known as the *horn*. An arrow is then 'nocked' or placed in position just above the handle of the bow with the notch of the arrow engaged in the string. The bow is then drawn, the arrow gripped by the first and second fingers and the string by the other two or three fingers. The bow was formerly drawn so that the rear of the arrow was level with the ear, but current practice takes it only to the chin. The pull of a bow, or the number of pounds of strength necessary to pull it fully, is largely a matter of taste and ability nowadays, combined with the purpose for which it is to be used, some American bows having 100 lb (45 kg) pulls, which give enormous power for large game.

Archery today

The use of the longbow for target shooting as an amusement was revived about 1780, and the Royal Toxophilite Society founded in 1781 to foster and regulate the sport. Archery has a large following today in Britain and North America, where frequent competitions are held with the bow. Some daring sportsmen in America have succeeded in taking most types of large game with the bow.

A small number of craftsmen have relearnt the art of bowyery and are capable of recreating most types of bow in use by modern archers. A few archers use traditional type longbows made from hardwood and having linen bowstrings, but most use the composite bow. This type of bow is laminated and consists of GRP (glass reinforced plastic) on the outside with maple laminations inside and hardwood on the *riser* (handle section). Lengths vary from 58 to 70 inches (1.54 to 1.78 m). The bowstring is made from a manmade fibre such as Dacron, while modern arrows are precision drawn aluminium. Bows for target shooting may also be equipped with adjustable micrometer sights. Marksmen in archery aim at the centre gold (9 inches, 22.8 cm, in diameter) at a range of 100 yards (91 m).

COLONEL BOEHM/PHOTOS: DAVID KELLY

LONG RANGE GUN

The first long range GUNS, with ranges beyond 20 miles, appeared in World War 1. To achieve such great ranges the gun barrels had to withstand very high pressures and were thus very heavy; they required heavy carriages and systems capable of dealing with the vast amount of energy contained in the recoiling gun. The guns were relatively immobile and, when transported by road, they impeded the movement of stores, equipment and vehicles. As a result the majority of long range guns were railway mounted.

World War 1 The French armies in 1915 to 1918 made considerable use of long range railway guns and the armament concern of Schneider made simple box mounts for guns intended for naval or fortress service. These mounts were placed directly on to railroad trucks which were run on to spurs constructed in a curve of the railroad track to enable the gun to be pointed in the required direction. The truck was driven back on recoil and then was hauled back into position for the next round. The British used a mounting designed for the 9.2 inch (23.4 cm) naval gun. This had a ramp up which the gun recoiled and it then ran back to its original position for firing again. This method, however, did not give enough elevation and later guns were specially designed for long range railway firing.

The Germans undoubtedly produced the most effective guns, and the most famous of all was the 'Paris' gun. This was designed by Rausenberger and produced by Krupp. It was a development of the 'Max E' railway gun which was used to bombard Verdun in 1916. The length of the barrel was increased by nearly 20 feet (6.1 m) and the bore was lined down from 36 cm (14.2 inch) to 24 cm (9.5 inch). The barrel was braced to withstand the muzzle whip on firing. The gun had a high muzzle velocity and drove its shell up into the stratosphere, where air resistance is much reduced, and so achieved the immense range of 82 miles (132 km) (see GUNNERY TECHNIQUES). The gun was, however, of psychological value only, for although the shells fell into Paris, the damage they did was minimal compared with the effort involved. The immense powder charge needed to produce the high muzzle velocity led to considerable erosion of the inner walls of the gun barrel, and the powder charge had to be increased after every round to keep the muzzle velocity constant as the chamber volume increased. Each successive projectile had an increased diameter of *driving band* (a band of soft metal surrounding the projectile to ensure a good fit with the inside of the barrel) to allow for the increasing bore diameter.

World War 2 During this period the Germans continued their tradition of long range railway guns. The 21 cm (8.3 inch) 'K-12' gun had a barrel length of 105 feet (32 m) and weighed 98 tons. Its maximum range was 93 miles (150 km) but, as far as is known, was used only to fire into the area of Dover across the Channel in 1940. The most efficient railway gun was probably the 28 cm (11 inch) 'K-5'. This fired a shell weighing 560 lb (254 kg) which was rocket assisted and *pre-engraved*—that is, the rifling was already engraved to fit the barrel. It had a solid cordite motor in the nose and a tube passed to the rear through the high explosive filling to carry the rocket exhaust to the base of the shell. The rocket motor was ignited as the shell reached the highest point of its trajectory and this extended the range to 53 miles (85.3 km). Like most rocket assisted projectiles it had a reduced target efficiency and was somewhat inconsistent. It was used to shell the Allied positions at Anzio and was nicknamed 'Anzio Annie'. An experimental

version with the same barrel bored out to 31 cm (12.2 inch) fired a 12 cm (4.7 inch) fin stabilized sabot round (see ARMOUR PIERCING SHELL) to 90 miles (145 km) but the five foot (1.5 m) projectile had a very limited target effect.

Probably the biggest railway gun of all time was the 80 cm (31.5 inch) Krupp gun of 1937, which fired a four ton high explosive shell to 29 miles (46.7 km). It weighed 1350 tons, had its own track laying crew and altogether required 1420 men to serve it. The detachment was commanded by a major general. The gun was used at Sevastopol and at Warsaw during the 1944 rising. Its ultimate fate is one of the unsolved mysteries of the war.

The 'V3' One long range gun system which was developed towards the end of the war was the 'V3', a type of *multi-chambered* gun. The idea behind the 'V3' was not a new one;

Below: the 'Paris' gun in the final stages of construction. The gun was used in 1918 to bombard Paris from a distance of more than 60 miles (97 km). It fired a projectile weighing 264 lb (119 kg) and had a maximum range of more than 80 miles (129 km).

multi-chambered guns had previously been design topics. The 'V3' was designed by Condors, and it differed from the first known multi-chambered gun project of 1870 only in the size of the proposed gun. The basic idea was very simple; a primary charge initiated the movement of the projectile and as it passed up the bore of the gun it uncovered a succession of secondary chambers each of which had a propellant charge which was initiated by the burning gases following the projectile, and so the velocity of the shell was constantly increased along the length of the barrel.

Condors planned to have 28 side chambers arranged alternately on each side and building up the velocity of the 15 cm (5.9 inch) shell to more than 5000 ft/sec (1524 m/sec) at the muzzle. This would have produced a range of nearly 200 miles (322 km). Scale models appeared to work well

enough and although a short barrel, full bore system was very erratic, Hitler is said to have ordered a fifty barrel model, each barrel having 28 secondary chambers, and each barrel being 150 metres (492 ft) long. To avoid detection and counter battery measures the system was to be built into a hillside near Calais. Before the digging was completed, however, the RAF photographic reconnaissance units located it and the gun was bombed out of existence. Like many excellent German ideas the project was not pursued actively until it was too late.

After World War 2 the US 280 mm (11 inch) gun, the 'M-65', on a road mounting, was the first gun designed to fire an atomic shell and therefore probably rates as the most lethal long range gun ever produced. With the advent of the free flight rocket the very heavy long range gun became redundant and went out of service.

Below: the remains of a German multi-chambered gun, a forerunner of the 'V3'. The projectile was accelerated up the sectional barrel by successive firing of charges in the side chambers. Operation of the gun was hazardous as the barrel tended to burst after a few firings.

Below: the American 'M-107' 175 mm (6.9 inch) mobile gun. The gun crew is kept to a minimum by extensive use of power assisted mechanisms for moving the barrel and loading. The gun is capable of firing a nuclear shell.

PHOTRI

LOOM

The loom is among the most ancient of devices. It was in use in 4500 BC, according to evidence found in tombs, and certainly long before that. Hand looms are still used for WEAVING in underdeveloped countries throughout the world, the way they were in English cottage industry until a few hundred years ago. They are also found in hobby and handicraft activities. The modern high-speed industrial looms work on the same basic principles.

In a piece of woven cloth, the lengthwise threads are called the *warp*. The threads which go across are called the *weft* (*woof, filling,* or *shoot*). The edge of the cloth is called *selvedge*. (In modern industrial weaving, the selvedge is about $\frac{1}{4}$ inch (6 mm) wide and may contain a woven trademark.)

In the loom, the warp threads are held in tension by the machine. In the simplest, most common pattern, called *plain* or *tabby* weave, every other thread is pulled upwards and the rest are pulled downwards. The separation of the threads into two *sheets* is called *shedding*, and the space between is called the *shed*. The weft thread is passed through the shed; this is called *picking* and each weft thread is called a *pick*. Then the pick is beaten in (pushed up tightly into the weave) and the upper and lower sheets change places, so that they hold the pick in the weave. The beating in is accomplished by the *reed*, a screen or gate made of wire, so called because it was originally made of reeds. The *batten* is the part of the machinery which operates the reed. The batten is sometimes called the *sley*, and *sleying* is threading the warp threads through the reed.

Thus the operation of the loom is a continuous cycle of shedding, picking, beating in, shedding, picking, and so forth.

History Primitive weaving was a slow process analogous to darning. The earliest loom probably comprised sticks in the ground to hold the thread with the operations carried out by hand. Thousands of years ago, shed sticks were invented to form the shed and keep the sheets separate. Before that it would have been necessary to accomplish shedding by hand, one thread at a time.

The next improvement was the invention of the *heddle*, or *heald shaft*. Again, we do not know when this took place. The heddle at first may have been a stick with a hole in it; later it became a piece of wire with an eye in it, and still later a strip of metal with a hole. The heddle is mounted vertically at the front of the machine; there is usually a heddle for each warp thread. The thread passes through the hole in the heddle and the shed is formed by raising and lowering the *harness* (frame which holds the heddles). (In more complicated weaving patterns, the heddles are raised and lowered in various combinations according to the pattern. The pattern is supplied to the weaver on graph paper of 8×8 point size; see FABRICS.)

On primitive looms there were several ways of providing tension on the warp. On the *weighted* loom, the warp threads were hung over a crossbar with weights on the ends. In the *backstrap* loom, the operator had a strap tied around his back and added tension by leaning back. On these primitive looms, the pick was passed back and forth through the shed by hand with the thread wrapped around a stick; in the modern looms, this is accomplished by a *shuttle*, which in its simplest form is a hollowed out piece of wood containing the *weft package* (a *cone* or *spool* of thread).

The heddles and the shuttle were operated by hand until recent times, except that a single harness could be operated by foot, an innovation that first occurred in the East. Throughout the mediaeval period in Europe, looms were simple

machines, but in about the thirteenth century the *shaft loom* appeared, also copied from an oriental idea. To this a number of heddles can be fitted; they are suspended above the loom from a shaft and can be operated by a treadle. This makes possible more weaving patterns because each shed variation can have its own heddle rod.

In modern times the improvements to the loom have been ways of conveniently or automatically operating the heddles and the shuttle, and finally using steam or electricity to drive the machine. Automating the shuttle is one of the many ideas to which Leonardo da VINCI gave some thought. Real progress, however, was not made until the seventeenth century, and the process of development has continued until the present day. The improvement in textile machinery together with the invention of the STEAM ENGINE sparked off what we call today the Industrial Revolution, and each improvement to the loom caused riots and violence by weavers who were afraid they would lose their jobs.

Drawloom The shaft loom was still not capable of weaving intricate patterns; the drawloom was invented for this purpose. The drawloom can make a greater variety of sheds because it uses, in addition to heddles, slipcords tied to the warp threads. They were operated at first by a *drawboy*, who sat on top of the machine and pulled the cords in various combinations according to the pattern. (If he made a mistake it would show up in the cloth.) The drawloom was improved gradually until the jacquard, a mechanical selective shedding attachment, was perfected by J M Jacquard in about 1805. Hooks instead of slipcords were used, and they were operated by an endless chain of punched cards (see JACQUARD LOOM).

Automated looms The flying shuttle was invented in 1733 by an English maker of broadcloth, John Kay. Because of the width of the cloth, the weaving process required two operators to pass the shuttle back and forth through the shed. Kay realized that automatic operation would make better cloth because there would be no need to stop the shuttle and reach through the shed, which resulted in imperfections. He devised a *driver* attached to the batten. The weaver could send the shuttle in the right direction by sharply pulling a cord, operating the driver.

Other inventors devised mechanical arms for the shuttle, spring-loaded beating-in devices, overhead cranks to operate the heddles, and so on. These devices all had to be combined with means of feeding the machine with thread and winding up the finished cloth. A mechanically limiting factor was that the shuttle speed must be much faster than the other operations. Power operated looms did not become common until the nineteenth century, but nowadays some industrial looms run at a speed of well over 200 picks a minute.

The greatest number of modern industrial looms can be divided into three types: *hand-replenished, automatic,* and *shuttleless.*

Hand-replenished looms For weaving special patterns or fabrics, the power operated looms of the nineteenth century have been refined to a high degree. They run more smoothly and more safely, but not much faster, than their predecessors. Their operation is precise and dependable because of modern engineering advances; for example, their essential parts can be made by MACHINE TOOLS today rather than by casting processes, which leave rough edges. Hand-replenished machines are especially useful for inserting single picks or odd numbers of picks of a certain colour, since no fully automatic machines have been built which can do this.

Left: a German illustration from about 1389 showing a shaft loom, which was a recent innovation at that time. On this model the cords operating the heddles are suspended on pulleys, which in turn are suspended from the shaft.

Below left: a Turkish loom of the type in use since ancient times.

Above: a nineteenth century Platt power loom for plain weaving.

Below: carpet weaving in Persia. In weaving this type of carpet, a pile yarn must be knotted on each warp thread by hand; then the weft thread is sent through 2 or 3 times for each row of knots.

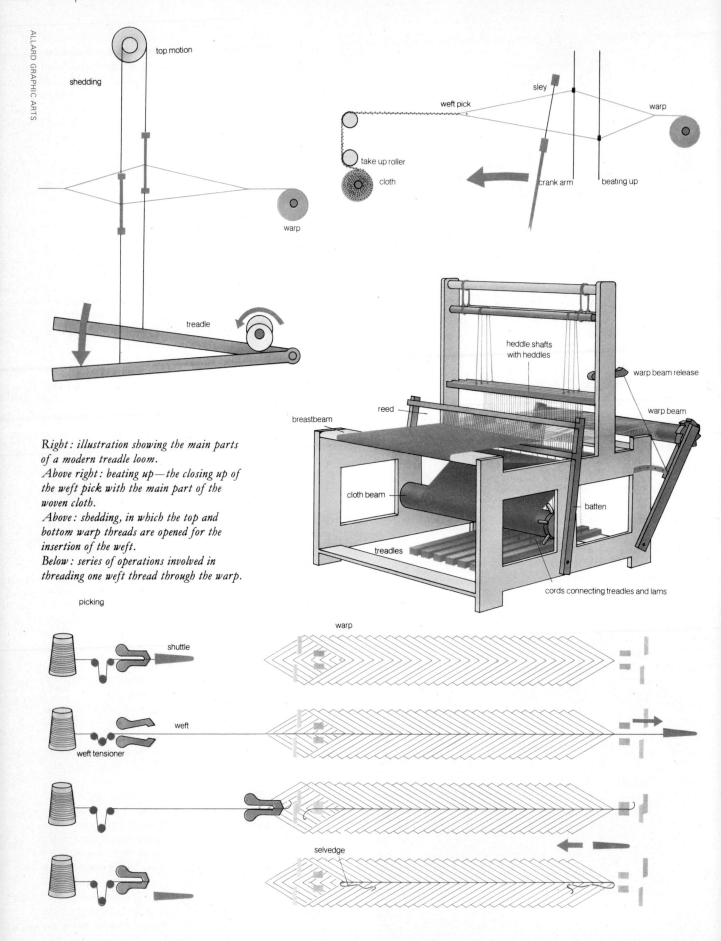

top motion

shedding

warp

weft pick

sley

warp

take up roller

cloth

crank arm

beating up

treadle

Right: illustration showing the main parts of a modern treadle loom.

Above right: beating up—the closing up of the weft pick with the main part of the woven cloth.

Above: shedding, in which the top and bottom warp threads are opened for the insertion of the weft.

Below: series of operations involved in threading one weft thread through the warp.

heddle shafts
with heddles

warp beam release

reed

warp beam

breastbeam

cloth beam

batten

treadles

cords connecting treadles and lams

picking

shuttle

weft

weft tensioner

warp

selvedge

The shuttle contains a supply weft package and is propelled across the loom by means of a slinging action from an *overpick* or an *underpick* device, which pivots in a short, powerful arc from above or below the shuttle. The underpick is becoming more common because it is safer and cleaner.

Automatic looms The largest number of modern looms are the automatically replenishing type. Looms which automatically replaced the shuttle when the weft package was used up have been superseded by an improved type which replaces the bobbin of weft in the shuttle when it is at rest in the shuttle box at the side of the machine, with no break in production. Sensors, which may be mechanical, electrical or optical, determine when the weft is about to run out and the fresh bobbin is inserted, at the same time ejecting the old one. An air suction device takes care of any loose ends before they become woven into the fabric, causing an imperfection.

Shuttleless looms The noise level in textile mills is extremely high, and the advantage of shuttleless looms is that they are quieter, as well as potentially faster. There are three

Below: a cotton weaving loom in Blackburn, Lancashire. An automatically replenishing loom has several full bobbins at the side, ready to go. It senses when a shuttle bobbin is almost empty, then ties the new weft onto the end of the old.

types: *dummy shuttle, rapier* and *fluid jet*. All have the weft package stored at the side of the machine.

The dummy shuttle is a small steel projectile which travels back and forth on a track. It has a gripping spring in the back end and takes the weft with it. It returns more slowly than it travels across, so some machines have several dummies going at once. Several picks a second are possible.

The rapier is essentially a piece of wire with an eyelet in the end. Some rapiers are flexible steel tapes which are reeled up at the side of the machine. The latest design has a double rapier; one rapier carries the weft from one side of the machine and another rapier meets it half-way. Transfer takes place inside the shed. The rapier is not as fast as the dummy shuttle.

The latest type of loom is the fluid jet. In this machine, for the first time, nothing enters the shed but the weft itself; it is propelled from a nozzle by a jet of air or water. Since the propelling pressure is not great enough to pull the weft off the bobbin, the machine has an additional device which draws the yarn off ahead of time, storing it loosely so that it can be propelled at zero tension. The water jet is more efficient, but cannot be used except with waterproof (synthetic) fibres and machines built of non-corrosive materials.

LOST WAX PROCESS (see casting)

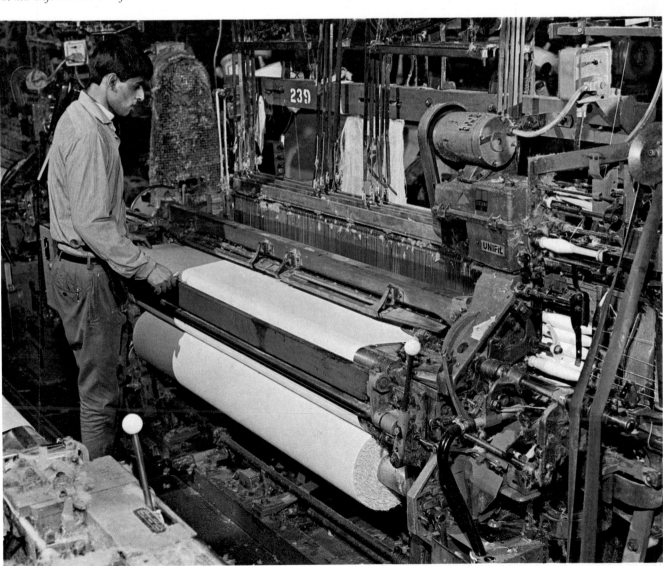

ZEFA

Above: a German acoustic record player synchronized with a film projector in an early attempt at motion picture sound. The hinged device at the foot of the horn is the sound-box; the mechanical vibration of the groove was amplified by the horn. Horns were made even larger than this. The invention of electrical systems made an immediate improvement in sound quality and frequency range. (Film soundtracks were not invented until after loudspeakers.)

Below: a typical modern speaker system of high quality. This is a two-way system for a room size about 5000 cubic feet, using 15 to 25 watts of amplifier power and reproducing about 50 Hz to 30 Khz. The box is sealed so that the air inside is a cushion.

Below right: a co-axial system, with the tweeter inside the woofer.

LOUDSPEAKER

In the 1920s, discoveries were made which allowed sound waves to be recorded and reproduced by electrical means. Before that time, the RECORD PLAYER worked on simple mechanical principles. As the pick-up (or *sound box*) traced the record, the mechanical vibrations of the needle were coupled to a flared horn mounted on top of the instrument, and this produced the sounds directly. Later, however, the theories of electricity became more closely allied to those of acoustics (the science of sound), and pick-ups were made which became known as *transducers,* because they converted energy from one form into another; that is, the tiny mechanical movements of the needle on the record into an electrical signal. Such an electrical signal could be amplified by the newly developed valve [vacuum tube] AMPLIFIER, but it could not be fed to an acoustic horn. Hence some means had to be found of converting an electrical signal back into sound waves, a requirement which is met by the loudspeaker we know today.

The first 'hornless' loudspeakers were described in 1924–5. Probably the most important single contribution came from C W Rice and E W Kellogg of America, whose work led to the commercial success and establishment of this new transducer. The system they described has remained essentially unchanged to the present day. The experience of the past fifty years has shown that it would be difficult to find an alternative to this system which would give the same performance quality together with constructional simplicity.

A moving-coil loudspeaker (abbreviated *speaker*) consists of a light circular (or elliptical) *diaphragm* or *cone,* freely suspended from a metal frame by springy suspensions both around its edge and near the centre. Firmly attached to the

KEF ELECTRONICS LTD

RANK LEAK WHARFEDALE

centre of the cone is a cylindrical former and wound on this is a coil of wire called the *voice-coil*. The former and coil are positioned between the poles of a magnet. The early speakers used electro-magnets, and were energized by a direct voltage derived from the amplifier, but nowadays permanent magnets of soft iron or ceramic materials are used. When a signal is applied to the coil, a force is exerted, according to the theory of ELECTROMAGNETISM: the coil is a current carrying conductor in a magnetic field and being rigidly attached to the diaphragm causes it to move. The movement of the diaphragm closely follows variations in the electrical signal and sets up sound waves in the air. The early loudspeakers of this type had a great advantage over horns, in that an increased level of sound could be produced simply by increasing the signal level fed to the speaker, whereas previously this could only be achieved by greatly increasing the size of the horn.

Enclosures

The audible frequency range extends from about 30 to 16,000 cycles per second (Hz) or more, and it was known long before the first cone loudspeakers were developed that certain problems arose when radiating such a wide range of frequencies. Firstly, the sound from the rear surface of the cone had to be isolated from that of the front, otherwise sounds leaving the two surfaces would cancel each other at low frequencies. Secondly, sounds are not radiated in all directions, but become concentrated in a narrow beam at high frequencies. This effect would be more noticeable with large diameter diaphragms. To improve reproduction and efficiency at low or bass frequencies, a loudspeaker is mounted in an *enclosure* or cabinet. The cabinet is effective only at frequencies below a few hundred Hz.

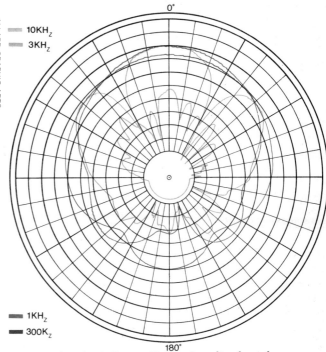

Above: polar plots indicate uniformity in radiated sound pressure from a loudspeaker. This is done at various frequencies—at low frequencies the sound is fairly evenly distributed, but at higher frequencies the obstacle effect leads to uneven distribution.

Below: electrostatic speakers (left) move the diaphragm by electrostatic forces (like charges repel) but in electromagnetic types it is moved by electromagnetic forces between coil and magnet.

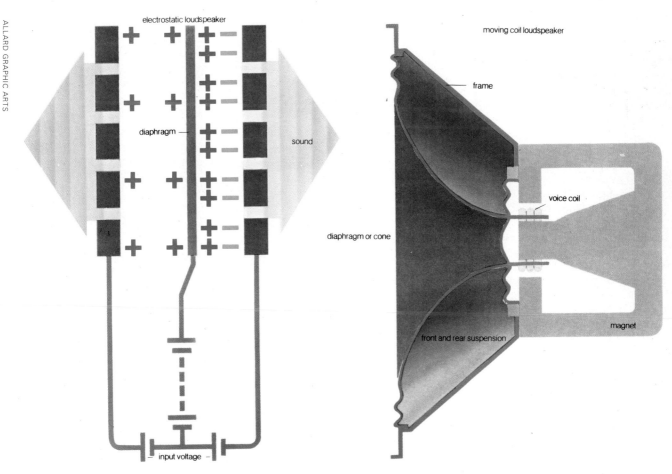

Nowadays the speaker is often mounted in a sealed cabinet which is packed with sound-deadening material, so as to isolate sound radiation from the rear surface of the cone. This is the acoustic suspension type, which is less *efficient*, that is, it requires more power from the amplifier, but gives good bass response from a conveniently smaller enclosure. In other designs, the rear radiations are arranged to aid those from the front, after being delayed slightly within the cabinet. An example of this type is the *tuned* or *reflex* enclosure, where a *vent* or *port* at the front magnifies the sound pressure at a specially tuned bass frequency range. The *labyrinth* or *transmission line* enclosures *guide* the back radiations to the front of the cabinet where they augment the speaker's front radiation. These developments took place during the 1930s and are in very wide use today.

Single loudspeaker units are used in radios, television sets and portable record players, but for sound reproduction of the highest quality more than one speaker is required to cover the full audible frequency range. Quite small units, with cone diameters of only an inch or two, are often used to cover the treble frequency range. Such small diaphragms overcome the problem of narrow directional radiation and their design can be optimized to give a more accurate response than a single large cone. High frequency speakers do not need enclosures, because their cone movements are very small. This allows the rear of the frame to be sealed, so that their operation is not affected when mounted in low frequency enclosures.

In a modern loudspeaker system of high quality, there might be a bass unit of about 10 inches (25 cm) diameter, covering the range from 30 Hz to about 500 Hz; a mid-range unit of about 6 inches (15 cm) diameter working from 500 Hz to around 4 kHz, and a small high frequency (or 'tweeter') unit for the treble range. The speakers are fed from an electrical filter or *crossover* circuit, which divides the audio spectrum appropriately between units. Considerable attention is paid in design to producing a single integrated sound from the system, rather than a collection of separate sound sources. Many modern speaker systems use tweeters having a 'domed' diaphragm, which is more rigid than a cone and so gives a more accurate response. Acoustic horns are also sometimes used in front of tweeters to improve efficiency, and also to load bass speakers in special cabinet designs.

Other types

Other types of loudspeaker were developed in the 1950s and have since become established alternatives for certain applications.

The *ribbon* loudspeaker, used for high frequency reproduction, uses a magnetic field in which is placed a light metal ribbon, a few inches long and about $\frac{3}{8}$ inch (9 mm) diameter. The ribbon acts as both voice-coil and radiator, but because it is so small an acoustic horn is often used with it to improve efficiency. Its very tiny mass allows very accurate re-creation of subtle transient sounds, because there is so little energy stored in the light ribbon diaphragm.

The *electrostatic* speaker has proved successful as a full range system. In this speaker, the diaphragm is a light, taut metal or metal sprayed plastic plate, placed close to a similar, but fixed plate. A very high direct voltage (several thousand volts) is connected between the two, which polarizes the system and creates a mechanical force between the two fixed plates, which are perforated to allow sound radiation to take place. The signal from the amplifier is connected between the plates via an isolating transformer. When a signal appears, the electrically produced force between the plates is modified or 'modulated',

and this causes movement of the diaphragm and hence radiation of sound. Because the diaphragm is light and tightly stretched, it moves accurately and can re-create the subtle tonal qualities of music with near perfect fidelity. A limitation of the system is that at low frequencies, when diaphragm movements are large, there is the danger of the two polarized plates touching. Hence the low frequency performance of the system is somewhat restricted. In general, the moving-coil loudspeaker is preferred for realistic bass reproduction, while the electrostatic speaker can give more faithful treble performance, though there are a few moving-coil dome tweeters which do meet the highest standards.

Recent development on moving-coil loudspeakers has tended to concentrate upon making their responses more accurate, so as to capture the subtle tonal qualities of music and speech sounds. There are many different speakers systems available today, and very few of them sound alike. This is because of the complex way in which the diaphragm moves, which upsets the precise timing of the component frequencies contained in music and speech waveforms. It is doubtful that any new type of loudspeaker will become as well established as the present ones, because it would have to be both cheaper and better than the moving-coil system. It is true, however, that the differences between different speakers are becoming smaller, and their performances more accurate, than was the case a few years ago.

Below: a British make of electrostatic speaker. The sound is generated by a large membrane which is caused to vibrate electrostatically. One American design is about 4 ft (1.2 m) high and can hang on the wall like a picture. There are also small designs for high frequencies only.

QUAD

LUBRICATION

Lubrication is the process of controlling FRICTION to reduce the wear of surfaces in rubbing contact with each other, such as those in BEARINGS and GEARS, by introducing a lubricant between the surfaces. Many different materials including liquids, solids and gases can be used as lubricants; the most common are mineral oils, which are products of OIL REFINING. Whichever lubricant is used, however, there are only three basic modes of lubrication: *boundary lubrication, fluid film lubrication* and *mixed lubrication*.

Boundary lubrication Boundary lubrication usually occurs either under conditions of high load and low sliding speed between two surfaces, or if there is insufficient lubricant because of unfavourable surface geometry. The entire load is carried by a thin, multi-molecular layer of lubricant between the surfaces.

It has been known for a long time that many animal and vegetable fats and oils can provide effective boundary lubrication and significantly reduce friction and wear. For example, it is thought that axles of ancient Egyptian chariots were lubricated with tallow. The lubricating agent in all these natural organic substances is a fatty acid (an organic acid derived from a HYDROCARBON) of high molecular weight, such as *stearic* or *oleic* acid (see CARBOXYLIC ACID). The molecules of these fatty acids are long chain compounds which can attach themselves to suitably reactive metal surfaces with sufficient strength to maintain adherence during rubbing contact. This reaction produces a 'soap' film of low shear strength, protecting the metal and reducing friction. Unrefined mineral oils do not contain a large percentage of fatty acids and are therefore not very good boundary lubricants. Refined mineral oils, however, with an addition of from $\frac{1}{2}$ to 5% of fatty acids are effective boundary lubricants.

Various solid lubricants can also be used to provide boundary lubrication, particularly in hostile environments or where contamination must be minimized. Typical solid lubricants are molybdenum disulphide (MoS_2), graphite and polytetrafluoroethylene (PTFE). These materials are used to provide a surface film of low shear strength between two sliding surfaces. They can be rubbed on to surfaces in powder form to produce a 'burnished film', usually about 0.000004 to 0.0004 inch (0.0001 to 0.01 mm) thick, or dispersed with resin in volatile fluids and sprayed on to surfaces to produce a layer 0.0002 to 0.001 inch (0.005 to 0.025 mm) thick, or dispersed in non-volatile fluids and used directly as a lubricating medium.

Fluid film lubrication The best way to minimize surface damage of rolling or sliding contacts in machines is to separate the solids completely by a film of lubricant. The lubricant can be a liquid or a gas and the load-supporting film can be created by the motion of the surfaces or by supplying the fluid under pressure, as in *hydrostatic bearings*. The main feature of fluid film lubrication is that the surfaces are separated by a fluid film that is considerably thicker than the surface films formed by boundary lubricants. Friction is only caused by viscous shearing of the lubricant and is reduced to about one tenth of the value which would be achieved by boundary lubrication. The main factors which affect the formation of fluid films are the load, the relative speed of the surfaces, the lubricant viscosity and the density if the lubricant is a gas.

The theory of fluid film, or *hydrodynamic,* lubrication is based on the experimental work of Beauchamp Tower who developed suitable methods for lubricating railway axle bearings in 1883. The conclusions of this work led Osborne Reynolds to formulate his classical theory of fluid film lubrication in 1886. The rotation of a shaft in its bearing will demonstrate the principle of hydrodynamic lubrication. There must be some clearance in the bearing so that the shaft can rotate, and thus when the loaded shaft is stationary it is positioned eccentrically. As the shaft rotates within its bearing, lubricant is drawn into the convergent channel and causes an increase in pressure. This in turn pushes the shaft back to its central position and maintains a film of lubricant between the shaft and the inner surface of the bearing. Under some conditions, such as start up, a film will not exist and boundary lubrication will occur. Because of the extremely high pressures which occur in some bearings, local elastic deformation of the surfaces leads to a condition known as *elastohydrodynamic* lubrication. This is the principle mode of lubrication in many gears, rolling bearings, cams and some soft rubber seals. The effects of operating temperature and pressure on the lubricant have to be considered when designing a hydrodynamic bearing. In some systems boundary and fluid film lubrication can exist simultaneously, and this is called mixed lubrication.

Lubricants Plain mineral oils are used in many lubrication systems, but because of the demands of modern high speed machinery they are often enhanced with additives. A mineral oil is a mixture of hydrocarbons having an average molecular weight ranging from about 150 for a light machine oil to about 1000 for a heavy gear oil. Oils are usually rated according to their viscosity, and the Society of Automotive Engineers (SAE) have devised a series of numerical values each of which represents a range of viscosities. Thus an oil whose SAE value is 30 will have a viscosity in the range 180 to 280 centistokes (cSt) at 25 °C (77°F). By using appropriate additives, oils can be formulated which will have different SAE values under different conditions; these are called *multigrade* oils. Common additives include *viscosity index improvers* which counteract the

Below: a fluid-tight seal for a rotating shaft. This is an example of fluid film lubrication; a layer of lubricant, which is coloured red, can be clearly seen between the rotating shaft and the inner surface of the seal.

tendency of oils to become thinner as temperature increases, *pour point depressants* which improve fluidity at low temperatures, *antioxidants* which prevent the formation of sludge by reaction of the oil with atmospheric oxygen, *antiwear additives* which neutralize the corrosive acid gases present in the exhaust of internal combustion engines, *extreme pressure additives* which improve the ability of an oil, for example a hypoid gear oil, to maintain lubrication in high pressure conditions, and *dispersants* which prevent the build up of particles, such as carbon particles, on the lubricated surfaces.

Under certain conditions it is advantageous to use a more viscous form of lubricant, for example in bearings which are lubricated and sealed for life, and in dirty environments where maintenance is difficult; for this purpose greases have been developed. Greases are generally mineral oils thickened with a *metallic soap* (a metal salt of an organic acid) or clay. Additives can be used as with oils. Calcium or lime greases are satisfactory for lubricating plain and rolling bearings at low speeds, but for higher speeds sodium or lithium based greases are preferred.

In extreme conditions, such as in aero engines where very high temperatures are encountered, it is impossible to provide the right characteristics with a lubricant based on mineral oil. More expensive synthetic lubricants are then used, typically *esters, diesters* (compounds obtained by reacting acids with ALCOHOLS) or *silicones* (see SILICON).

ESSO PETROLEUM CO LTD

ESSO PETROLEUM CO LTD

Right: the principal action of a lubricant is to keep moving surfaces separated so there is no actual contact between them, allowing them to move with a minimum of friction and wear. The rotation of a shaft within a bearing creates a film of oil around the shaft which supports it and keeps it clear of the bearing. In an engine like the one in the diagram the pump draws oil from the sump and forces it under pressure to the bearing surfaces, from where it eventually returns to the sump for re-circulation. As well as lubricating the engine, the oil also assists cooling.

Above: shaping a stainless steel cup for a ball and socket joint on a profiling machine. A medium to low viscosity oil is applied to the tool to assist the cutting operation. The oil contains additives which improve its lubricating ability under conditions of extreme pressure.

Left: greasing a slipway prior to the launch of a ship. The grease has a very high compression strength and a high tenacity so that it adheres to the slipway.

LUBRICATION SYSTEM, car

Lubrication of automotive engines serves not only to reduce FRICTION and wear of the moving parts but also to disperse heat, reduce corrosion, and help the sealing action of the piston rings.

Modern lubrication systems used in diesel engines and four-stroke petrol [gasoline] engines have developed by stages from the crude 'total loss' systems used in the early INTERNAL COMBUSTION ENGINES. In these early systems the driver operated a manual PUMP which delivered oil to the crankcase, from where it was splashed around the engine by the moving parts. The oil in the engine was eventually 'lost' by being burned in the cylinders or by leakage through joints and bearings, and then was replenished by further operation of the pump.

This method was eventually replaced by a pump system in which oil was pumped to a trough beneath the crankshaft, where it was picked up by scoops on the big-end bearing caps and carried to the big-end bearings.

In most modern engines, oil is carried in a SUMP [oil pan] and fed to the moving parts by a pump via a FILTRATION system. The sump usually forms the lower part of the crankcase and fulfils the combined duties of reservoir and cooler. Cooling is achieved because the sump protrudes into the airstream below the vehicle, and can be improved by adding cooling fins to increase the surface area. The pump is normally fitted to the crankcase and its drive is taken from the camshaft or the crankshaft. The commonest forms of oil pump in use are of the gear type, using two intermeshing gears to pump the oil up, or the rotor type.

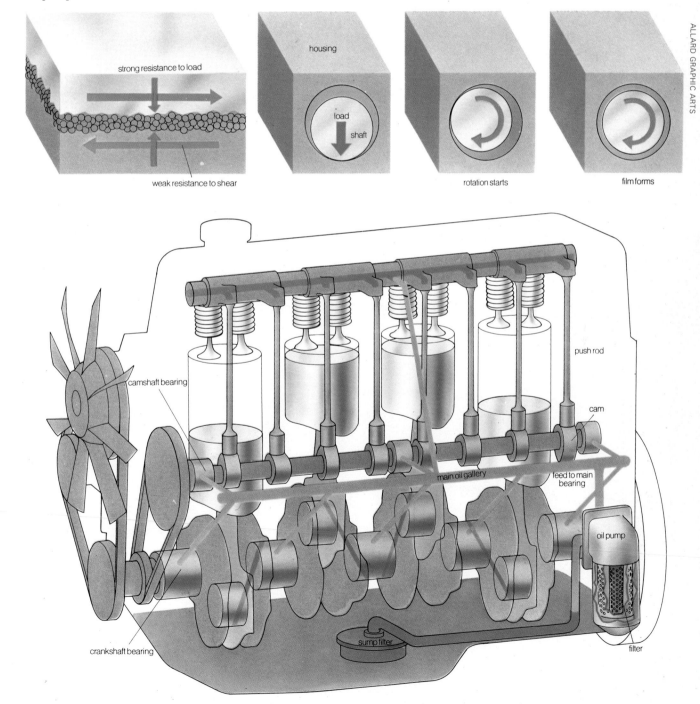

ALLARD GRAPHIC ARTS

strong resistance to load

weak resistance to shear

housing

load
shaft

rotation starts

film forms

push rod

camshaft bearing

cam

main oil gallery

feed to main bearing

oil pump

crankshaft bearing

sump filter

filter

The rotor type pump has a rotor mounted off-centre within the casing, and sliding vanes around the edge of the rotor carry the oil from inlet to outlet in a similar manner to the operation of a rotary vane COMPRESSOR.

Filters Oil usually enters the pump through a strainer, submerged in the oil, which is designed to trap any large particles of dirt. The oil then passes through a fine filter of either the bypass or full flow type. In the bypass system, some of the flow is fed to the filter and then returned to the sump while the rest is fed direct to the engine. Full flow filters handle all the pump's output before delivery to the engine, and incorporate a pressure relief valve which returns oil to the sump if the filter element becomes blocked or when the oil is cold and too thick to flow through the filter.

Filter elements can be made from various materials, but must be capable of restricting the flow of fine particles without restricting oil flow. A common filter element comprises resin-impregnated paper folded into a multi-pointed star, enclosed in a perforated cylinder. Oil enters the filter through the perforations in the cylinder, passes through the filter element, and leaves through a central outlet tube.

Typical full flow filters retain all particles over 15 microns in diameter, 95% of all particles over 10 microns, and 90% of all particles over 5 microns. During use the elements eventually become blocked and therefore less efficient, and so have to be replaced periodically.

Distribution From the filter the oil, at a pressure of about 40 to 60 psi (2.76 to 4.14 bar) in modern engines, is fed to a main passage or *gallery*, which is connected by drillings in the cylinder block to the moving components such as the main bearings, camshaft bearings, valve rockers and timing gears. After passing through the main bearings some of the oil drains back into the sump, and the rest passes through drillings in the crankshaft to the big-end bearings.

Cylinder walls and gudgeon pins are generally lubricated by oil thrown out of the big-end bearings, or else via an oil channel in the connecting rod.

In engines where high oil temperatures are expected an oil cooler may be installed in the pressurized circuit. On some high performance engines a 'dry sump' system is employed. In this system oil is retained in a storage tank, which may also function as a cooling radiator. The oil is pumped to the engine through a filter and then scavenged by a second pump in the sump and returned to the tank.

In most two-stroke petrol engines the crankcase is used to provide initial compression of the fuel-air mixture, and cannot be used as a sump. In these engines lubrication is usually provided by adding a small percentage of oil to the fuel.

Gauges To monitor the performance of a pressurized system many vehicles have oil PRESSURE GAUGES. These are connected to the main oil gallery by a thin pipe, and any drop in oil pressure or persistent low pressure will warn the driver that there is either a fault in the lubrication system or else a lack of oil in the system. On many cars the oil gauge has been replaced by a warning light which comes on when the oil pressure is low. It is connected to a pressure-operated switch in the oil gallery, whose contacts close when there is insufficient pressure in the system.

Below left: greasing the front suspension of a car. Oil is used for the lubrication of the engine and transmission, but most of the other major lubrication points on a car use grease.

Below: many bearing assemblies are packed with grease and sealed so that they do not require further lubrication during their working lives. The picture shows rear wheel bearings being packed with grease which is forced in under pressure.

Bottom: a complete oil filter assembly, on the right, together with a replaceable filter element.

LUMIERE, L (1864-1948), A (1862-1954)

Louis and Auguste Lumière invented the cinema as we know it today. Though they were not the first to photograph movement, having been preceded by such pioneers as MAREY, MUYBRIDGE and EDISON, they were the first to project moving pictures on to a screen before a paying audience.

The Lumières' father, Antoine (1840–1906), was a French painter who turned to photography. When his sons were about twenty, they established a factory near their home town of Lyons to manufacture photographic materials, producing one of the early *stripping films* (films with a paper base which is stripped off before processing). In 1894, they saw in Paris Edison's Kinetoscope, patented three years earlier. The Kinetoscope's successful illusion of movement was achieved by viewing thirty pictures a second through a narrow slit, and this limited it to being a peep-show: not enough light reached the eye from each image to make projection possible.

The Lumière brothers (their very name is the French for 'light') perceived that any improvement on the Kinetoscope would require each picture to be held completely still for a split second. Louis, the mechanic (Auguste provided the business brain), set to work developing a mechanism which would move film intermittently rather than continuously: the clue to solving the problem seems to have come from studying the movement of a sewing machine needle. Louis also realized that the peculiarity of the eye known as *persistence of vision,* the blending together by the brain of a series of still images into one continuous moving one, would work at a speed much slower than that used by Edison, and he settled on sixteen frames per second, which remained standard for cameras and projectors until the coming of sound to films over thirty years later.

On 13 February 1895, the Lumières patented a machine to photograph, develop and project moving pictures. The fact that it did all three overcame problems of 'registering' (the positioning of images in precisely the same place on any piece of equipment) and ensured that its pictures were always steady. It was the vital breakthrough, and it is entirely proper that the name the Lumières gave to their portable, all-in-one box—the Cinématographe—should be that by which the industry which sprang from their invention would be known.

The first public performance of the Cinématographe was given in the 'India Room' of the Grand Café, Boulevard des Capucines, Paris, on 28 December 1895. On that date, cinema was born.

Though the Lumières had other achievements in the cinema, notably their 70 mm stereoscopic presentation at the 1900 Paris Exposition, their other greatest success took them back to still photographs. In 1904 they patented the Autochrome process. By covering photographic plates with tiny colour filters (actually, grains of potato starch dyed violet, orange and green), they made positive glass transparencies with very realistic and attractive colours, though the starch grains made them rather dark. The Autochrome, put on the market in 1907, was the first commercially successful photographic colour process.

Above right : the 'cinématographe' which was used to give regular motion picture shows. This illustration shows it set up as a projector, with the carbon arc light source separate from the mechanism, but this could be closed up to make a light-tight camera. The picture at right shows Louis (wearing spectacles) and Auguste Lumière working in their laboratory at Lyons, France.

LUMINESCENCE

Light can be produced by two processes which are fundamentally quite different. If it is the result of something getting hot, such as an electric lamp filament or a gas mantle, it is called *incandescence,* while the emission of light without this intense heat is known as *luminescence.*

The earliest known form of luminescence, recorded over 3000 years ago, was the glow emitted by fireflies and glow-worms to attract their mates. Such bioluminescence in these and other species has been the subject of frequent literary musing but, until recently, evoked little scientific study. Of far greater interest was the first, accidental, synthesis of a luminescent material in about 1603 by an Italian named Cascariolo. In his search for gold he heated some interesting looking stones with coal. On cooling he had a porous cake which looked very ordinary by day but gave out a dark blue glow at night. This substance was absorbing sunlight and giving a luminescent emission which was too feeble to see except in the dark.

Luminescent materials As a material is heated its atoms become agitated and collisions occur between them causing the energy that has been put into the material to be emitted. This energy is normally noticed as radiant heat but, as the temperature rises, a proportion of the energy is emitted as visible light, in other words the material becomes incandescent. In luminescent materials the atoms are excited by the energy input to an internally unstable condition. They have an electron out of place and in this way are storing the energy, which is then emitted as visible light when the atom returns to its original state.

There are two forms of luminescence, *fluorescence* and *phosphorescence.* A simple distinction between these is that fluorescence stops as soon as the cause of excitation of the atoms or molecules is removed, whereas phosphorescence continues after such removal. The period over which phosphorescence continues can range from a millionth of a second to days depending on the material.

There are also several categories of luminescence, but these merely refer to the various ways in which the energy is supplied to the luminescent material. Thus, in *chemiluminescence* the energy comes from a chemical reaction, in *bioluminescence* the energy comes from a biochemical reaction, in *photoluminescence* the energy comes from absorbed light, in *electroluminescence* the energy comes from added electrons, and in *roentgenoluminescence* the energy comes from X-rays.

Uses The most obvious use of a process which produces light is to produce enough light to act as a means of illumination. Bombardment of gas molecules by electrons in an electric DISCHARGE TUBE causes excitation of these molecules, which then emit light. This is an example of electroluminescence. The first public lighting installation using discharge tubes was in 1904 at Newark, New Jersey, and the tubes contained air at low pressure. Nowadays discharge tubes use gases such as neon (for advertising signs) and sodium vapour (for street lighting). The colour of the light emitted by a discharge tube is characteristic of the gas used and cannot be modified except by coating the tube with a photoluminescent material. In a common type of discharge tube mercury vapour is used to produce a discharge light which is absorbed by a photoluminescent coating on the tube. The coating then re-emits light of a different colour. By using mixtures of photoluminescent materials, different tones of white light can be produced. These are the fluorescent strip lights currently in widespread

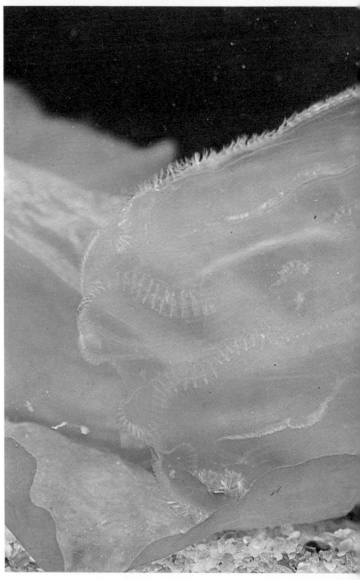

AMERICAN CYANAMID CO

PICTUREPOINT

use, and much attention is paid to determining the tone of white most suitable for shops, offices and domestic use.

Applications of luminescence other than for lighting are extremely varied; the most important is probably in the CATHODE RAY TUBE which is the basis of RADAR and TELEVISION. The source of the picture that we see is electroluminescence caused by accelerated electrons striking a screen of luminescent material at the end of the tube.

One of the most common uses of luminescent materials is in optical brightening agents for fabrics. Most fibres in their undyed state are slightly yellow and the old method of whitening them was to add a trace of blue dye to counteract the yellow tint. The modern way is to add a fluorescent compound which absorbs the ultra-violet component of daylight and emits blue light to counter the yellow tint. A white fabric is obtained which is brighter than by the old route. The effect is most readily noticed in clubs and discotheques where ultra-violet lighting is used for special effects and white garments are seen to have a blue-white glow. Optical brighteners are usually included in DETERGENTS for washing clothes.

One advantage of luminescent materials is that minute quantities are more easily seen than the same amount of a dye of the same colour. The luminescent organic compound *fluorescein*, for example, can be detected at a concentration of as little as one part in 40 million. This has led to the use of such materials in medical diagnosis, air-sea rescue, detection of leaks and even confirmation of the source of the river Rhône. Roentgenoluminescent materials are used in X-ray FLUOROS-COPY. Because luminescent materials are so noticeable to the eye they are sometimes included in paint compositions. Whereas an ordinary paint has a dye which reflects one colour and absorbs the others, a luminescent paint additionally contains a luminescent material which emits the same colour as the dye reflects making the resulting paint unnaturally bright. The luminescent material can either be fluorescent or phosphorescent depending on the intended use of the paint, for example on instrument panels, road signs and luminous watches.

Some of the more modern applications of luminescence include LASERS, light emitting DIODES, emergency lighting for aircraft (by chemiluminescence) and automatic sorting of mail by the colour of emission from the stamp.

LUNAR ROVER, LUNOKHOD (see space probes)

Above left: bioluminescence exhibited by a glow-worm. A chemical called luciferin is formed in the luminous cells of the glow-worm and is oxidized in the presence of an enzyme called luciferase. Light is emitted during the oxidation process.

Above right: a chemiluminescent emergency light. The light consists of a flexible, transparent tube containing two liquid components, one of which is contained in a glass ampoule. To actuate the light, the tube is bent sufficiently to break the ampoule, which allows the two liquids to mix and sets off the chemiluminescent reaction. Because the light is 'cold' it can safely be used in atmospheres where flammable gases or vapours may be present, for example in mines or petrol [gasoline] filling stations.

Left: a luminescent marine organism called a ctenophore, or comb jelly. The luminescent cells are in the hair-like cilia which the ctenophore uses to propel itself through the water.

MACHINE GUN

The earliest hand-held GUNS equipped with *matchlock* or *flintlock* FIRING MECHANISMS were slow to load and immediately after firing were of no more value than a bludgeon. In an effort to improve the volume and rapidity of fire many efforts were made to find devices which permitted one man to control a number of weapons. These usually took the form of a number of muskets mounted on a frame or on a wagon and so arranged that the application of the sparks from a match or flint to a black powder train set off a number of barrels in very quick succession. These weapons were known as organ guns from the similarity of the arrangement of the barrels to that of the pipes of a church organ. Although known to have existed in the fourteenth century, they reached the height of their popularity in the fifteenth century when a variety of types were produced, some firing a concentration and some producing dispersed fire. Among many others, Leonardo da VINCI produced several different versions.

Puckle's gun of 1718 was a remarkable revolver type weapon mounted on a tripod and allowing a rate of fire of 63 rounds in seven minutes, according to the London Journal of 31 March 1722. This weapon is on display at the Tower of London.

The first really successful rapid fire gun was that of Dr Gatling. It was a multi-barrel weapon with the barrels rotating around a central axis and each firing in turn. It was first demonstrated in 1862 and eventually was used all over the world, remaining in service with the United States Army until 1911. It was manually operated and the complete cycle of operations was carried out by the operator rotating a crank.

Below : Puckle's gun of 1718. Apart from its flintlock firing mechanism it had many features in common with the first Gatling gun introduced nearly 150 years later.

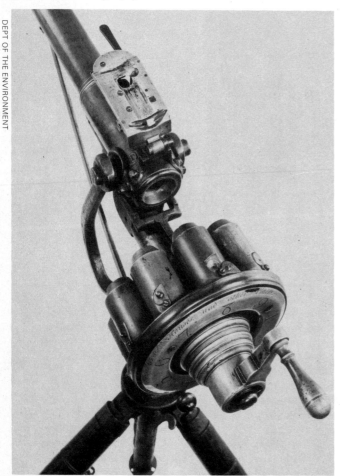

A German MG 42 machine gun which operates on the recoil system, and simplified representations of gas operated and blowback systems. In the MG 42 the bolt is driven forward by the recoil spring when the trigger is depressed. The bolthead drives a cartridge into the barrel chamber and is locked in position by the locking piece. A further small movement forward of the bolt (red arrow) fires the round, the barrel and the bolt recoil, and the locking piece releases the bolthead. The cycle is then repeated.

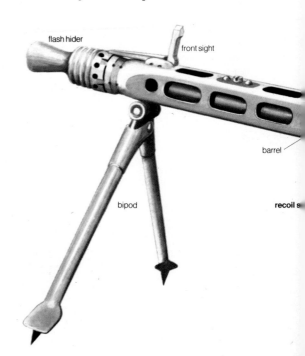

flash hider

front sight

barrel

bipod

recoil s

Above : a Gatling gun mounted on a camel saddle. The gun had a number of parallel barrels which rotated around a central shaft, and it fired the newly introduced brass cartridge ammunition.

The Maxim gun

In 1883 came MAXIM's first machine gun. This differed from all its predecessors in that the power to carry out the cycle of operations, that is feeding, chambering, locking, firing, unlocking, extraction and ejection, and cocking, all came from energy contained within the propellant and needed no external source of energy such as hand operation. Maxim's gun was sold all over the world, and was used by all the major powers. It was operated by the recoil of the barrel and lock (breech block) caused by the gas pressure. This principle is still used in a high proportion of modern machine guns and it results in a sturdy weapon with a high rate of fire. It has proved to be particularly successful when used in armoured fighting vehicles because there are no toxic fumes emitted into the confined space of the crew compartment.

The Maxim gun was followed by the guns designed by Browning, another American. Although Browning's first commercial machine gun, the model of 1885, was gas operated he was most successful with his 0.3 inch (7.6 mm) recoil operated machine gun, presented in 1917. The American army adopted his machine gun as soon as it appeared, and it has been developed both in its original calibre and in 0.5 inch (12.7 mm) calibre. It is still widely used in the larger calibre all over the world.

The lighter form of machine gun used by infantry is considered best operated by the simple ducting of gas from the barrel to drive back a piston which unlocks the breech block and carries it to the rear. *Gas operation*, as it is called, has been used to power many famous guns such as the Lewis, the Bren, and the current American M-60 machine gun. It permits a light, reliable weapon which, unlike a recoil operated one,

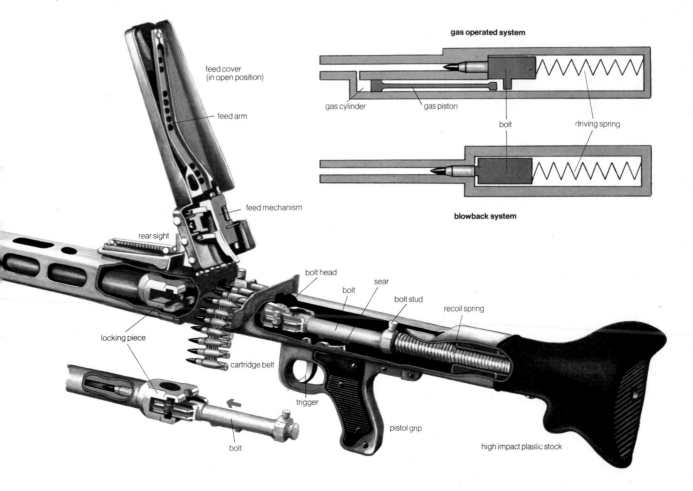

gas operated system

gas cylinder   gas piston

bolt   driving spring

blowback system

feed cover
(in open position)

feed arm

feed mechanism

rear sight

bolt head

bolt   sear

bolt stud

recoil spring

locking piece

cartridge belt

trigger

pistol grip

high impact plastic stock

bolt

allows adjustment of the power to cater for such contingencies as fouling and the ingress of dirt into the mechanism.

Blowback operation   Another way of using propellant energy to operate a machine gun is in the process known as *blowback*. This system does not have a locked breech block but relies on the inertia of the breech block to withstand too rapid an acceleration to the rear while the pressure is high. This inertia was, in early days, produced from a simple massive block but in later designs various mechanical linkages were used, connecting the breech block and the body of the gun, and producing a mechanical disadvantage which prevented undue acceleration of the breech block.

The light machine gun used by infantry seems unlikely to change much in its essential characteristics but it is of interest to note that the larger 20 mm type machine gun and those used in armoured vehicles appear to be reverting to the idea of using external power for their operation. This is shown in such weapons as the Vulcan 20 mm gun and the latest experimental armour machine guns produced in America by Hughes, which are electrically powered.

The machine gun has proved to be one of the most appalling weapons of war in history. The entire concept of trench warfare in 1915–1918 was produced as an answer to the terrible efficiency of the machine gun. The tank originated simply as a means of moving across the battlefield in the face of machine gun fire, while aerial warfare could hardly have occurred without the machine gun.

MACHINE TOOLS

A machine tool is a power driven machine for shaping metal by a series of repeated cuts. Machine tools are the only machines capable of reproducing themselves, but they are also used in the manufacture of nearly all other types of machines. Accuracy of construction of machine tools is essential, for machines reproduce or multiply their own errors.

Broadly, there are three types of machining: surface operations (*shaping* and *planing*); cylindrical operations (*turning*); and production of holes, slots and so forth by drilling and *milling* machines. Where great precision is required, as in bearing surfaces on motor shafts and *slideways* for machinery, *grinding* machines are employed to produce highly polished surfaces to precise sizes.

Shaper and planer   *Reciprocating* machine tools are those in which the cycle of operation commences with a cutting stroke, followed with a return stroke in which no metal removal takes place. Since the return stroke is non-productive, the machine is designed to effect a rapid reversal to reduce idle time. Shapers and planers are used to remove metal from flat surfaces.

In the *shaper*, the *ram* reciprocates across the surface of the workpiece, which is held stationary in a vice. The workpiece is advanced across the path of the cutting tool after each stroke of the ram, and the rate of its travel is adjustable. The tool box, or tool holder, is mounted on the end of the ram, and can be swivelled to cut vertical surfaces. The work table can be raised or lowered.

The length of the ram stroke can be adjusted from zero to a maximum according to the size of the piece. A *slotted link motion* is used in the ram drive to effect a return stroke of about double the speed of the cutting stroke. (The ratio of cutting time to return is not constant, but is reduced when the stroke is shortened.) The mechanism comprises a crank adjustable for length and fastened to a wheel. By means of a die which slides and drives the slotted link, the link is caused to swing and move the ram back and forth on its slideway. An alternative system of ram drives is by means of a hydraulic piston operated by a variable-speed pump.

The *planer* performs a similar function on larger workpieces, except that the cutting tool is stationary and the work is mounted on a reciprocating table which passes back and forth under the tool. This much larger machine has the advantage that milling heads (see below) as well as multiple tool boxes can be fitted to the cross slide and the side uprights. With multiple tool locations, cutting passes can be intermittent or at different heights.

Because planing takes place at table speeds varying from 20 to 220 ft/min (6 to 67 m/min), while milling speeds are from 1.5 to 38 in/min (38 to 965 mm/min), two separate drive mechanisms are required. An interlocking clutch prevents them from being engaged simultaneously. The table is driven by means of a rack and gear.

Lathe   The LATHE, the oldest and most important machine tool, is used for cylindrical work, such as making motor shafts

Above left: a Vickers machine gun. This gun was based on a design by Maxim who invented the first fully automatic machine gun, and it was widely used in World War 1. To prevent overheating, the barrel was fitted with a water jacket which had to be refilled after firing 2000 rounds of ammunition.

Left: a modern general purpose machine gun, which is gas operated.

and cutting threads. The work is turned by the headstock of the machine, and the tool, mounted on a *carriage*, is drawn past the turning work piece by the feed mechanism of the machine. There are two feed drives operated by the gear box of the lathe, one for ordinary turning and one for cutting threads.

Milling machine Unlike machines which use 'single-point' tools to cut metal, the operation of *milling* is based on rotation and travel of a multi-toothed cutter. The teeth of the cutter do not cut steadily but intermittently, on the side of the cutter being fed into the work. With the use of modified cutters and attachments, more complicated machining can be done. There are two general types of milling machines: those with vertical spindles and those with horizontal spindles. Machines with horizontal spindles use a round flat cutter with teeth around its perimeter, roughly resembling a circular saw blade; vertical spindles used an *end mill*, which resembles a twist drill except that it is flat on the end rather than pointed, has more teeth and is more precisely manufactured from higher quality steel. Both types of machine can also use a variety of other tools by means of sleeves and chucking devices. Either type of machine can have automatic or manual table traverse and cross feed; vertical milling heads can also feed up-and-down.

The use of a *dividing head* with either type of milling machine renders it more versatile. The dividing head is mounted on the table and has a vice or other chucking device which holds the work piece. It has an indexing crank with a pin which fits into a hole in a plate; the plate has a geometrical arrangement of holes which allow the work to be turned the required number of degrees between cuts. There are often a number of interchangeable plates. In addition, helical work such as flutes in twist drills or teeth on helical gears can be performed if the dividing head is geared to the lead screw of the table, so that the dividing head turns the work as it goes past the cutter.

The most versatile vertical milling machines have an *offset head* feature, so that the spindle turns in an arc as it rotates the tool, allowing elliptical holes and other unusual configurations to be generated. Threads can also be cut in milling machines, using cutters designed for this job. *Die-sinking* is an operation in which contoured surfaces can be generated, again using modified cutters.

Jig bore *Jig bores*, *mill bores* or *boring mills* are essentially large, versatile milling machines. The spindle projects horizontally from a column which can be raised or lowered; the spindle can be advanced or withdrawn; there is also the usual traverse and crossfeed of the work table. Some such machines are as large as rooms. They can use a wide variety of cutting tools with interchangeable collars, tapered sleeves and so forth, which adapt the tools to the spindle. A large workpiece, such as the body casting of a machine, can be mounted on the table; holes, slots, flat surfaces and other configurations can be machined on it within precise distances of each other. Jig bores are often used to remodel machinery to accept new work heads or special attachments.

Drillpress The simplest drillpress, often found in a handyman's workshop, is a clamp on a vertical column designed to hold an electric drill (see DRILL, ELECTRIC) above a work table. The clamp travels up and down on a rack and gear, operated manually. The industrial drillpress has a spindle operated by an electric motor; drills of various sizes are adapted to the spindle, usually by means of tapered sleeves. For a large number of identical workpieces, the table will have a fixture into which the pieces can be clamped one after the other. The vertical travel of the spindle may be automatic or manual;

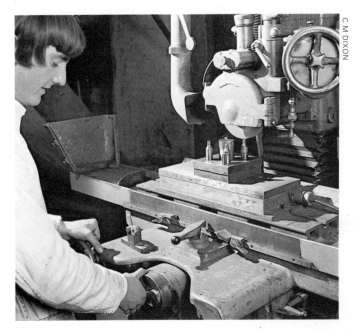

Above: surface grinding. The tips of tools are being ground perfectly flat and smooth; the tools are first hardened by heat treatment. A small grinding job like this can be carefully done without the use of coolant. The table passes back and forth beneath the grinding wheel.

Below: a machine hand makes adjustment to grinding stones. On this type of grinding machine the wheel head revolves and the work table revolves slowly underneath it, also moving in and out. Large amounts of coolant fluid are used.

in industrial mass production a drillpress may have multiple spindles. For drilling holes of precise size, a slightly small hole is drilled first and then a *reamer*, having straight flutes designed to remove only small amounts of metal, is used to bring the hole to size. A *tap* can also be used in a drillpress; this is a fluted, multi-toothed cutter which cuts threads on the inside of a hole. Drilling and tapping operations, especially at speed, normally require a constant stream of cutting fluid. A multiple spindle radial drilling machine is illustrated on pages 194–95.

Automatic transfer For all the tons of *swarf* (metal chips) made by metal cutting, more than 90% are from drilling operations. This can be seen from the large number of holes in pieces such as cylinder blocks for INTERNAL COMBUSTION ENGINES. Where high production is needed, the *indexing automatic transfer* system may be used, where the component is moved automatically from one machine station to the next. At each station a *unit head* is arranged as required in a vertical, horizontal or angular attitude to the work piece. Each unit head is driven by its own electric motor, and is provided with 'pick-off' gears for the feeding motion instead of an elaborate gearbox. The actual feed may be hydraulic, pneumatic or cam operated, but simplicity of construction keeps repairs to a minimum.

A unit head can be designed and equipped to perform more than one cutting operation. Each head advances at its station and retracts when its cutting job is complete; when all heads have retracted and tripped their respective limit switches, the machine automatically indexes to the next work station. Many such machines are of radial design: the stations are arranged in a circle; the operator stands in one place; each time the machine indexes, the operator removes a finished piece from a fixture and inserts a fresh one. The use of unit heads is not restricted to automatic transfer machines; an example of a Cincinnati automatic multiple unit head is illustrated on page 194. (See AUTOMATIC CONTROL.)

In-line transfer machine For greater mass production, the *in-line transfer* system is used. A typical installation for machining cylinder blocks for Austin cars is 65 feet (20 m) long and has fourteen stations. Its operation commences with a casting picked up by an air-operated carriage which places it on a *transfer bar conveyer*. The piece is located at the first station. The tools advance, carry out their machining operation, and retire. The piece is then advanced to the next station, located, machined and so on until it reaches the end of the line. Meanwhile other castings are following it. A finished block comes off the end of the line about every four minutes. Such an installation may perform drilling, reaming, tapping, boring, *honing* (see below) and milling operations with only two operators, one to put the casting on the line and one to take off the finished block. (There are usually also inspectors to see that the machining is being carried out correctly.) The blocks are then ready to go to the engine ASSEMBLY LINE.

Below left: a cylindrical grinding operation. The shaft is held between centres and rotated while the grinding wheel rotates at high speed in the opposite direction. Coolant flow can be seen.
Below: a rotary transfer machine. There are four milling heads. The coolant is piped from the centre. The turntable indexes when all four heads have advanced and withdrawn; the operator removes a piece from a fixture and installs a fresh one.

The transfer bar itself is usually operated by a hydraulic piston, and the blocks are located against positive stops, then clamped in place while machining goes on. The failure of any part of the system registers on a bank of lights on a control panel; all functions must take place before transfer can be effected. Repairmen are available to replace broken and worn-out tools so that downtime is at a minimum.

Other machine tools

Honing is the polishing and finishing to size of a hole, such as the cylinder bore in an engine block, by a *hone*. The hone is a cylindrical tool holder mounted in a spindle which holds a number of honing stones on its perimeter. It is inserted into the hole while rotating at a relatively slow speed compared to drilling; the exact speed depends upon the amount of stock to be removed, the size of the stones and their number. The stones are made of bonded abrasive material. Hones are also used when overhauling engines, for example, to polish cylinder walls which have been damaged by worn piston rings.

An *automatic screw machine* is a type of automatic lathe. It holds lengths of bar stock and indexes them in a circle. At each station in the circle a machining operation is performed; at the last station the finished piece is cut off, the chuck opens,

Below: the shaper is often used to rough out a piece of work to its external dimensions before more intricate machining is done. The work is held in a vice, or the vice is removed and the work clamped to the table by means of T slots. The reciprocating ram carries the tool across the work; the table feeds across in small increments with each return stroke. The length and speed of the stroke as well as the rate of table traverse are adjustable.

the bar is advanced to a positive stop and chucked up again, usually by hydraulic pressure. The automatic screw machine makes small round pieces such as screws, bolts, nuts and small gear blanks. One operator can service several machines.

Grinding machines are used to machine metal surfaces to precise sizes. All the bearing surfaces on a crankshaft, for example, must be finished to a precise uniform size, which also means they must be absolutely smooth and highly polished; more than 300 grinding operations are required in the manufacture of a motor car. Pieces such as slideways for machines must be hardened by heat treatment; once they are hardened, they can only be finished to size by grinding.

Grinding machines must be in good repair and isolated from external vibration. Round stock is turned relatively slowly *between centres* (see LATHE) while the edge of the grinding wheel, which turns in the opposite direction at hundreds or thousands of revolutions per minute, is carefully brought to bear. Flat work pieces are passed under the edge of a grinding wheel on a reciprocating table, or are revolved on a turning table under the recessed side of a horizontally turning wheel. Electromagnets are often used to hold flat work on the table. A grinding wheel must be *dressed* frequently with a DIAMOND tool to keep it straight and true.

Coolant fluid must be continuously used during heavier grinding operations. Inherent in grinding is the production of heat because of friction; if the surface being ground is allowed to expand because of heat, the wheel will 'dig in', ruining the work and probably causing an accident.

Conditions of careful manufacture, handling and storage of grinding wheels must be adhered to. The wheels are very

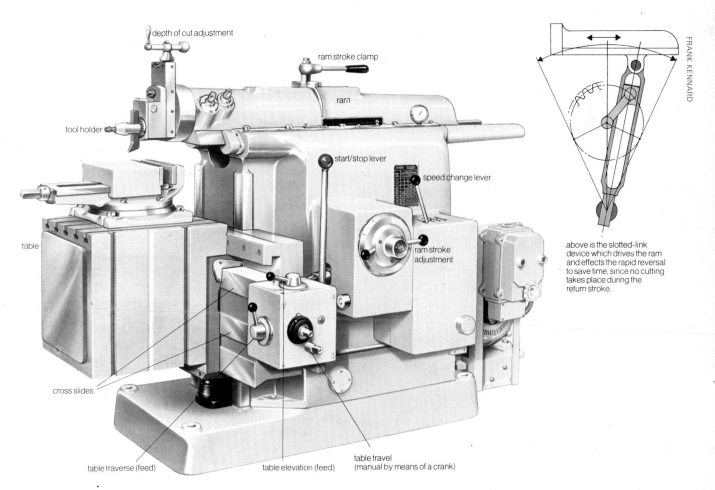

FRANK KENNARD

depth of cut adjustment

ram stroke clamp

ram

tool holder

start/stop lever

speed change lever

ram stroke adjustment

table

cross slides

table traverse (feed)

table elevation (feed)

table travel (manual by means of a crank)

above is the slotted-link device which drives the ram and effects the rapid reversal to save time, since no cutting takes place during the return stroke.

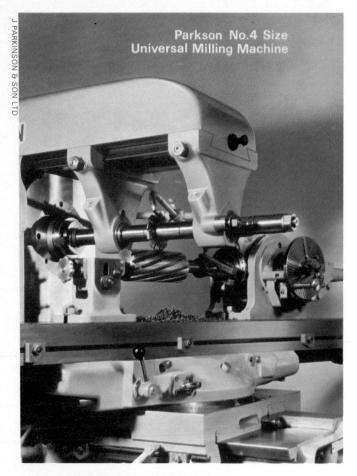

Parkson No.4 Size
Universal Milling Machine

J PARKINSON & SON LTD

CINCINNATI MILACRON

brittle, and the strength of the bond is limited by the necessity for tiny pieces of the abrasive material to come loose in the grinding process. The turning speed of the wheel is specified by the manufacturer, and must not be exceeded: tremendous CENTRIFUGAL FORCE is generated by the high speed, and a disintegrating grinding wheel will cause grave damage to operator and equipment. (See also ABRASIVES.)

Machine tool automation DIGITAL READOUT DEVICES for machine tools are now becoming common. On a lathe, the digital readout screen will have two lines; the inward travel of the tool and the lengthwise travel of the carriage causes transducers to transmit dimensions to the readout device. The operator stops the machine when the required size is reached.

For grinding machines, automatic work sizing is accomplished by a Microtonic feed whereby the wheel head is actuated by an electric stepping motor, controlled by digital information programmed on the control panel. The system uses solid state electronics with printed circuits; the stepping motor can advance the wheel in increments as small as .000025 inch (.006 mm) as finish size is approached.

In *plugboard* control, the board comprises a grid pattern of holes, each horizontal row representing a machine function. Insertion of plugs completes circuits when scanning by an indexing uniselector, and actuates air cylinders connected to slideways.

Numerical control (NC) is economic if used with large machining units in mass production, and if checking, inspection, adjustment and so forth can be kept to a minimum. NC is also used to perform the maximum number of machining operations on a large, complicated work piece. Numerically controlled co-ordinate settings are recorded as sets of 'numbers' on punched tape, which may be paper, film or MAGNETIC TAPE. The information is 'read' by the machine and transferred into movement of machine heads.

In the 'point to point' system, used for drilling or straight milling, the tool must be at 'A' and perform some operation, then get to point 'B' and so forth. The path of travel between points is not important because no cutting is taking place. In the 'continuous path' the path is important and so is the speed of travel, because this is the actual feed rate, dictated by the type of tool, material being worked and other considerations. A typical tape one inch (25 mm) wide may have eight channels for instructions; the TAB code is a spacer between instructions and EOB means End Of Block, telling the 'reader' to stop the tape and act on instructions up to that point.

Unit heads are in use which can change their own broken or worn-out tools, or change tools in spindles for alternate operations, and machinery is under development which repairs itself. In addition, non-machining processes are in use for certain applications, such as ultrasonic grinding, LASER and ELECTROCHEMICAL metal removal. (See also SHEET METAL FORMING.)

Above left: a milling machine with a horizontal spindle. A blank milling cutter is being machined. It is held between centres and the dividing head is geared to the lead screw of the table, so that it turns at the right speed as the table moves past the spindle of the machine. The coolant tubing can be seen above the cutter. Below left: a vertical milling machine with end mill installed. A machine body casting is being finished; cast metals can often be machined without coolant. The machine head can be tilted; the table can feed laterally, in-and-out or up-and-down. Drills and other tools can also be fitted to the spindle of the machine.

MAGNETIC TAPE

Magnetic recording tape consists of a layer of powdered magnetic material held together by a plastic binder, and coated on to a plastic base film which provides support and mechanical strength.

The base film is usually made of a polyester material, the thicknesses used ranging from 0.002 inch (0.051 mm) in the standard tapes to only 0.00033 inch (0.0084 mm) for the very thin tape used in C120 CASSETTES. The width varies from 0.15 inch (3.81 mm) for cassettes to 0.25 inch (6.35 mm) for cartridges and open reel sound recorders, 0.5 inch (12.7 mm) for computer tapes, and up to 2 inches (5.08 cm) for professional studio and broadcasting sound and vision recording.

The magnetic coating is even thinner, being between 0.000125 and 0.0005 inch (0.0032 to 0.0127 mm) thick, but every inch of the tape contains many millions of particles of the magnetic powder. Each particle behaves like a tiny magnet, and the particles are so small that they can only be seen with an ELECTRON MICROSCOPE.

The magnetic material of most tapes is one of the oxides of iron, known as the *gamma* oxide, Fe_2O_3, which gives the tape its characteristic brown colour. Some tapes are black in colour because finely divided carbon black has been added to conduct away any electrostatic charge which might accumulate on the tape as it moves through the recording or playback equipment. New materials used in place of iron oxide to improve performance include cobalt-iron oxides and chromium dioxide (CrO_2).

Recording During recording, the input signals are amplified and fed to the recording head, essentially a coil of wire through which the signal current passes and which is wound round a core of magnetic material. The core has a narrow gap cut into it at the point where the coated surface of the tape passes across it. As the incoming signal varies, so does the magnetization of the core, and a corresponding magnetic flux is created across and around the gap, setting up a similarly varying magnetic field in the coating of the tape adjacent to the gap.

The magnetic particles pass through the field at the gap as they are carried past it by the moving tape. The particles cannot physically move in the field, being fixed in the coating of the tape, but their magnetism is taken around a *hysteresis loop* (see MAGNETISM) and they leave the head having some remanent (remaining) magnetism, the strength of which depends on the strength of the field from the gap at the instant each piece of tape is in contact with it. The tape thus retains along its length a magnetic 'memory' of the changes in the field, and therefore of the original signal.

Playback When the tape is played back by passing it across a replay head, similar to the recording head, the process is reversed. The varying magnetic fields on the surface of the tape head due to the remanent magnetism stored on the tape

Top right: magnetic tape is made from wide rolls of plastic base film which is cleaned, coated, and dried, then slit to the required width on this machine, which cuts accurately to within about a hundredth of a millimetre.

Centre right: preparing leader tape which is spliced to the ends of the magnetic tape. Open reel tapes for sound recording usually have a red leader on one end and a green leader on the other.

Right: tape slit to width for use in cassettes.

set up corresponding flux changes in the core, and thus induce currents in the coils. These are amplified and will reproduce the original signal when played back through the appropriate device, such as a television or loudspeaker.

The magnetism in the tape remains unaffected by the replay process, and the signal can be replayed time and time again. The tape can be erased for re-use by passing it across an erase head, which has a larger gap than the recording or playback head, and a strong high frequency current flowing through the coils. As the particles move through the field from this head, their magnetism is taken round a series of hysteresis loops of progressively reducing size until no nett magnetism remains.

Multi-track recording
By making the longest dimension of the head gaps much shorter than the tape width, and including several gap, core and coil assemblies magnetically screened from each other in one head unit, a number of tracks can be recorded on a single tape. This multi-track working can be used to increase the playing time of the tape by playing it through first on one track and then on another, or to provide more than one signal at a time such as the two channels of a stereo recording or the sound and vision of a television recording.

Uses
One of the main uses of magnetic tape is for sound recording, on open reel tape or on cassettes or cartridges. Typical tape speeds are $1\frac{7}{8}$ inches per second (4.75 cm/sec) for cassettes, and $3\frac{3}{4}$ ips (9.5 cm/sec) for cartridges. Open reel tapes may be run at $1\frac{7}{8}$, $3\frac{3}{4}$, $7\frac{1}{2}$ or 15 ips (4.75, 9.5, 19 or 38 cm/sec), the higher speeds being used mainly for professional and hi-fi applications.

In computer DATA STORAGE applications, the tapes may run at as much as 200 ips (508 cm/sec) and the signals are in the form of a series of pulses 'written' in seven or nine channels across the tape.

By using a thinner polyester base, more tape can be wound on to a given size of reel. 'Standard play' and computer tapes are about 0.002 inch (0.051 mm) thick, and this tape is also used for professional sound recording. 'Long play', VIDEO and scientific information recording tapes are usually 0.0015 inch (0.04 mm) thick. 'Double play' tape, used for domestic sound recording, is 0.001 inch (0.0254 mm) thick. 0.00075 inch (0.019 mm) thick tape is used for 'triple play' tape and for C60 cassettes, and the C90 and C120 cassettes use 0.0005 inch (0.0127 mm) quadruple play and 0.00033 inch (0.0084 mm) quintuple play tapes respectively.

MAGNETISM

Magnetism is often thought of as a force in its own right, yet it is just one manifestation of the *electromagnetic force* (see FIELDS and FORCES). It is closely linked with electrostatic force: the difference is that while a stationary charged particle has just an electric field associated with it, a moving particle has a magnetic field as well. Yet it is possible to produce *permanent magnets*—indeed, these are the most familiar type—which have no apparent associated electric field. Modern physics has explained permanent magnets in terms of electromagnetism, though as with all scientific explanations, the theories only show the way in which things work, and fail to clarify just why they should do so in the first place.

FARADAY, in the 1830s, demonstrated clearly the relationship between electric charge and magnetism. When electric charge moves it is said to constitute an *electric current*. When an electric current flows, it generates a magnetic field in the space around it just as if the current system had been replaced by a magnet system with a particular shape. It takes a force, analogous to the pressure needed to cause water to flow in a pipe, to make a charge move, that is, to produce an electric current. This force is known as an electromotive force (emf). Faraday showed that when an object capable of conducting electric current was moved through a magnetic field, an emf was set up in the conductor, capable of producing electric current. He also demonstrated that when the magnetic field which 'threaded' a conducting object was *changed*, an emf was also produced. So electricity produces magnetism and magnetism produces electricity.

Magnetic circuits
The concept of magnetism existing only in closed loops is a useful one and was known to Faraday. It can be shown experimentally that the 'driving force' in a magnetic circuit of an electromagnet (analogous to emf in an electric circuit) is proportional both to the number of turns which form the coil and the current in that coil. This is called the *magnetomotive force* (mmf) and measured in *ampere-turns*. We then invent an imaginary 'substance' which we consider to be the result of this mmf; this we call *magnetic flux* (or sometimes 'induction') and is measured in *webers*. Then we can write an equivalent of OHM's law (see CIRCUIT, electrical) for a magnetic circuit and use it to calculate the mmf needed to set up a certain flux or the reverse. In electrical circuits emf equals current times resistance, and in magnetic circuits mmf equals flux times *reluctance* (the impediment to the flow of flux).

Below: microphoto of the magnetic particles in two kinds of tape coating. Chromium dioxide particles, on the right, have better high frequency performance than the iron oxide particles on the left.

BASF

40 MILLIONTHS OF AN INCH

(a)   (b)   (c)

MAGNETIC FIELD H

BELL TELEPHONE LABORATORIES

Above: domain structure in Alnico 5 alloy. In A the alloy was heat treated without a magnetic field and the domains are at right angles to each other. B was heat treated with a magnetic field applied and the domains align. C is a cross section of B—the domains are 0.012 microns thick, 0.025 microns long and 0.05 microns wide.

Below left: Gilbert's experiment demonstrating induced magnetism in iron wire (A & B) by magnet (C) causing repulsive force.

Below right: these four pictures show magnetostrictive energy in domain structure of pure iron, nickel and cobalt crystals. When magnetized, the crystals change in length and create internal strain.

Bottom: At a few degrees above absolute zero temperature the pan, which is made of lead and normally a poor conductor of electricity, becomes a superconductor (no resistance). As the magnet is lowered on the chain into the pan (1) currents are induced which set up a magnetic field to oppose the magnet. Finally, the magnet will drop no lower (2) because the induced magnetic field is large enough to support it. The chain then becomes slack (3). Superconductor electromagnets can create very large magnetic fields.

Permanent magnets

This tidy pattern of what is universally known as ELECTROMAGNETISM is, however, upset by an aspect of magnetism that has no precise counterpart in electricity. Some elements, having been placed in a magnetic field and then removed from it, adopt and retain an apparent internal source of mmf and they continue to drive a flux pattern in the space around them. These we call permanent magnets and the phenomenon 'ferromagnetism', because one of the elements is iron (Latin *ferrum*). The others are the less common metals cobalt and nickel and still rarer elements such as gadolinium and dysprosium.

Many textbooks on magnetism and electricity begin with the discovery of lodestones in the Chinese desert in 3000 BC. This, and the fact that horseshoe and bar magnets have been available in toyshops for many generations, has resulted in a demand

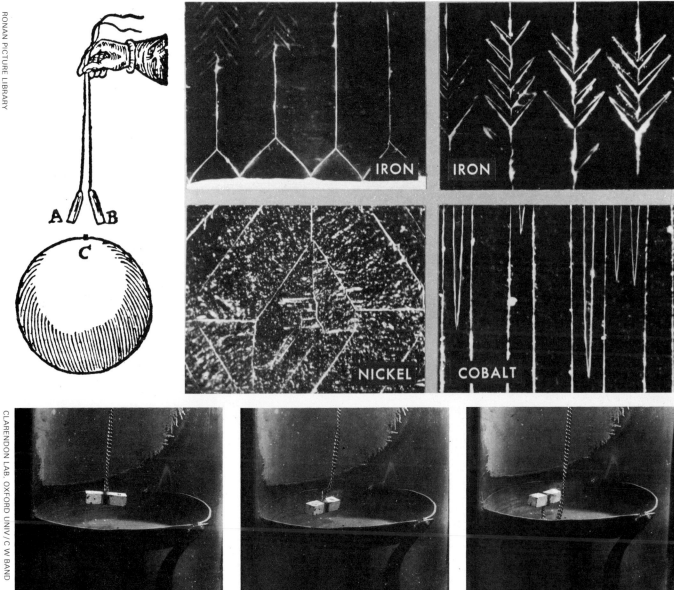

RONAN PICTURE LIBRARY

BELL TELEPHONE LABORATORIES

CLARENDON LAB. OXFORD UNIV / C W BAND

A   B
C

IRON   IRON
NICKEL   COBALT

1   2   3

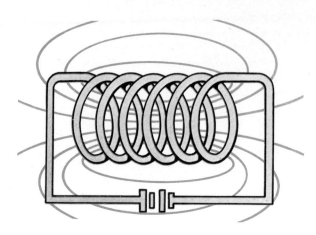

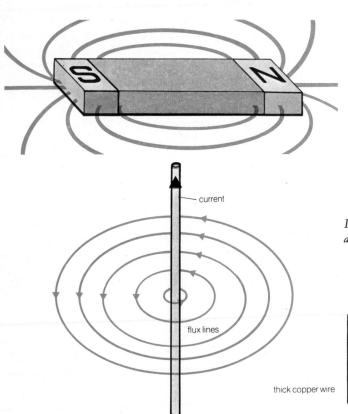

Left and above: a coil of wire carrying an electric current sets up a magnetic field the same shape as that from a bar magnet.

- current
- flux lines
- thick copper wire

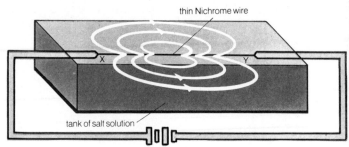

- thin Nichrome wire
- X
- Y
- tank of salt solution

Above: current flowing in a straight wire sets up a magnetic field pattern which may be represented as concentric circles of 'flux'.

Above: there is no such thing as a magnetic insulator and all materials 'conduct' magnetic flux. Magnetic circuits are therefore rather like a conducting electric wire immersed in a salt bath. The current through the solution gives the appearance of poles at X and Y.

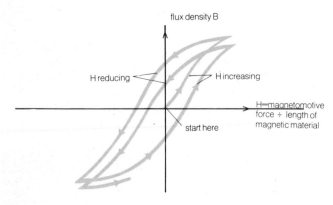

flux density B

H reducing / H increasing

H=magnetomotive force ÷ length of magnetic material

start here

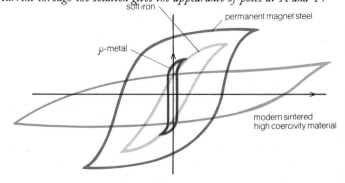

- soft iron
- μ-metal
- permanent magnet steel
- modern sintered high coercivity material

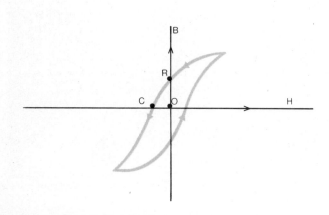

B

R

C O

H

Above left: a typical magnetic 'journey' as the result of an oscillating magnetomotive force (mmf) in a ferromagnetic material. The ultimate steady cycle after millions of cycles is shown at left. The point R is called the 'Remanence point', the distance OR being what is left of the flux density B after the magnetizing force H has been removed. The distance OC is called the 'Coercivity', being the value of H required to demagnetize the specimen completely.

Above: the shapes of hysteresis loops of various ferromagnetic materials useful in engineering. Permanent magnet steels have small additions of other elements to make OC and OR as large as possible and the total enclosed area of the loop as large as possible. For magnetic screens in electron optical systems such as television tubes the highest magnetic conductivity possible is required; the loop should have a small area and the sides should be steep.

OSBORNE/MARKS

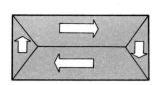

Above: arrangement of saturated domains in an unmagnetized iron crystal.

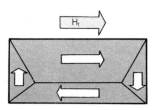

Above: domains resulting from application of magnetizing force H₁ in direction shown.

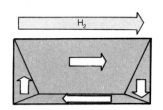

Above: when the magnetizing force is increased to H₂ the domain in that direction grows in size.

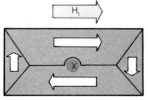
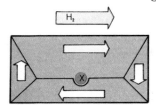

Above: this shows the result of an impurity X being crossed by a Bloch wall during magnetization. There is a sudden jump between (a) and (b) detectable as an earphone 'click' (Barkhausen effect).

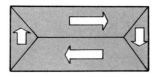

Above: no external field.

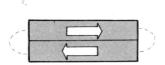

Above: some magnetostatic energy as particle size is reduced.

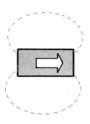

Above: no Bloch wall energy in a single domain.

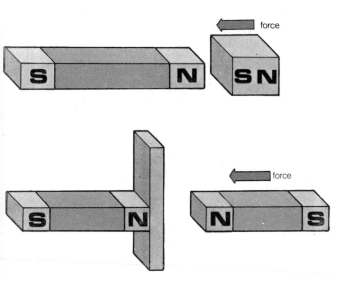

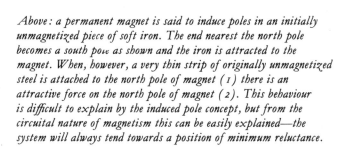

Above: a permanent magnet is said to induce poles in an initially unmagnetized piece of soft iron. The end nearest the north pole becomes a south pole as shown and the iron is attracted to the magnet. When, however, a very thin strip of originally unmagnetized steel is attached to the north pole of magnet (1) there is an attractive force on the north pole of magnet (2). This behaviour is difficult to explain by the induced pole concept, but from the circuital nature of magnetism this can be easily explained—the system will always tend towards a position of minimum reluctance.

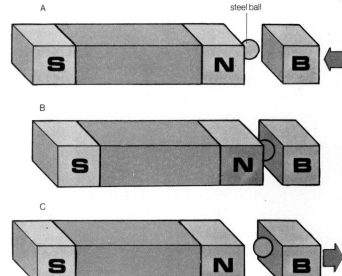

Above: the steel ball, initially unmagnetized, can always be pulled off the primary magnet's pole face by touching it with an unmagnetized piece of iron (B) which is then pulled away as shown in the sequence (a) to (c). The pole concept of magnetism cannot explain this behaviour but the circuit concept can. It can be shown that the 'circuit' has a minimum reluctance when the ball is attached to the iron (B) rather than to the magnet.

for an 'explanation' of their behaviour at a very early part of a school curriculum. The fact that the Earth itself is magnetized along an axis roughly corresponding to its axis of rotation was used by the ancient Chinese, who found that a freely suspended lodestone would always set itself in the same geographical direction. Simple rules were needed to deal with a simple action-at-distance experience, and soon the rule emerged that the lodestone had 'poles' that pointed north and south. This was followed by the rule that 'like poles repel, unlike poles attract'.

From an educational point of view it is doubtful whether the readily available 'permanent' magnets are a blessing or a curse, for they focus attention away from the circuital nature of magnetism, which is far more useful in engineering than is the pole concept. Arguments against the circuital concept are that unlike electric circuits, magnetic circuits cannot be insulated (see INSULATOR, electric) because the corresponding *magnetic conductivity* of air or empty space is finite and only about a thousand times smaller than that of the best magnetically conducting steel. Faraday himself likened the design of magnetic circuits to the design of electric circuits using bare copper wire in a bath of salt water (which is a good conductor of electricity). The result is that while the electric circuits of most electrodynamic machines are complex and consist of coils of thin wire, multi-turned, their magnetic circuits are simple, short, fat and consist of a single turn.

The disadvantages of the pole concept however are first that it presupposes isolated poles in space; these have not been found, despite searches (isolated electric charges, however, do exist); and second, that troubles arise when trying to predict reactions between permanent magnets and other, initially unmagnetized, pieces of ferromagnetic material. For this purpose the law of *induced magnetism* is invented, implying that the proximity of a primary magnet pole to a piece of soft iron induces an opposite pole in the latter nearest to the magnet and a similar pole at the point most remote from the magnet. There are a number of experiments which are very hard to explain on the basis of poles alone, while the circuit concept sees no difficulty in such arrangements: the pieces will always take up a position of *minimum reluctance* (that is, minimum

impediment to the flow of flux), within the prevailing mechanical constraints. The circuit theory sees a magnet's pole merely as a change in reluctance between different parts of a magnetic circuit.

The hysteresis loop The difficulty with permanent magnets does not end here. The magnetic flux density B (the number of flux 'lines' crossing unit area—measured as webers per square metre) that can be induced in a ferromagnetic material by imposing an mmf on it is not directly proportional to that mmf. Furthermore, if flux density is plotted as a graph against magnetizing force H, (a quantity obtained by dividing mmf by magnetic length and measured in ampere-turns per metre) the state of magnetization of a piece of ferromagnetic material is seen to depend on its entire magnetic 'history'. If taken through many circles until a repetitive pattern occurs, the loop so obtained is called a *hysteresis loop* whose area can be shown to be the *work done* in taking the magnetic material around one cycle and which appears as heat in the material itself.

The ratio B/H is given the name permeability (μ) but it is clear that μ is not constant as B varies. It is this aspect which becomes such an easy concept in magnetic circuits involving no ferromagnetic material, for μ is then constant and is the magnetic conductivity directly usable in the magnetic circuit version of Ohm's Law.

Theories of ferromagnetism The behaviour of ferromagnetics is one of the hardest phenomena to explain in terms of conventional physics. For several generations, Weber's theory that all ferromagnetic substances were effectively made of a mass of tiny particles, each of which was a permanent magnet, remained the only plausible model, but the imagination had to be strained to account for various degrees of difficulty being encountered in forcing the 'micromagnets' to line up, as exhibited in the hysteresis effect.

The modern (*domain*) theory of ferromagnetism could be said to begin with the observation of the Barkhausen effect, whereby audible 'clicks' were heard in a telephone receiver when connected to a coil of wire surrounding a ferromagnetic specimen that was being magnetized by a *very gradually increasing* mmf. Most of the pioneering work was done at the Bell Tele-

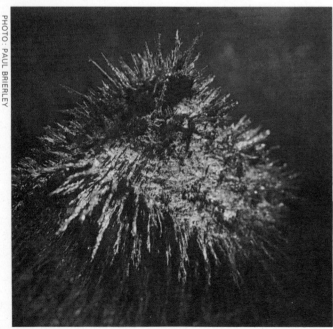

PHOTO: PAUL BRIERLEY

FERROFLUIDICS CORP

Left: permanent magnet in a sample of lodestone from Utah, USA. At the pole, iron filings indicate lines of flux.

Right: magnetic fluids (or ferrofluids) are fluids which react with magnetic fields. This shows liquid spikes forming at the surface of a magnetic fluid subject to a vertical magnetic field. Spike formation is attributed to energy balance between magnetic and interfacial tension at the surface.

Far right: Despite their rigid appearance, the burrs or spikes are completely fluid and are due to the component of magnetic field that is at right angles to the free surface.

phone Laboratories in the USA by a team that included Bozorth, Dillinger, Shockley (of TRANSISTOR fame) and Williams. The technique they evolved was to polish the surface of a specimen and then etch it with acid. This revealed patterns of 'walls', later to be called *Bloch walls* dividing regions of different magnetic orientation. The theory of these domains was then built up to the following detailed picture.

A clue to the essential difference between a ferromagnetic element and a non-ferromagnetic one is to be found in their atomic structures. The ELECTRONS orbiting the nucleus of an atom are arranged in *shells*, beginning with the simplest atoms 'filling' the innermost shell and shells of large radius then being used for the electrons of elements higher in the PERIODIC TABLE, and therefore with more electrons. In order to balance the forces and energies within an atom it is necessary to credit orbiting electrons with a spin (even though it is sometimes necessary to describe an electron as energy and therefore without shape).

One feature that is unique to the ferromagnetic elements is that their atoms each have at least one electron with an uncompensated spin in one of the outer shells. Latching on to this as the basis of the mechanism, it was soon shown that atoms finding themselves in relative positions such that the axes of the uncompensated spins were parallel, were likely to stay thus related and thereafter to regiment neighbouring atoms in this direction. This build up process is rapid and implies that every crystal of a ferromagnetic metal structure is self-magnetizing to saturation level.

In the case of each single crystal, however, what had hitherto been defined as the degree of magnetization was not due to each part of the crystal being magnetized to the same fraction of its saturation level. Rather the crystal is divided into portions or domains, each of which is self-saturated, but not all domains are lying in the same magnetic direction. The rules for the domains can be investigated both experimentally by the etching process and theoretically, for the crystal as a whole tries to assume a pattern of minimum total energy.

The various forms of energy in a magnetic metal crystal may be classified as follows. Firstly, there is magnetostatic energy, where the flux has to emerge from the crystal and pass through space. Secondly, there is magnetostriction energy due to the crystal increasing or decreasing in length because of magnetization, producing mechanical strain energy. Thirdly, there is Bloch wall energy due to strain in the atomic lattice where, within a distance only a few atoms thick, the spin must reverse.

When a ferromagnetic metal is reduced to finer and finer particles, the minimum energy condition is reduced to magnetization in one direction only. This knowledge gave rise to a whole new magnet technology in which fine metallic powders were shaken so as to allow them to line up with each other (just as Weber's theory stated) and the whole then heated (sintered) to make a permanent magnet with a very large coercivity. (This is the magnetizing force required to 'pull' the flux down to zero after its initial magnetization). This technique can be extended to include substances other than pure metals known as *ferrites*. These are CERAMIC material consisting basically of iron oxide and small quantities of TRANSITION metal oxides such as cobalt and nickel. It was found that in the case of non-metallic magnetic materials not all the electron spins within a domain were aligned in the same direction. Instead, a portion of the atoms had their uncompensated spins aligned in one direction while the rest of the atoms had their spins aligned in the opposite direction. Externally, therefore, such materials cannot contain as high a flux level as can metallic substances. These ferrite substances are said to display *ferrimagnetism*. They are used in MICROWAVE apparatus where it is essential that the substance is not capable of conducting electricity. Furthermore, the flux saturation level can be controlled by mixing different materials.

More recent developments have produced flexible and even liquid magnetic materials by the powder-metallurgy process, suspensions of barium ferrite and other similar materials being held in a base of rubber, polyvinyl chloride and other plastic materials. In the case of liquids, each particle of ferrite is encapsulated in a single layer of molecules of a long-chain polymer. The capsules slide over each other with virtually no frictional resistance, so when made as a suspension in water, the liquid has the viscosity of water but the particles are so small that thermal agitation prevents them from settling.

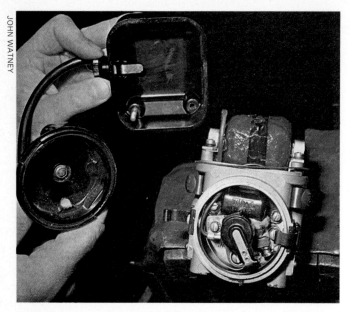

JOHN WATNEY

MAGNETO

The magneto is an ignition device for spark-ignition INTERNAL COMBUSTION ENGINES, and it combines most of the features of a coil IGNITION SYSTEM into a single unit. Driven directly from the engine, it performs the same functions as the coil and DISTRIBUTOR of a conventional system, and in addition it generates its own electrical energy thus eliminating the need for a BATTERY to power the ignition system.

Battery ignition systems are standard on most car and many motorcycle engines today, but magneto ignition is still in common use on lightweight motorcycles (particularly those with two-stroke engines), aircraft piston engines, stationary engines, and lightweight engines such as those used for lawn mowers and small pumps.

The three main types of magneto are the *rotating coil*, *rotating magnet*, and the *inductor* magnetos.

Rotating coil
The rotating coil magneto has a rotating armature wound with two coils: the primary, which consists of a few hundred turns of thick insulated copper wire, and the secondary coil which has many thousands of turns of fine copper wire and is wound around the primary. The armature rotates between the poles of a permanent magnet, and the magneto also has a contact breaker to switch the primary current and a distributor unit which delivers the high tension secondary current to the SPARK PLUGS.

One end of the primary coil is connected to earth [ground] and to one end of the secondary coil. The contact breaker and a CAPACITOR (which prevents arcing and aids the build-up of the secondary current) are connected between the ends of the primary coil. The secondary current is collected by a carbon

Above: a view of the end of a magneto, showing the contact breaker points and the capacitor. The capacitor is connected across the points to prevent arcing when they open, and this minimizes pitting of the point surfaces and assists the rapid build-up of the current in the secondary winding.

Below: an early magneto, built by Robert Bosch, which was fitted to a 1902 Panhard-Levassor. Bosch, who worked for a time with Edison in the USA, made many innovations in automotive engineering.

BOSCH

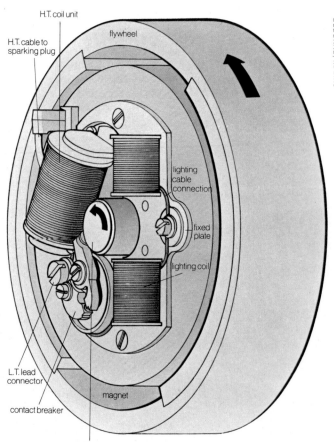

OSBORNE / MARKS

H.T. coil unit

flywheel

H.T. cable to
sparking plug

lighting
cable
connection

fixed
plate

lighting coil

L.T. lead
connector

magnet

contact breaker

flywheel boss and cam

brush which contacts a brass slip ring connected to the other end of the secondary coil.

As the armature rotates the coils pass through the magnetic flux between the pole pieces of the magnet, and with the contact breaker closed an alternating current is *induced* in the primary winding (see ALTERNATOR and DYNAMO). The maximum induced current flows when the coils are at 90° to the lines of flux between the pole pieces. At this point the flux in the coils is zero, but its rate of change (which determines the value of the induced current at any instant) is at a maximum.

When the armature is in this position the contact breaker points open, interrupting the current flow in the primary. The magnetic field associated with this current collapses rapidly, and a very high voltage is induced in the secondary winding, as in an INDUCTION COIL. This voltage is discharged through the slip ring and brush to the distributor part of the magneto which delivers it to the appropriate spark plug.

Rotating magnet
An improvement on the moving coil magneto is the rotating magnet type, in which the coils are wound around a stationary core. The core is mounted across the ends of a pair of pole pieces, forming a U-shaped magnetic circuit, and a permanent magnet, fixed to a shaft driven by the engine, is rotated between the pole pieces. This produces a changing flux in the core which induces an alternating current in the primary and when this current is interrupted by the opening of the contact breaker a high voltage is induced in the secondary. This voltage passes directly to the distributor section; there is no need for a slip ring because the coils are stationary.

Inductor magnetos
In the inductor magneto both the coil assembly and the magnet are stationary, the flux changes being created by the action of a soft iron inductor. The inductor has four lobes, and the magnetic circuit is completed through them. As the inductor rotates the lobes move in and out of the magnetic flux, causing the flux changes which create the current in the primary coil.

The current in the primary is interrupted by a contact breaker operated by a cam on the drive shaft, and the secondary current is passed to the spark plugs by means of a distributor unit at the end of the magneto.

Flywheel magnetos
On many small engines, such as two-stroke motorcycle engines, the coils are mounted on a fixed aluminium plate and the magnets are carried on an aluminium flywheel on the end of the engine crankshaft. As the crankshaft turns the magnets are rotated around the coils, which produces the primary current, and the primary circuit is broken by a contact breaker mounted on the plate and operated by a cam on the flywheel hub. These units often have additional coils which generate the power for the motorcycle's lights and horn.

Left: the flywheel magneto used on lightweight motorcycles provides electrical power for both ignition and lighting. The magnets are fitted into the rim of the flywheel, the coils remaining stationary on the baseplate. As the flywheel turns the magnets induce currents in the coils, the primary circuit of the ignition coil being opened and closed by a contact breaker, which is operated by a camming surface on the hub of the flywheel.

Right: inside an early 40W MHD generator. High velocity, hot ionized gas is generated by a small rocket and passes between two graphite electrodes (left and right). Two pole pieces at front and rear (removed for picture) create flux densities of 1 tesla in the plasma.

MAGNETOHYDRODYNAMICS (MHD)

Just as hydrodynamics deals with the way in which water and other fluids move, magnetohydrodynamics or MHD is the science of the way in which fluids which are good conductors of electricity (see CONDUCTION, electrical) move and interact with magnetic fields (see MAGNETISM and FIELDS). The fluid can be either a liquid (such as mercury, molten sodium or brine) or a gaseous conductor, which is called a *plasma* (see MATTER). Gases can become ionized, and therefore able to conduct electricity (see ION), under the influence of heat (as in a FLAME) and many other sources of ENERGY.

When any conductor moves through a magnetic field, an electromotive force (emf) is generated, which drives an electric current in a direction at right angles both to the field and to the direction of motion. A typical example is a dynamo with solid copper conductors, but the same effects applies with a fluid conductor. But with a fluid, the forces can change the flow inside it so the details of the fluid movements must be considered in addition to the ELECTROMAGNETIC effects. It is this coupling together of the equations of motion with the electromagnetic equations that complicates MHD theory.

When dealing with gases, the subject is sometimes called *magnetogasdynamics* (MGD)—that is the Russian term—or *magnetoplasmadynamics* (MPD). The French use the term *magnetoaerodynamique,* but its unfortunate abbreviation, MAD, has prevented its use in English.

MHD generation
When a hot ionized gas is driven through a magnetic field, the current which is generated magnetohydrodynamically can be picked up by a pair of electrodes. In this way, power can be extracted directly from

CEGB

a high temperature flame without the need for all the usual intermediate stages—boiling water to raise steam to pass through a steam turbine to drive a shaft to turn a dynamo. So, as a direct generation process, MHD potentially has considerable advantages.

An important factor in MHD generation is the conductivity of the gas and this depends on the type of gas involved and its temperature. Typically, at a temperature of 3000°C the concentration of ionized atoms is only about one part in a million. At 4000°C this may have increased to one part in 10,000, but this is still far too low for efficient conduction through the gas.

One way of increasing the ionization concentration is to 'seed' the gas with an element more easily ionized at the temperatures involved. For example, at 3000°C the addition of a percent or so of potassium to the gas increases the ionization concentration to about one part in 1000. The gas then has a conductivity of about 40 to 50 mhos per metre (that is, a resistivity of about 0.02 ohm-metre).

Unfortunately, even when the gas is seeded with some easily ionizable material such as potassium and it is raised to temperatures as high as 3000°C to 4000°C, its conductivity is still only a millionth of that of copper. The volume of an MHD generator is therefore much bigger than that of an equivalent copper wound dynamo, its internal resistance is much higher and its efficiency as a generator is lower.

When the power taken from the hot flame, however, has reduced the temperature to around 2000°C, the conductivity is too low for further MHD use but the gas still contains a great deal of heat and this can be used in a conventional generating station. So the MHD generator is a thermodynamic 'topping' device which can increase the total efficiency of conventional plant.

The MHD electrical power which is generated comes from slowing the gas down to extract kinetic energy and from expanding it to release compression energy. The hot gas leaves the combustion chamber at around its sound speed of 2250 mph (1000 m/s)—sound travels about three times faster at flame temperatures than it does at normal temperatures.

The very high flame temperatures can be obtained by burning the fuel (gas, oil or even powdered coal) in oxygen. For large scale use, however, it will be necessary to burn the fuel in air suitably preheated by the hot exhaust gases before they are cleaned, to recover all the seeding material, and released to the atmosphere.

The heat and friction losses at the electrodes and at the insulating side wall surfaces are enormous—conditions are

NOVOSTI PRESS AGENCY

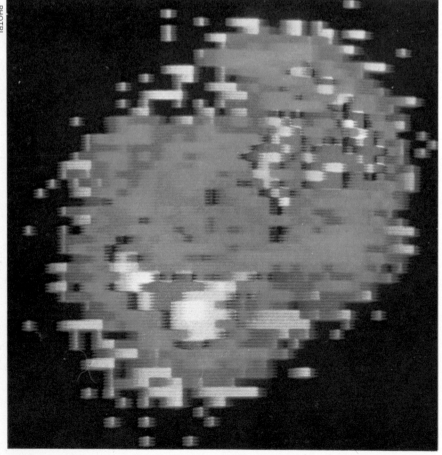
PHOTRI

Above: a pilot commercial MHD generator being installed for operation.
Left: spectroheliograph in digital form (by satellite) of solar storm activity. MHD can be studied in the motion of solar plasma. White regions are areas of intense storms with yellow and red clusters denoting lesser intensities. This storm was one of the most intense in recent years—it created waves in the Earth's magnetic field that caused disruptions in communications around the world.

Top right: this shows the basic configuration for MHD generation. The hot ionized gas (plasma) enters the chamber at high velocity and because it is ionized it behaves like a fast moving conductor. The magnetic field is arranged to be at right angles to the flow of gas so that the gas 'conductor' cuts the maximum amount of flux—this is the same principle as used in a conventional dynamo. The current thus created moves at right angles to both the field and the flow of gas and is 'tapped' from between the two electrodes (top and bottom).

Right: proposed MHD open cycle combustion plant with conventional steam turbine.

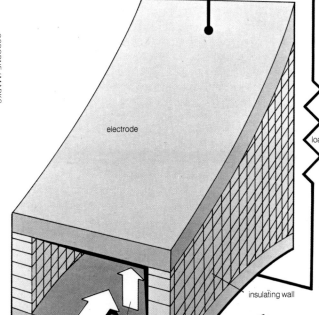

electrode

load

insulating wall

gas

electric current

magnetic field

very similar to those in the nozzle of a Saturn rocket—but the MHD power is generated from the whole volume. To produce more power than is lost, it is necessary to build large multi-megawatt generators whose volumes are large in relation to their wall area.

Russia and the USA have both built MHD generators which burn oil, or natural gas to produce tens of thousands of kilowatts of electricity for a minute or so, a few thousand kilowatts for a few hours and lesser powers for hundreds of hours; they aim to develop MHD power stations which will generate millions of kilowatts.

An alternative source of energy would be a very high temperature NUCLEAR REACTOR which could heat helium and force it round a closed MHD cycle. Since the temperature from a reactor is not high enough to ionize even a seeded gas, some extra non-equilibrium ionization is needed and the development of such a system will take time.

Liquid metal MHD systems are being developed. The heat from a reactor would boil a metal such as sodium and the vapour would force the liquid metal through an MHD duct. Although the conductivity of the liquid metal is very high, the bubbling and foaming of the boiling process causes great problems that have yet to be solved.

The electromagnet needed to provide a very high magnetic field (many Tesla) over the large volume of MHD duct (many cubic metres) calls for hundreds of tons of copper and steel and many megawatts of electrical power. An alternative would be to use a very large SUPERCONDUCTING magnet.

So the successful development of MHD generation will call for new materials and techniques to handle some of the very highest and very lowest temperatures which can be produced.

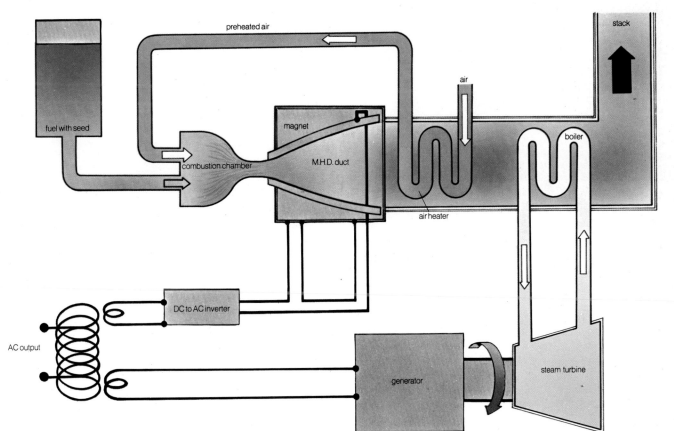

preheated air

stack

fuel with seed

air

combustion chamber

magnet

M.H.D. duct

boiler

air heater

DC to AC inverter

AC output

generator

steam turbine

MAGNETOMETER

The need to measure the strength of magnetic fields in science and industry has resulted in the production of magnetometers of many different types. Early magnetometers consisted of spring loaded magnets in which the field strength was measured by the extension of the spring. These were soon superseded by electronic systems, the most common nowadays being the *proton, fluxgate* and *Hall effect* magnetometers.

Proton magnetometer This is probably the most accurate type of magnetometer available at present, and it relies for its operation on the alignment of PROTONS—the positively charged particles in atoms—within a proton rich source such as paraffin [kerosene], which has a comparatively large number of hydrogen atoms (see HYDROCARBON). The paraffin, which is contained within a bottle, is magnetized to a very high level by means of surrounding coils. When it is fully magnetized the protons are all accurately aligned in the same direction. The moment the exciting field is removed the protons begin to fall back to their original random orientation, and as they do this they induce a voltage in a sensing coil system. The rate at which the proton orientation decays is a measurement of the surrounding magnetic field.

The main advantage of the proton magnetometer is that the decay rate can be extremely accurately measured and therefore the field strength can be obtained very precisely. Its disadvantages are that it cannot be used to measure a rapidly varying or alternating field, the field direction, or, because of the recycling time, the field at any instant in time.

Fluxgate magnetometer This depends for its operation on the rapid AC magnetization of a pair of high permeability (easily magnetizable) cores. Each core has a primary and a secondary winding, one outside the other. An AC current applied to the primary magnetizes the core, which in turn induces a current in the secondary windings. If an external field is present, the core will be magnetized more, and by using two cores, arranged so that their outputs will reinforce each other, the signal is doubled for a given external field. This shows up as an AC voltage of twice the original frequency.

Magnetometers based on this principle can measure fields over a small area (as small as 5 × 2 mm), can detect rapidly varying fields (up to several kilohertz) and can measure field direction as well. They operate within the range 1 to 100,000 gamma: the Earth's field strength is about 50,000 gamma.

Fluxgates are ideally suited to the detection of sunken objects such as ships, bombs, mines and so on. Their directional properties make them useful aboard aircraft as compasses,

FAIREY SURVEYS

Above: a high sensitivity proton magnetometer being towed behind an aircraft, away from the plane's magnetic fields.

Near right: an archaeologist uses a fluxgate magnetometer to detect below-ground magnetic differences. The vertical pole has a detector at each end, the lower one being affected more by buried structures. A long cable connects it to a pen recorder. A three-probe fluxgate magnetometer was used on the Apollo 12 Moon mission (centre right, foreground).

DEPT OF THE ENVIRONMENT / A J CLARK

PHOTRI

with one on each wingtip. Other uses include measurement of magnetic fields in deep space, and detection of the weak magnetic fields of geological and archaeological specimens.

Hall effect The principle of the Hall effect magnetometer was discovered in 1879, but it has only been applied quite recently with the introduction of semiconductor materials such as indium arsenide and indium antimonide. When a current is applied between two edges of a slice of the material, a small voltage is induced across the other two edges by the movement of the electrons carrying the current through the magnetic field. This voltage can be measured, and its magnitude is a measure of the magnetic field strength.

Such a device is particularly suitable for measuring strong magnetic fields—from 100,000 to 20 million gamma, for example—and will work at frequencies up to a megahertz. Because the semiconductor material may be only 0.1 mm thick, it is ideally suited to measuring very strong fields in small spaces in machines such as electric motors.

A common design of magnetometer, of any type, has a probe containing the measuring head connected by cables to the electronics and meter in a separate box. This forms a handy and portable device. Proton magnetometers, however, can be more cumbersome, requiring a vehicle to carry them.

MANOMETER

A manometer is a device for measuring the pressure of a gas; it is a type of PRESSURE GAUGE. In its simplest form it consists of a U-shaped glass tube filled with a liquid, usually mercury. One of the limbs of the tube is open to the atmosphere while the other is connected to the system whose pressure is to be measured. The difference in the level of the mercury in the two limbs of the tube is a measure of the pressure in the system as compared with atmospheric pressure. For example, if the mercury level in the limb connected to the system is 10 cm (3.94 inch) above the level in the limb open to the atmosphere, and atmospheric pressure, which can be measured by a BAROMETER, is 76 cm (29.9 inch) of mercury, then the pressure in the system will be 66 cm (26.0 inch) of mercury. The units centimetres or inches of mercury (cm Hg or in Hg) are commonly used to measure pressures, particularly where barometers or manometers are involved.

Uses An example of a manometer is the *Riva-Rocci sphygmomanometer* which is used by doctors to measure blood pressure

Below: a doctor using a sphygmomanometer to measure arterial blood pressure. The cuff is inflated until no pulsation can be heard in an artery in the forearm, and the pressure is then read off.

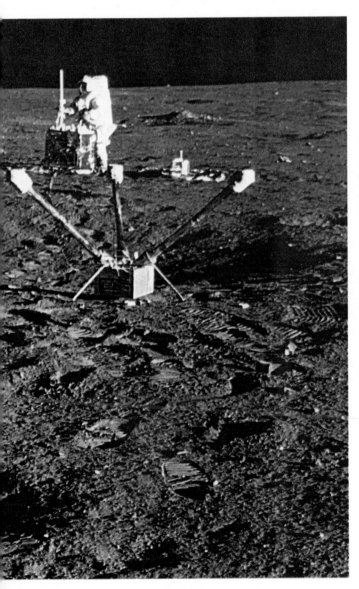

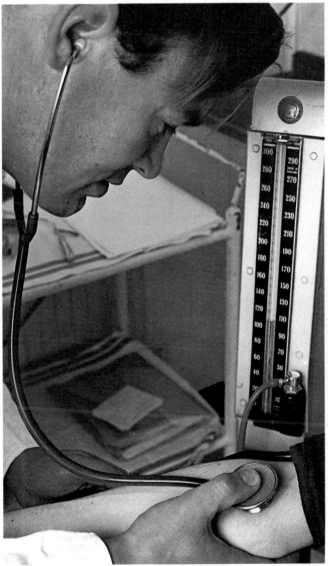

KEN MOREMAN

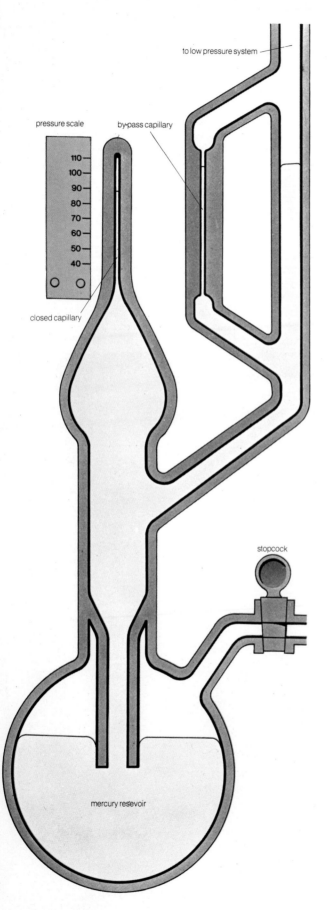

to low pressure system

pressure scale

by-pass capillary

110
100
90
80
70
60
50
40

closed capillary

stopcock

mercury resevoir

in the arteries. The manometer is connected by means of a flexible tube to an inflatable cuff positioned around the patient's upper arm. The cuff is inflated by means of a small hand pump until the pressure is just sufficient to stop pulsation in an artery in the forearm below the cuff. When this point is reached the difference in mercury levels in the manometer is read off and this gives the arterial blood pressure. A similar method is used to measure blood pressure in the veins except that instead of a cuff, an inflatable rubber bag with a glass plate in its upper surface is used. The bag is positioned over a vein and inflated until the vein collapses, and the pressure is then read off on the manometer.

In research and industry, processes are often carried out at very low pressures, and a type of manometer called a *McLeod gauge* is sometimes used for measuring the pressure in such systems. McLeod gauges are commonly built to measure pressures of about one thousandth of a millimetre (0.000039 inch) of mercury. A McLeod gauge consists of a closed reservoir containing mercury which is connected by means of a tube firstly to a chamber of known volume having a closed glass *capillary tube* (a tube with a very small inner diameter) at its top end, and secondly to the system whose pressure is to be measured. The tube to the system is provided with a capillary tube by-pass which runs parallel and close to the closed capillary tube. The mercury level in the by-pass capillary is adjusted by allowing air into the mercury reservoir until it is aligned with the top of the closed capillary, and the level of mercury in the closed tube is then a measure of the pressure in the system.

Right: a simple oil-filled manometer. When in use the difference in oil levels in the two limbs represents a pressure difference which can be read off on the vertical scale. Manometers of this type are often filled with mercury rather than oil, and they can be used to measure pressures relative to atmospheric pressure (one of the limbs is left open to the air) or to measure pressure differences between two different parts of a chemical apparatus (one limb is connected to each part of the apparatus).

Left: a McLeod gauge which is used for measuring very low pressures. The mercury level in the by-pass capillary is adjusted by means of the stopcock until it is level with the top of the closed capillary. The level of mercury in the closed capillary is then read off on the pressure scale, and this is a measure of the pressure in the low pressure system.

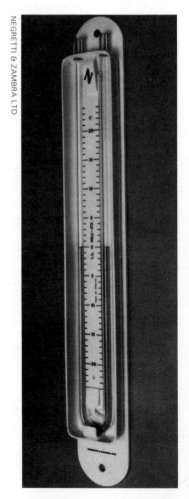

MANUFACTURED BOARD

Plywood, *particle board* and various kinds of *hardboard* are ingenious and useful wood products made possible by twentieth century technology. Particle board is also called *chipboard* or *pressed wood*; hardboard is called *fibreboard* and sometimes *Masonite*, which is a trade name.

Plywood is constructed of several thin layers of wood, called *veneers* or *plies*, glued together with the grains at right angles to one another, with the result that plywood is difficult to split and has far more tensile strength, as well as resistance to changes in humidity and temperature, than solid timber. Poor grades of wood can be used for the interior plies, or for all the plies in the case of plywood which is to be used where it will not be seen, as in sub-flooring. Alternatively, any kind of finishing quality wood can be used for the outside ply; finished properly, sheets of such plywood make attractive wood panelling. Despite the high strength of plywood it can be worked with ordinary woodworking tools.

Particle board makes use of waste material from timber processing and of forestry thinnings (undersized trees). These are chopped into small chips, which are coated with resin and pressed into sheets by machinery, using heat. The sheets can be used for panelling, shelving and so forth, like plywood but without its extraordinary strength.

Hardboard is made by subjecting wood chips to high steam pressure and then suddenly releasing the pressure, which causes a fresh activation of the lignin, the natural plastic substance which binds wood fibres together. The chips are then pressed into large thin sheets on heated presses. Hardboard is used mostly for interior panelling, and is available in a wide variety of finishes simulating, for example, trowelled plaster or brickwork. One of the most familiar uses of hardboard is *pegboard*, which has holes in it to accept wire attachments for hanging up tools or kitchen utensils, and for displaying goods in shops.

Attempts to make such wood products were unsuccessful at first because the necessary adhesives and other technology had not been developed. Manufactured board, as well as other technical processes, received a great impetus during both world wars when combatants, especially Germany, were short of raw materials and had to make do with substitutes. *Urea formaldehyde* (UF) is the most common adhesive used for making plywood and particle board, although many different formulae and additives are used to make these products more moisture proof, flame resistant, insecticidal, and so forth.

Particle board manufacture Wood from thinnings and wastes from industrial timber processing are cut into small chips by a rotating disc with cutting edges around its face, or by a cylindrical cutter block with knife blades set in it. The chips are crescent shaped. If the equipment has knife blades, they can be adjusted to make large or smaller chips. The chips are then passed through a grading machine which, with a winnowing action, eliminates large chips and particles of foreign matter. (At this stage or sometimes later, magnets are also used, because if particles of metals are pressed into the board they will ruin a saw blade.)

Regardless of source, chips contain a moisture content which must be reduced to two or three per cent. The chips are dried by being tumbled in heated drums. They are then conveyed to the tops of mixing cylinders through which they are allowed to fall; nozzles in the cylinder walls spray them with UF resin as they fall. (They still feel dry because the resin content does not exceed ten per cent.) Alternatively, the chips can be sprayed while being tumbled in drums.

Next the chips are spread on a continuous band or a line of linked steel plates. They used to be spread by hand, but this resulted in uneven distribution and subsequent weak places in the finished board. Some types of machinery can spread the chips so that they fall with the smaller chips on the top and bottom and the large chips in the middle; this makes a smoother finish on the board and a more uniform density.

The layer of chips on the plate is called a mattress. At this point the chips have a flow characteristic similar to that of coarse sawdust. To prevent loss on account of mechanical vibration or stray air currents, they go through a cold press which exerts a relatively light pressure to consolidate them. They are also slightly dampened to replace moisture lost by evaporation and to compensate for losses during subsequent

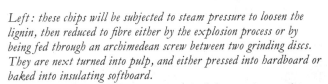

Left : these chips will be subjected to steam pressure to loosen the lignin, then reduced to fibre either by the explosion process or by being fed through an archimedean screw between two grinding discs. They are next turned into pulp, and either pressed into hardboard or baked into insulating softboard.
Below : pulp is poured on to a moving wire belt to make a wetlap.

heat pressing. Then the units are loaded into heat presses. For 15 mm boards (0.6 inch) the pressure is 1 N/mm² (150 psi), the temperature is 121°C (250°F), and this is applied for ten minutes.

The boards are then stacked to cool and to allow localized inner stresses to become evenly distributed. This takes several days. The boards are then trimmed and sanded by drum sanders on both sides.

An alternative process is *extrusion*, in which a reciprocating ram forces the chips horizontally through parallel heated metal plates, which are adjustable for thickness. Continuous lengths of thicker board can be produced this way, but the internal structure of the board is slightly different because of the longitudinal rather than vertical pressure on the chips. Extruded board has higher tensile but lower bending strength.

Particle board is made in three densities. High density board weighing 640 to 800 kg/m³ (40 to 50 lb/ft³) is used for high strength and stability, as in flooring. Medium density board weighing 480 to 640 kg/m³ (30 to 40 lb/ft³) is used for such applications as panelling, partitions, shelving and FURNITURE MANUFACTURE. Lower density board is used for roof decking, ceilings, and core material for composite panelling. Particle board has sound insulating properties which improve with lower density. The bulk of particle board manufactured in the UK (175,000 tons in 1969) is of medium to high density in the range 12 to 18 mm (½ to ¾ inch) thick.

Plywood manufacture

Trees are chosen and inspected carefully before manufacture to ensure that they are used to best advantage. Manufacturers have to import wood from all over the world; trees with long cylindrical clear trunks which can be easily peeled are necessary, and many of these grow in tropical areas.

First the logs are boiled or steamed in large vats. This softens them, ensures that moisture is evenly distributed, and reduces the likelihood of splitting or tearing of the veneers during subsequent processing. Tropical hardwood especially requires this treatment; some species (such as birch and beech) can be peeled without it. In Finland, the practice is to leave the logs in the log pond for months, injecting steam into the pond to keep it from freezing.

The logs are then peeled of bark and cut to convenient lengths. The peeling of the veneers from the logs is carried out on a large LATHE which rotates the logs against a knife blade running the full length of the log. Strict quality control begins at this point, for the veneers obtained must be of uniform thickness throughout. The rate of feed and the angle of the blade are adjustable for individual logs and species. Veneers are cut from about 1 mm to 4 mm (0.03 to 0.16 inch) thick. The veneer is then *clipped* automatically or manually to predetermined widths in such a way that defects are clipped off.

Next the veneers go through continuous tunnel driers to ensure that they are of uniform moisture content; otherwise the finished product will warp or twist. The permissible content varies from 5 to 14%, depending on the type of adhesive to be employed. (There are also wet and semi-dry cementing processes which do not require this careful drying; these result in a cheaper but poorer grade of plywood which is used where cost rather than finish is the consideration.)

The dried veneers are then sorted and graded. Veneers for faces of the most expensive grades of plywood are often full width, but joins are permissible. Joins must be smooth and parallel; this is accomplished by *veneer guillotines* or *edge joiners*. Materials used for core veneers may be edge joined using staples (which are removed later) to prevent core gaps which would lower the strength of the finished board. Veneers for face joins are carefully selected for colour and are joined by an *automatic tapeless splicer*, which draws the edges together and

Below left: in wetlap forming, the pulp is laid on to a wire mesh belt conveyer 1220 mm (about 48 inches) wide. Interlocking of fibres takes place, and this photo shows a finer top layer of sawdust added to make a smooth surface on the board.

Below right: plywood veneers going through a glue spreader.

makes a join which is nearly invisible and as strong as the veneer itself.

Next the glue is applied for the sandwich construction. It must be evenly applied, for too much glue will result in a poor bond. An alternative method is the use of resin impregnated paper, which is cut to size and placed between the plies. (Three-ply construction describes itself; *multiply* comprises a face, a back and usually three or more inner plies. The plies are arranged with the grain of each at a right angle to that of the plies on either side; nearly all plywood has an odd number of plies, but if the number is even, the centre two plies can have the grain following the same direction.)

The veneers are sometimes pre-pressed cold. The hot pressing is then carried out in hydraulic machinery between multiple heated platens. Temperature, pressure and so forth are adjusted to the type of construction under production. The finished boards are then stacked to allow stresses and uneven moisture content to work out, and trimmed and sanded.

Blockboard, *laminboard* and *battenboard* are constructions of face and back veneers with cores made of strips of wood placed together face to face. Block or ply constructions can be made with a saving in weight by using wood of lower density for the core material, such as pine. They can be made to order with a core material of cork, foam or fibre for applications where sound or heat insulation is important, or can be covered with plastic or metal sheeting for other special purposes. Plastic faced plywood is used for building forms for pre-cast concrete units, because it can be re-used several times and leaves a smooth finish on the concrete. Plywood can be veneered and pre-finished in several ways; choosing decorative veneers is an art in itself, because veneers from the same batch or even from the same tree may not be a perfect match. Research continues on ways to weatherproof plywood for exterior use. Moisture-proofing is not perfect yet because trimming of plywood sheets will leave the edge liable to penetration; nevertheless plywood is one of the most durable and versatile of construction materials.

BORDEN (U.K.) LTD

MAP MAKING TECHNIQUES

The task of the cartographer (map-maker) is to represent the topographical (natural and artificial) features of the Earth's surface at a greatly reduced scale in a convenient form, usually on flat sheets of paper. His first and fundamental difficulty arises from the curvature and irregularity of the Earth's surface, and although the curvature can be ignored for maps of small areas, the surface irregularities—hills and valleys—make it necessary to show the ground features as plan projections on a plane (flat) surface. Thus, unless the ground is level, the distances shown on the map do not agree exactly with those on the surface. With larger areas, such as Great Britain, the curvature has to be taken into account and the plan projection is made on a regular curved surface conforming as nearly as possible to the shape of the Earth; this is known as the *spheroid of reference*.

Maps on curved surfaces, however, are inconvenient objects to handle, and a transformation has to be made from the curved to a plane surface by means of a map projection. There are many different map projections, but they all result in the distortion, in one way or another, of the pattern of features on the curved surface. This distortion is very obvious in atlas maps of the whole world (as on Mercator's or Mollweide's projections), but it is possible, by using particular projections, to retain some elements of correctness.

Orthomorphic projections are widely used for large scale topographical maps. In an orthomorphic projection the scale does not remain constant over the whole area, but at every point the scale is the same in all directions for a short distance, thus preserving the correct shape in small areas. The orthomorphic Transverse Mercator projection is used for the official maps of Great Britain, and in this comparatively small area, the scale variation caused by the projection does not exceed one part in 2500, which is negligible for most purposes.

Primary mapping   A distinction must be made between the two classes of mapping. *Primary* mapping is produced directly from a topographical survey; *derived* mapping at smaller scales results from the reduction and generalizing of primary maps, or from the compilation of map material drawn from either or both categories.

When undertaking primary mapping, it is not possible to fit together individual surveys of small areas in order to complete the survey of a large area. The errors in such independent local surveys would accumulate and produce discrepancies that would be unresolvable. A consistent framework has first to be constructed covering the entire area to be mapped. This framework must be located and oriented correctly on the Earth's surface, and this is accomplished by astronomical observations at several points within it.

Since the middle of the eighteenth century the classical control framework for mapping large areas has been produced by *triangulation*, in which the angles of a system of triangles are measured to a high degree of precision with a *theodolite* (an instrument consisting basically of a telescope moving around a circular scale graduated in degrees—see SURVEYING). The linear dimensions are determined by *base measurement*; that is, by measuring the lengths of several sides in different parts of the system, and thereafter by calculation. Accurate base measurement was first carried out in Great Britain with glass measuring rods on Hounslow Heath in 1784. At about the same time great improvements were made in the design and manufacture of theodolites, particularly by Jesse Ramsden (1735–1800), and the national triangulation of Great Britain was begun. The lengthy and laborious operation of base measurement with glass rods (1784), bimetallic bars (1826), and later with steel tapes suspended in catenary (the curve a string makes suspended between two supports), was gradually replaced from the 1950s onwards by ELECTROMAGNETIC methods.

Instruments such as the tellurometer and Geodimeter, which measure distance by recording the time taken for an electromagnetic wave to travel to and from a remote station, enable the whole operation to be completed in a few hours and make it possible to incorporate many more linear measurements into the triangulation framework. The subdivision of the main or primary triangles into secondary and tertiary triangles is continued until a density of fixed control points is obtained, which meets the requirements of the topographical survey method chosen.

A similar control network for heights above the sea level datum is obtained by a pattern of intersecting lines of spirit levelling. In Great Britain evidence of the levelling may be seen in the broad arrow *benchmarks* (fixed points of reference used for levelling in surveying) on permanent objects and buildings. The height of each benchmark is shown on the large scale national maps.

Air surveys

The topographical survey can be undertaken on the ground or by means of aerial photographs. The ground surveys of the eighteenth and nineteenth centuries were carried out with compass, *plane table* (essentially a drawing board mounted on a tripod together with an alidade consisting of a rule with sights at both ends to give direction of survey points from the table) and chain; in the second half of the twentieth century, new instruments which combine the theodolite with either an optical or an electromagnetic distance measuring device came widely into use. The method most commonly practised, however, in recent years for topographical mapping is air survey, because of its speed and economy (see AERIAL PHOTOGRAPHY).

Except when the ground is absolutely flat, and when the photographic exposure is made with the camera pointing vertically downwards, an air photograph cannot be used directly to make a map because of the scale variation caused by the ground relief and the tilt of the camera. To solve the problem, stereo plotting machines, such as the WILD PHOTOGRAMMETRIC MACHINE, are generally used. Pairs of overlapping air photographs are set up in the machine in accordance with the control data already obtained, so that their positions and orientations in space at the two moments of exposure are recreated. It is then possible to create in the machine a three dimensional 'model' of the ground from which planimetric detail (distances and positions of features), contours and spot heights can be derived. The 'model' is formed by the intersection of the images of the two photographs.

In primary mapping, the task of the cartographer is to show all the information collected by the surveyor in the way that enables it to be most clearly and readily comprehended. With primary mapping at large scales (1:500 to 1:10,000) the preservation of positional accuracy is of first importance, and the cartographic process of generalization has little part to play.

Printing

One method commonly used in drawing offices for making a single colour primary map is to scribe the detail on plastic sheets. A clear plastic sheet is covered with a semiopaque waxy coating on which the image of the surveyor's work is printed by a photographic process. The draughtsman

JOHN R FREEMAN & CO

Left: an illustration from an old German book, showing a surveyor at work. Cartographic surveying is based mainly on triangulation; the first country to be completely mapped by triangulation was France, a task which took 39 years and was finished in 1783.

Below left: digitizing the information on a map—turning it into a series of numerical co-ordinates which are fed into a computer. The position of the cursor is sensed electromagnetically, and the features are encoded with the buttons on the cursor.

Below right: checking an edited map on a computer display screen.

ORDNANCE SURVEY

EXPERIMENTAL CARTOGRAPHY UNIT/N E R C

cuts away the waxy coating along the lines of the surveyor's drawing, leaving very sharply defined lines of clear plastic. This operation produces a negative from which a positive on another sheet of film or plastic can be made by contact photography. Names and symbols are usually added at this stage; these are printed on strips of very thin film which are stuck to the film positive. A lithographic printing plate is made, also by contact photography, for printing on a rotary offset litho machine (see LITHOGRAPHY).

The combination of scribing and photographic processes compares very favourably for speed and quite well for quality with the copper plate ENGRAVING used in the early nineteenth century for map reproduction. In this process a hand-drawn tracing was made of the surveyor's drawing and this was transferred to the copper plate which was coated with wax to take the transfer. The engraver then cut along the transferred lines into the copper; the outline, names, symbols and ornamental drawing, including the *hachures* (lines used to shade a plan) representing the hills, were all engraved in this way. Ink was then rubbed into the engraved lines and, after the surface of the plate had been cleaned, impressions were taken on paper. Revision was carried out by hammering the copper flat in the area to be revised, and then engraving the new detail.

The revision of primary mapping in a highly developed country depends upon a flow of new information from surveyors who may be permanently occupied in surveying changes as they occur. In the drawing office it is important that the new work should be incorporated into the map without having to redraw the whole, as this would lead to a progressive deterioration in accuracy. The combination of new and old is therefore achieved by photographic methods.

Derived mapping   Small scale derived maps are made either directly from the primary mapping or from other derived maps. Here there is great scope for the cartographic designer because it is generally necessary to make a selection of detail for showing at the smaller scale, to generalize the outline of some features, and to exaggerate the size of others so that they are given the prominence the designer requires. Because of the closeness of detail on small scale maps, it is usual today to use colours to distinguish one type of feature from another, such as red for main roads, blue for water, and green for woods.

A typical procedure for making a smaller scale derived map from primary mapping is as follows. A print of the primary map is made in a 'non-photographic' blue colour (which will not show up in a photograph), either at the scale of the primary map or at a scale intermediate between it and the derived map. The features for the derived map are selected, generalized and penned in black on the blue print, which is then photographed and reduced to the final scale. Several blue prints (depending on the number of colours) are made of the reduced drawing, and separate drawings in black ink are made for each colour.

A printing plate for each colour can then be made from the separate drawings, and, after printing, the colours will all be in correct register. Although each colour is printed separately, it is possible to produce several shades of the same colour by means of rulings or stipple. The relief of the ground, which in

Below: in triangulation an area is measured by means of a series of triangles built up from a set of base triangles, using a second set as a check. The diagram on the right shows how a map is drawn from pairs of aerial photographs, which are viewed together to produce a 'geometric model' from which the map is traced.

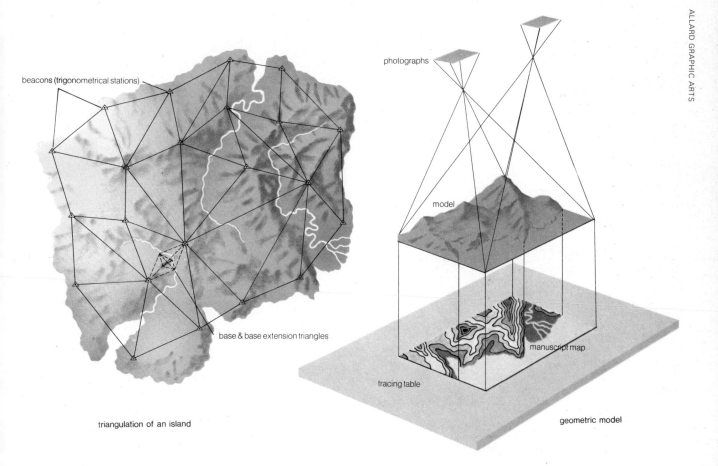

beacons (trigonometrical stations)

base & base extension triangles

triangulation of an island

photographs

model

manuscript map

tracing table

geometric model

the nineteenth century was generally shown by hachures, is now normally depicted by contour lines, which may be enhanced by hill shading or by layer colours. In the latter method, the spaces between the contours are filled with a progressive series of tints, often with green for the lowest level, and deepening shades of buff and brown for the higher levels.

Maps of sea areas, made for the guidance of mariners, are known as *hydrographic* charts. They show coastlines and coastal features, navigational lights and marks, soundings and underwater contours. Because of the changing character of the sea bed in coastal areas, up to date information is essential, and careful arrangements must be made to disseminate revisions.

Computer drafting The application of COMPUTERS and automatic drafting machines to mapping has been extensively studied since the late 1960s. The concept of a computer based topographical data bank containing classified and coded information, any selection of which could be plotted at a wide range of scales, has great interest both for the makers of atlas maps and for those responsible for topographical map series. The lines representing the features of a map can be stored in coded numerical (digital) form on magnetic tape. For example, a straight line can be represented by the map coordinates of its two ends; curved lines by a series of such coordinates.

Trials have shown that the information on large scale maps can be stored in digital form and then drawn automatically by high speed drafting machines. The same information, or selected categories from it, can be drawn automatically at smaller scales, and the possibility of producing a whole family of derived scales in this way is very attractive to map makers. The generalization required, however, for small scale maps, such as the widening of roads, the simplification of outlines, and the adjustment of adjacent features to conform with these changes, presents programming difficulties.

MARCONI, Guglielmo (1874-1937)

Guglielmo Marconi was an Italian, born in Bologna, but much of his pioneering work on wireless telegraphy, which led to his later development of RADIO communication and BROADCASTING, was done outside his home country, mainly in Britain, because the Italian government declined to give him financial support when he badly needed it.

Marconi was always more of a practical person than an academic and from an early age, to the displeasure of his father, he preferred tinkering with objects to studying. It was natural therefore that he should seize on the discovery by Heinrich Hertz, a German physicist, that energy could be transmitted from place to place in the form of ELECTROMAGNETIC RADIATION, just as James Clerk MAXWELL had earlier predicted, for Marconi immediately saw the practical potential of 'Hertzian waves' as a means of communication.

Marconi was 20 when he first learnt of Hertz's work and he immediately embarked on a period of intense experimentation in two attic rooms of his family's country mansion outside Bologna. He filled these with equipment, including a coil and spark gap—for creating the electromagnetic waves—and a receiver for detecting them. Soon Marconi was able to show his mother (she was a source of constant encouragement, unlike his father) how a key which was pressed at one end of a room could cause a buzzer to sound 30 feet away.

Using his capacity for improving and inventing, Marconi gradually developed his apparatus so that he could transmit over greater and greater distances. And he soon discovered that a hill between transmitter and receiver was no obstacle. At that stage he emigrated to England in search of support, which he got, from both the Post Office and the War Office. By 1897, when he was 23, Marconi was sending wireless signals over a distance of nine miles.

AEROFILMS

Left: a stereoplotter used for the preparation of large scale maps, which use a series of pairs of overlapping aerial photographs as the input data. The photographs are viewed stereoscopically to produce a correctly proportioned image.

Below: cutting away a plastic film which will be used to produce a photographic negative of the map.

EXPERIMENTAL CARTOGRAPHY UNIT/N E R C

STAATSBIBLIOTHEK BERLIN

The setting up of a company by Marconi and some British relatives, and the first transmission across the English Channel, followed in quick succession. In 1899 he visited the United States to demonstrate his technique—which by that time had to compete with those developed by other people and other companies—but the mission was not a great success because Marconi was reluctant to show off his then unpatented improvements to possible rival businesses. His aim by then, however, was to transmit across the Atlantic and this he attempted in spite of serious storm damage on both sides of the Atlantic to his original transmitters. The one at Poldhu in Cornwall was rebuilt and a temporary receiving AERIAL was flown on a kite in St John's, Newfoundland. Success came in late 1901 when he was 27, in the shape of the three dots that make up the letter 'S' in the MORSE code, which was the basis of all wireless communication in those days.

Marconi was closely involved in the commercial development of wireless and saw it installed in countless places including ships such as the Titanic, which sank in 1912, and the Montrose which carried the murderer Crippen to his arrest as the result of a ship-to-shore message in 1910. Marconi weathered a financial scandal surrounding his company (but not himself) in 1912 and after World War 1 devoted more of his time to his home country, both in a political and a technical sense. When he died in 1937 at the age of 63 the world paid the simplest and most impressive tribute—two minutes of radio silence.

Below left: this 1896 photograph shows Guglielmo Marconi seated behind his first wireless telegraph.
Below: in 1901, Marconi (centre) and his assistants received the first signals to be broadcast across the Atlantic. They were sent from Cornwall and received at Signal Hill, St John's, Newfoundland.

MAREY, Etienne Jules (1830-1904)

Dr Etienne Marey combined a knowledge of medicine with a love of mechanics. This combination led him to invent a number of instruments for recording physiological change in animals and humans, and to realize that photography could arrest movements otherwise invisible to the eye. The result was a scientific measuring device which was in fact the first movie CAMERA.

Marey was born in Beaune, in the French wine district of Burgundy. His father was a wine merchant, his mother a schoolteacher. He was sent to Paris to study medicine and, after taking his degree, began to develop measuring machines for use in diagnosing illnesses. His first such device, described in a scientific paper published in 1860, was the *sphygmograph*, which counted human pulse beats and recorded them on a revolving smoked glass disc. He went on to measure the wing movements of bees and pigeons, and the leg movements of horses and men. His machines were very ingenious: the horse, for instance, had a hollow rubber ball fitted inside each hoof, from which rubber tubes led, transmitting the variation in air pressure to a paper recorder in its rider's hands.

Marey, by now a Professor of Medicine, heard of the work of Eadweard MUYBRIDGE and was his host in Paris in 1881, arranging for him to give a demonstration to scientists there. From Muybridge's results, Marey perceived that photography was the answer to his problem of recording movement but, instead of Muybridge's many cameras, he used one. In 1882 his *fusil photographique* ('photographic gun') took twelve consecutive pictures per second. The images, the size of a postage

Below: although unacknowledged as the inventor of cinematography, Dr Etienne Marey developed the first modern cinematographic films which enabled accurate scientific study of movement.

stamp, were arranged round the edge of a revolving circular photographic glass plate, a development from the daguerreo-type disc used nearly ten years earlier by the astronomer Pierre Jules Cesar Janssen (1824–1907) to capture the movement of the stars. Janssen's apparatus only made on exposure every seventy seconds and could hardly produce the illusion of movement. It was the advent of the dry photographic plate in 1880 which made possible Marey's shorter exposures and genuine analysis of motion.

The glass plate used in the photographic gun made it heavy and slow, and its pictures too small. But when George Eastman introduced gelatin-based film in 1885, Marey progressed to exposing sixty images per second, each 3.6 inches (9 cm) square. These were truly the first modern cinematograph films: lengths of film moving constantly, but stopping for a split second in front of a lens which was covered by a shutter while the film was moving. His experiments with cine techniques also involved time-lapse methods to speed up slow movements.

Marey was a scientist. He developed the inventions of Janssen and Muybridge, as he himself freely admitted, until they were capable of the split-second accuracy which he sought. He published his results freely. His pioneer work was continued by the famous Institut Marey, founded in Paris a year before he died. Had he been an entertainer, or businessman, he would probably now be acknowledged as the inventor of cinematography, instead of Louis and Auguste LUMIÈRE, or any of the other claimants to that title.

MARGARINE PRODUCTION

The high butter prices in France in the period before the Franco-Prussian War of 1870–71 prompted Napoleon III to organize a competition for the invention of a cheaper and less perishable substitute for butter that could be used to alleviate the fat shortage among the low-income sections of the population and supply the armed forces with a source of food energy. The competition was won in 1869 by Mège Mouriès who produced a butter subsitute by forming an emulsion of skim milk (the aqueous phase) dispersed in beef fat (the oil phase), which was subsequently solidified by chilling and worked to improve the texture. The product was called 'margarine' because of the pearly lustre of the fat crystals, a name derived from the Greek word for pearl—*margarites*.

Although the basic principle of producing margarine remains the same, it is now firmly established as a food in its own right and the manufacturer draws on a wide range of vegetable, animal and marine oils and fats to form the desired oil blend to be emulsified with cultured skim milk.

Oil blend Manufacturers in Britain use imported vegetable oils (for example, palm, groundnut, coconut, sunflower, cotton seed and soya bean), animal fats (for example, EEC or American lard) and marine oils (for example, herring and pilchard) for the oil blend. In the United States the oils for margarine are largely derived from the soya bean and cotton seed.

Before the oils can be blended they must be refined to purify

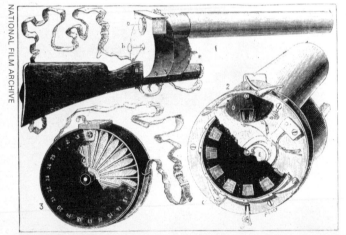

Right: a diagram showing the various stages in margarine manufacture: oil refining, milk preparation and emulsification. Refining results in oils that are pure and free of taste, smell and odour. It involves degumming, neutralizing and bleaching, and subsequent filtration. Often oils are hydrogenated to raise the melting point. After deodorization the oils are blended. The milk, the aqueous phase, is pasteurized and then cultured with bacteria to impart flavour and acidity. Oil and aqueous phases are mixed with additives before emulsification.

Left: Marey invented the 'fusil photographique' in 1882 to enable him to photograph objects in motion. The photographic gun resembled a rifle with a revolving magazine of photographic film. Below: Unsatisfied with the photographic gun, Marey developed the 'chambre chronophotographique', the first modern movie camera, which recorded a great variety of movements for scientific study.

them. The first stage of purification is *degumming*, which removes impurities such as carbohydrates, proteins, phospholipids and resins. The oil is heated to about 90°C (194°F) with 5% water so that the impurities are hydrated to form an oil-insoluble gum which can be separated by centrifuging. In the next stage of refining, the oil is neutralized to remove free fatty acids (see CARBOXYLIC ACIDS) which would impair taste and cause rancidity as a result of oxidation. Neutralization is often carried out in 25 ton (25,400 kg) batches by treatment with caustic soda (sodium hydroxide) solution at 75 to 96°C (167 to 203°F) for 30 minutes, during which time the free fatty acids combine with the caustic soda to form a soap which can be run off. After soap separation the neutralized oil is washed with water and dried under vacuum.

Colouring matter in the oil, such as carotenoids and chlorophyll, is removed by bleaching with 1% fuller's earth (a form of non-plastic clay) in stirred tanks held at a temperature ranging from 90 to 110°C (194 to 230°F). The bleaching is carried out under vacuum for a period ranging from 10 to 60 minutes depending on the amount of colour originally in the oil and, when the process is complete, the fuller's earth is removed by passing the mixture through a plate-and-frame filter press.

Unsaturated oils are deficient in hydrogen and therefore melt at low temperatures. They are also unstable and more likely to deteriorate. The melting point can be raised by controlled hydrogenation (addition of hydrogen atoms to the molecule) with a nickel CATALYST at 180°C (356°F) at a pressure of 3 atmospheres. This process is particularly important for modifying fish oils, which are highly unsaturated. The melting point of an oil can also be altered by a process of *interesterification* in which the molecular structure of the components of the oil is rearranged. Hydrogenation and interesterification produce side products which must be removed by neutralization and bleaching.

Deodorization is the final step in the preparation of the oil for blending. Any volatile flavours, which might render the flavour of the oil unsatisfactory, are removed by steam DISTILLATION. In this process the oil is heated to a temperature of 180°C (356°F) and steam passed through, while the pressure is kept at a low level of 0.1 inches Hg (2.5 mm Hg) to prevent oxidation of the oil.

The blending of refined oils depends upon the type of margarine to be produced. Table margarines must be spreadable over a wide temperature range and still be capable of melting readily in the mouth. For a good melting range a blend of liquid oil and hard fat can be used and melting in the mouth is improved by incorporating hydrogenated oils which have a melting point less than 34°C (93°F).

Aqueous phase   The water content of all brands of margarine made in Britain must not exceed 16%. This is derived from the aqueous phase, which consists of a blend of cultured skim milk (milk 'ripened' with bacteria to develop flavour and acidity), skim milk, brine and water.

Skim milk arriving at the factory is pasteurized at 75°C

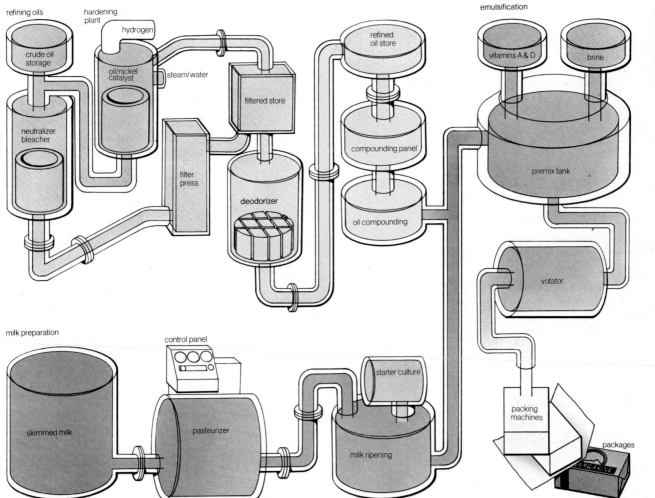

OSBORNE / MARKS

(167°F) for 30 minutes to remove unwanted bacteria. If the milk is to be cultured it is cooled to 22°C (72°F), otherwise it is stored at 5°C (41°F). Culturing is achieved by inoculating the milk with strains of the bacteria *streptococcus lactis* which convert the milk lactose to lactic acid and other short-chain organic acids. In the first stage of ripening, a 5 gallon (22.7 litre) can of pasteurized milk is inoculated with the culture and ripened for up to 24 hours. This milk is then transferred to an 800 gallon (3,630 litre) tank of milk to ripen for about the same period at a controlled temperature of 22°C (72°F) to achieve the correct flavour. After ripening, the cultured milk is cooled to 5°C (41°F) and blended with skim milk, water and brine such that the final margarine will have a salt content of between 1 and 2%.

Oil phase

The oil blend must contain a number of ingredients before it is emulsified with the aqueous phase. Legislation in Britain requires that margarine must contain 23 to 27 international units (IU) per gramme of vitamin A, and 2.8 to 3.5 IU per gramme of vitamin D. These used to be added to the oil blend in the form of concentrates of marine livers or palm oil, but nowadays synthetic preparations are used. Colour is also added in the form of *annatto* and *beta carotene*, derived from synthetic or natural sources.

Emulsifiers are also added to stabilize the aqueous emulsion oil once it has been formed mechanically. Egg yolk used to be used but, being susceptible to microbial attack, it has been replaced by monoglycerides (esters of an organic acid and the alcohol glycerol) and lecithin (an organic compound similar to a fat) in quantities up to 0.5%. Finally, some of the constituents known to exist in butter (for example, butyric acid, caproic acid and delta lactones) are added to improve flavour.

Emulsification, chilling and texturing

Metered quantities of the oil and aqueous phase are mixed and passed to an emulsion pump which feeds the mixture at 38°C (100°F) to a votator which chills the mixture to 10°C (50°F). The votator is a tube fitted with scraper blades rotating at about 1000 rpm and the cooling is achieved by an ammonia refrigerant circulating in the votator jacket at −18°C (0°F). As the emulsion crystallizes it is scraped off the votator walls by the rotating blades and forced into a tempering tube approximately 7 inches (178 mm) in diameter and up to 10 feet (3.05 m) in length, where the texture is developed for up to 2 minutes before extrusion and packaging.

MARINE PROPULSION

The power to propel any vessel through the water must come from one of three sources: man himself, the wind or an engine. There are, however, many methods for translating that power, from whichever source it comes, into a driving force.

Oars The earliest method for propelling a craft through the water in a desired direction was by paddles, and then subsequently by means of oars. An oar or paddle consists of a shaft with a rounded handle at one end and a blade at the other end. In rowing, part of the shaft of the oar rests in a notch or *rowlock* on the side of the boat, which acts as a fixed fulcrum, or turning point. The oar is therefore a simple lever which moves the boat by offering resistance to, and thereby pushing against, the water. Paddles, used for instance when canoeing, also move the boat by pushing against the water, but in this case there is no fixed fulcrum, and one arm of the canoeist acts as a moving fulcrum.

Sails The use of a sail or sails to catch the wind and thus propel a vessel has been known for almost as long as rowing; certainly sailcloth is mentioned in Homer's *Odyssey*. In any SAILING BOAT there must be firmly fixed into the hull the mast or masts from which the sails are suspended by a system of wires or ropes, known as the rigging. Sails vary in shape and size according to the vessel for which they are intended. The materials used today to make sails are canvas or Terylene or similar synthetic fabrics, although the earliest sails were made from animal skins or reeds flattened and woven into shape.

There are two major categories into which sails can be placed; the first of these is *square* sails. These are normally set across the longitudinal axis of the ship, and the wind pressure acts only on the afterside of the sail (the side facing the stern), to push the ship through the water. The second category is *fore-and-aft* sails, which are set along the longitudinal axis of the boat. Both sides of these sails are used for forward propulsion depending on the side of the boat from which the wind is blowing.

These sails can be considered as aerofoils, and taking a sailing boat 'beating into wind' as an example, the pressure of the wind on the sail produces a 'lift' force at right angles to the sail and a smaller 'drag' force along the sail. The resultant of these two forces can be further split into a force acting to drive the boat ahead along its set course, and a larger force perpendicular to it. It is this larger force that tries to heel the boat over and push it off course to leeward, and in small sailing boats this tendency is overcome as much as possible by the crew

Above: milk holding tanks. From here the milk is pumped to the culturing tanks.

Left: part of the main production area. From the votators (centre line), looking like groups of 3 torpedoes, the margarine passes to the extruders on the left.

balancing the boat by sitting to windward, and by HYDRO-DYNAMIC forces acting underwater on the hull and keel.

Mechanical power
The first known successful use of mechanical power to propel a ship was by the paddle wheel. The vessel was the tug *Charlotte Dundas* in 1802 on the Forth and Clyde Canal. The paddle wheel is a revolving wheel with a series of blades or paddles radiating out from the centre, and as the wheel revolves so each blade in turn is forced against the water and this pushes the ship along. ARCHIMEDES (287 to 212 BC) had demonstrated the power of a helical blade in moving water (see ARCHIMEDEAN SCREW) and in 1838 the first successful steam ship driven by a propeller was, appropriately, called the *Archimedes*. Her reciprocating STEAM ENGINES, operating at 26 rpm, were geared up to drive the propeller at about 139 rpm. Her original propeller was helical with one complete turn.

When turned by the engine a propeller's shape is such that it will 'screw' through the water and therefore exert a pressure on the water. Since, from the third of NEWTON'S LAWS, action and reaction must be equal and opposite, the water exerts a pressure on the propeller shaft and tries to push it forward. Somewhere along the propeller shaft there must be fitted a *thrust block* to transmit the thrust of the propeller to the hull, and thus move the ship through the water. Large thrust blocks are strong steel castings fixed to supports which are bolted to specially stiffened hull frames. In smaller ships and power boats the thrust block may be incorporated in the gearing or in the propulsion unit itself.

The first vessel to be powered by steam TURBINE machinery was the steam yacht *Turbinia* in 1894, the turbine having been invented by Sir Charles PARSONS. She had a three shaft arrangement with each shaft being directly driven (without any gearing). With only a single propeller on each shaft it was found that at high revolutions the propeller simply *cavitated* or 'dug a hole' in the water, and therefore eventually the *Turbinia* was fitted with three propellers on each shaft.

Cavitation is caused when the propeller blade is turning so fast that the surrounding pressure is not high enough to force the water that has been pushed aside back into contact with the blade. This leaves a vapour-filled cavity next to the blade, thus destroying the normal flow around the blade and reducing the thrust. In addition the vapour pocket will collapse either on the blade or just behind it, causing erosion to take place on the blades, and creating noise. It is this noise emanating from a SUBMARINE's propeller that can so easily be detected by any enemy warship. The larger the blade area of a propeller the faster the propeller can turn before cavitation takes place. In propeller design this fact has to be carefully balanced against the fact that larger blades cause greater drag and therefore decrease the propeller's efficiency.

In the early part of the twentieth century the DIESEL ENGINE was introduced to power ships, and as direct reversing of a diesel engine was a problem, the controllable pitch (CP) propeller was devised. As its name suggests, the pitch of a CP propeller can be changed while the ship is moving, as the propeller blades can be rotated in the propeller hub. This

Top right: a steam powered launch on Lake Windermere, England.

Centre right: a small marine steam engine. The boiler can be seen on the right of the picture while the engine itself is on the left.

Bottom right: an inboard diesel engine on a sailing yacht. Seawater is used for cooling the engine, so no radiator is needed.

PHOTOS : JOHN WATNEY

PHOTOS : JOHN WATNEY

ROLLS ROYCE (1971) LTD

means that in order to go astern, the blades of a CP propeller are simply rotated to reverse pitch, and the ship will go astern without reversing the direction of the engine. Early CP propellers were controlled by simple mechanical linkages, but the shaft horse power of ships became too great for them in about 1920 and so they fell from favour until 1934, when hydraulic power was introduced to provide the necessary forces to adjust the blade pitch. Today there are CP propellers fitted to container lines of nearly 35,000 shaft horse power.

Modern propulsion systems Modern ships are usually powered by marine diesel engines or steam turbines, while smaller boats often have petrol [gasoline] engines, for example in the form of OUTBOARD MOTORS, ELECTRIC MOTORS powered from storage batteries are used in non-nuclear submarines for underwater propulsion because conventional power units consume large quantities of oxygen and would require a complex exhaust system for underwater operation. When the submarine is on the surface or at periscope depth, the motors are powered by electric generators driven by diesel engines. Air is drawn in and exhaust gas vented through snorkel tubes. The generators are also used to recharge the batteries. NUCLEAR REACTORS have proved ideal for powering submarines since they do not consume oxygen or generate toxic waste gases. Coolant from the reactor is pumped through a HEAT EXCHANGER to generate steam which is used to drive the submarine's propulsion turbines.

A HYDROFOIL looks like many other craft at rest or at slow speeds, but underneath it is fitted with an arrangement of fins at the front and back which act as planing surfaces. The hull of a hydrofoil must be designed to give the lift, and the fins act like wings and develop extra lift as the speed of the vessel through the water increases. Eventually there comes a speed at which the hull lifts almost completely clear of the water, and the vessel planes on its foils. The resistance to the water when planing is very markedly reduced, and thus for the speed achieved the power required is far less than for a conventional craft.

The most modern propulsive system is the *water jet* drive. This consists of either a single or multi-stage pump directly connected to a gas turbine engine. The pump sucks water through an opening in the bottom of the hull and discharges it at a high velocity through a nozzle at the back of the vessel. Across the nozzle there is a velocity change caused by a sudden drop in pressure (the VENTURI effect) and, in a similar manner to the conventional jet engine, the reaction drives the vessel forward. Steering is achieved by turning the discharge nozzle, and reversing by means of deflector plates which reverse the direction of the water flow.

Top left: the propeller of an auxiliary motor projects through a well in the hull of a sailing boat. The propeller is shaped to combine minimum cavitation and drag with maximum thrust.

Centre left: a small water-jet propulsion unit which has been cut away to show the pump impeller. Water is drawn in through a grille which can be seen at the bottom of the unit and is expelled through a movable discharge nozzle (left). The pump drive shaft can be seen above the water intake grille.

Bottom left: three Rolls-Royce 'Proteus' marine gas turbine engines installed in a fast torpedo boat of the Swedish navy. The combined power of the three engines is nearly 13,000 hp and the ship has a top speed in excess of 40 knots.

MARSHALLING YARDS

Marshalling yards are groups of *sorting sidings*, in which wagons [freight cars] can be *marshalled*; that is arranged in order so that they can be detached from the train at their destination with the least possible delay. This is done in groups of sidings by a *shunter* or *switcher*, a small locomotive which moves 'cuts' of trains (groups of wagons), *shunting* them from one track to another until the desired order is achieved. Marshalling yards are also called *classification yards* and *switchyards* in North America.

As railways became more complicated in their system layouts in the nineteenth century, the scope and volume of sorting necessary became greater, and means of reducing the time and labour involved were sought. (By 1930, for every 100 miles that freight trains were run in Britain there were 75 miles of shunting). The sorting of coal wagons for return to the collieries had been assisted by gravity as early as 1859, in the sidings at Tyne dock on the North Eastern Railway; in 1873 the London & North Western Railway sorted traffic to and from Liverpool on the Edge Hill 'grid irons': groups of sidings laid out on the slope of a hill where gravity provided the motive power, the steepest gradient being 1 in 60 (one foot of elevation in sixty feet of siding). Chain drags were used for braking the wagons. A shunter uncoupled the wagons in 'cuts' for the various destinations and each cut was turned into the appropriate siding. Some gravity yards relied on a code of whistles to advise the signalman what 'road' (siding) was required.

In the late nineteenth century the *hump* yard was introduced

Above: the interior of the East signal box at Temple Mills marshalling yard. The layout of the board corresponds to that of the yard itself. The room can be connected by phone or radio to strategic points in the yard as well as to the head office. Below: the primary retarder at Temple Mills, looking toward the hump. The artificial elevation can be seen in the background; the clamps inside the rails slow the wagons as necessary.

to provide gravity where there was no natural slope of the land. In this the trains were pushed up an artificial mound with a gradient of perhaps 1 in 80 and the cuts were 'humped' down a somewhat steeper gradient on the other side. The separate cuts would roll down the selected siding in the fan or 'balloon' of sidings, which would end in a slight upward slope to assist in the stopping of the wagons. The main means of stopping the wagons, however, were railwaymen called shunters who had to run alongside the wagons and apply the brakes at the right time. This was dangerous and required excessive manpower.

Such yards appeared all over North America and north-east England and began to be adopted elsewhere in England; Wath on the Great Central Railway in 1907 and Feltham on the London & South Western Railway in 1921 are notable examples. In Germany, small hump yards appeared, some having only three sidings on which to do the sorting. Much ingenuity was devoted to means of stopping the wagons; a German firm, Fröhlich, came up with a hydraulically operated *retarder* which clasped the wheel of the wagon as it went past, to slow it down to the amount the operator thought necessary.

Modern developments   An entirely new concept came with Whitemoor yard at March, near Cambridge, opened by the London & North Eastern Railway in 1929 to concentrate traffic to and from East Anglian destinations. When trains arrived in one of ten reception sidings a shunter examined the wagon labels and prepared a 'cut card' showing how the train should be sorted into sidings. This was sent to the control tower by pneumatic tube; there the points [switches] for the forty sorted sidings were preset in accordance with the cut card; information for several trains could be stored in a simple pin and drum device.

BRITISH RAILWAYS BOARD / C F KLAPPER

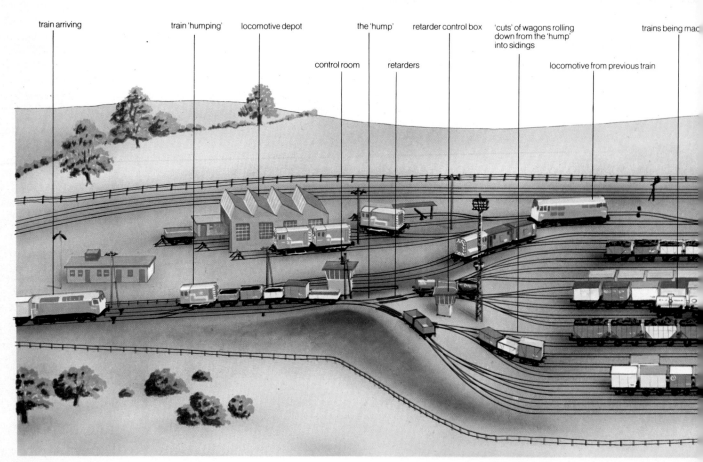

train arriving · train 'humping' · locomotive depot · control room · the 'hump' · retarders · retarder control box · 'cuts' of wagons rolling down from the 'hump' into sidings · locomotive from previous train · trains being mac

Left: the signal boards in many modern marshalling yards are located high above ground in a tower. This control tower is at British Rail's Tees yard.

Below: a typical marshalling yard. In early times natural elevation was used, but now the 'hump' is usually constructed artificially. The retarders are banks of automatically operated rams mounted by the rails which are individually replaceable. Some of them can boost wagon speed as needed as well as retard it.

Trains are sorted into groups of wagons for common destinations; there are also through roads for 'company' trains which do not need sorting. Brake vans are wagons from which the brakes of the train can be operated. The wagon repair works are served by a 'cripple' road. The control room is elevated for observation of the yard; the yard is floodlit at night and has its own telephone system.

The hump was approached by a grade of 1 in 80. On the far side was a short stretch of 1 in 18 to accelerate the wagons, followed by 70 yards (64 m) at 1 in 60 where the tracks divided into four, each equipped with a Fröhlich retarder. Then the four tracks spread out to four balloons of ten tracks each, comprising 95 yards (87 m) of level track followed by 233 yards (213 m) falling at 1 in 200, with the remaining 380 yards (348 m) level. The points were moved in the predetermined sequence by track circuits actuated by the wagons, but the operators had to estimate the effects on wagon speed of the retarders, depending to a degree on whether the retarders were grease or oil lubricated.

Pushed by an 0–8–0 small-wheeled shunting engine (see LOCOMOTIVE) at 1½ to 2 mph (2½ to 3 km/h), a train of 70 wagons could be sorted in seven minutes. The yard had a throughput of about 4000 wagons a day. The sorting sidings were allocated: number one for Bury St Edmunds, two for Ipswich, and so forth. Number 31 was for wagons with tyre fastenings which might be ripped off by retarders, which were not used on that siding. Sidings 32 to 40 were for traffic to be dropped at wayside stations; for these sidings there was an additional hump for sorting these wagons in station order. Apart from the sorting sidings, there were an engine road, a brake van road, a 'cripple' road for wagons needing repair, and transfer road to three sidings serving a *tranship shed*, where small shipments not filling entire wagons could be sorted.

Electronic developments British Rail built a series of yards at strategic points; the yards usually had two stages of retarders, latterly electro-pneumatically operated, to control wagon speed. In later yards electronic equipment was used to measure the weight of each wagon and estimate its rolling

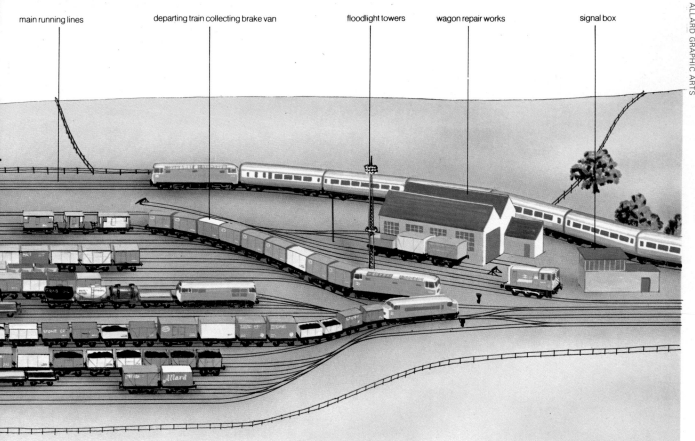

main running lines departing train collecting brake van floodlight towers wagon repair works signal box

resistance. By feeding this information into a computer, a suitable speed for the wagon could be determined and the retarder operated automatically to give the desired amount of braking. These predictions as to the running of wagons did not always prove reliable.

At Tinsley, opened in 1965, with eleven reception roads and 53 sorting sidings in eight balloons, the Dowty wagon speed control system was installed. The Dowty system uses many small units (20,000 at Tinsley) comprising hydraulic rams on the inside of the rail, less than a wagon length apart. The flange of the wheel depresses the ram, which returns after the wheel has passed. A speed-sensing device determines whether the wagon is moving too fast from the hump; if the speed is too fast the ram automatically has a retarding action. Certain of the units are booster-retarders; if the wagon is moving too slowly, a hydraulic supply enables the ram to accelerate the wagon. There are 25 secondary sorting sidings at Tinsley to which wagons are sent over a secondary hump by the booster-retarders. If individual units fail the rams can be replaced.

An automatic telephone exchange links all the traffic and administrative offices in the yard with the railway control office, Sheffield Midland Station and the local steelworks (principal source of traffic). Two-way loudspeaker systems are available through all the principal points in the yard, and radio telephone equipment is used to speak to enginemen. Fitters maintaining the retarders have walkie-talkie equipment. The information from shunters about the cuts and how many wagons in each, together with destination, is conveyed by special data transmission equipment, a punched tape being produced to feed into the point control system for each train over the hump.

As British Railways have departed from the wagon-load system there is less employment for marshalling yards. Freightliner services, block coal trains from colliery direct to power stations or to coal concentration depots, 'company' trains and other specialized freight traffic developments obviate the need for visiting marshalling yards. Other factors are competition from motor transport, closing of wayside freight depots and of many small coal yards.

Below: an aerial view of the Tees marshalling yard, opened May 21, 1963. The photo shows only part of the yard; such a yard can sort thousands of wagons a day. The use of marshalling yards is falling off because of competition from motor haulage. Railway mileage is actually falling in many countries, despite the fact that the true cost of railway haulage over 100 miles is cheaper.

MASS and WEIGHT

Mass (more correctly, *inertial mass*) is an intrinsic property of all matter and is a measure of its resistance to being accelerated by a force (see FIELD and FORCES). A cannonball, for example, requires a much greater force to set it rolling at a particular speed than does a football and this is as true on the Moon or in space as it is on the Earth.

The *weight* of an object is a more familiar concept to most people. It is the force which gravity exerts on the object and as such its magnitude can be found from Newton's second law of motion (see NEWTON'S LAWS). This states that the force on an object is equal to its mass multiplied by the acceleration this force produces. In a gravitational field therefore, the weight of an object is equal to its mass multiplied by the acceleration due to gravity. On Earth, the acceleration due to gravity (given the symbol **g**) is 9.81 metres per second per second (approximately 32 feet per second per second)—that is, every second the speed of a falling body increases by 9.81 m/s or 32 ft/s. On the Moon,

Brief periods of weightlessness are possible in aircraft flying in parabolic paths. The human body is relatively unaffected if fully exercised—three Skylab astronauts spent a record 84 days in free fall at the beginning of 1974 without any ill effects.

the acceleration due to gravity is only one-sixth that on the Earth and consequently objects on the Moon weigh only one-sixth of their weight on the Earth. As weight is the force exerted by gravity on an object, it is also equal to the force one must use to lift such an object *against* gravity.

Weightlessness It is possible for an object to have no weight. A man in a freely falling lift, for example, is *weightless*. He feels no force between himself and the lift floor because both are accelerating downwards at exactly the same rate. The period of weightlessness achieved in this way is necessarily quite short, for even in five seconds the man will have fallen 400 ft (120 m).

Trainee astronauts have been subjected to weightless conditions for several minutes by flying an aeroplane on a *parabolic trajectory*—the path in which a stone moves when thrown upwards. The pilot ensures that the aeroplane (and astronaut) moves along a parabolic path—as it travels upwards it is decelerating (negative acceleration) at 9.81 m/s² (32 ft/s²), it eventually reaches its topmost point (the *apogee*) where its upwards velocity is zero, and then continues to accelerate downwards like the free falling lift. At all points along the journey the aeroplane undergoes a downwards acting acceleration and the astronaut experiences weightlessness.

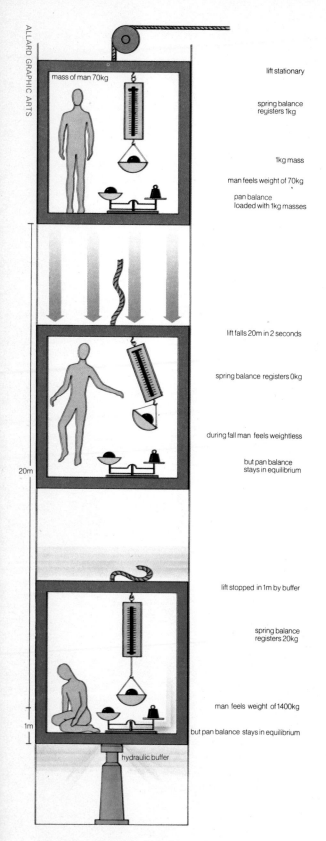

lift stationary

spring balance
registers 1kg

1kg mass

man feels weight of 70kg

pan balance
loaded with 1kg masses

lift falls 20m in 2 seconds

spring balance registers 0kg

during fall man feels weightless

but pan balance
stays in equilibrium

lift stopped in 1m by buffer

spring balance
registers 20kg

man feels weight of 1400kg

but pan balance stays in equilibrium

hydraulic buffer

mass of man 70kg

20m

1m

Mass in an unchanging property of matter, but weight depends on the environment. A man with a mass of 70 kg at rest on the Earth's surface feels a weight of 70 kg. If he is in a falling lift, he feels weightless until the car hits the bottom, when the abrupt deceleration causes a large temporary increase in his weight. All the time, however, his mass remains unchanged. Note that a spring balance measures weight, but a pan balance mass.

An astronaut orbiting the Earth in a satellite also experiences weightlessness. In this situation the CENTRIFUGAL force acting on the satellite and astronaut through their circular motion about the Earth counterbalances the Earth's gravitational forces on them. Also at such points in space which are remote from massive bodies, the gravitational forces are so weak that all objects are virtually weightless.

Units of mass and weight

Mass is a primary property of matter (see DIMENSIONS), that is, the units of mass are fundamental and cannot be reduced to other (more fundamental) units. Typical units are pounds, ounces, grammes, kilogrammes, tons and tonnes. In the metric system the unit of mass is the International Prototype Kilogramme, a block of platinum-iridium alloy, kept at the International Bureau of Weights and Measures at Sèvres (near Paris).

Because force equals mass times acceleration, the dimensions of force (and therefore weight) are [mass] $\times$ [acceleration] which can be written as $[M][L][T^{-2}]$ where M is mass, L is length and T is time. In the MKS (metre-kilogramme-second) system of units, force is measured in newtons, defined as the force required to move a kilogramme mass with an acceleration of one metre per second per second. It therefore has the units kg m/s^2.

For practical reasons it is often more conventional to use the weight of a standard mass within the standard gravitational field, **g**. That mass is then suffixed with the word 'weight' as in the 'kilogramme weight' (kg wt). The kg wt is approximately

Below: a stroboscopic picture of a disc sliding down a tilted air table. The regular strobe flashes show the rate of acceleration of the disc under the force of gravity.

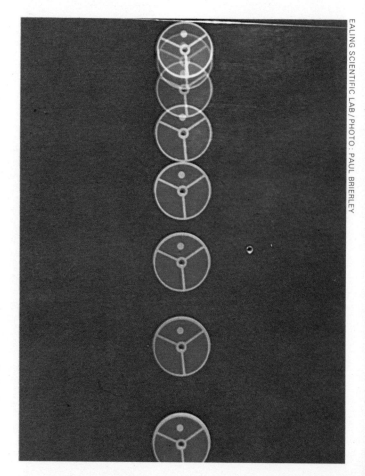

9.81 newtons (9.81 N) because **g** is 9.81 m/s² and the newton is defined as the force producing an acceleration of 1 m/s² on 1 kg mass. As **g** varies slightly over the Earth's surface, the kg wt also undergoes slight variations according to the position where it is being measured.

Balances A spring balance measures the *weight* of an object by opposing the force of gravity with the force of an extended spring. As such, its readings will vary from place to place according to the variations in gravity.

The beam balance, on the other hand, measures *mass*. The beam is balanced when the force of gravity on the object equals that on the combination of standard mass (unfortunately called 'weights') in the other scale pan. Because the acceleration due to gravity is the same at both ends of the beam, the masses must also be equal. Here, the actual value of **g** is unimportant—as long as it is not zero.

Inertial and gravitational mass The discussion of weight relies on the fact that the acceleration due to gravity is the same for all objects, regardless of their masses. This principle —sometimes known as the *equivalence of inertial and gravitational mass*—was first demonstrated by Galileo. He was supposed to have dropped two balls of different masses from the top of the leaning tower of Pisa. They hit the ground simultaneously. It is now known to be true to better than one part in a hundred thousand million, and EINSTEIN took this equivalence as the starting point in his General Theory of RELATIVITY to deduce his theory of gravity.

This equivalence could be of practical use in future space stations. By spinning the station quite slowly, an apparent gravity field will be set up towards the outside of the station, decreasing to zero at the centre of rotation.

MASS-ENERGY EQUIVALENCE

One of the most far-reaching results of Einstein's 1905 Special Theory of RELATIVITY is the one which states that mass and energy are equivalent. Mathematically, this is the famous statement $E = mc^2$: the total energy contained in a piece of matter is given by its mass multiplied by the square of the speed of light.

Einstein arrived at this conclusion from the basic assumption that the velocity of LIGHT is the same for any observer, whatever his velocity relative to the source of light. This goes against everyday experience, yet it is supported by every test that scientists have applied. Einstein's predictions, made from this assumption, are equally unexpected yet have nevertheless been supported by experiment—the most dramatic example being that of the A-BOMB, which uses the FISSION of a uranium isotope.

Although the equivalence of mass and energy is generally accepted, the problems of actually extracting the energy from matter are immense. The Sun, or an H-BOMB, uses FUSION of hydrogen atoms to make helium atoms, the difference between four hydrogen atoms and one helium atom being released as energy. This process is much more efficient than that of fission, yet if the difference between the two masses is compared with the total mass, it turns out that in the fusion process only 0.7% of the available energy is released.

This power station has coal stocks of 140,000 tons, capable of producing 260,000 megawatt hours of electricity in the normal way. If it could be completely converted into energy, however, it would produce 4000 million million MWh of energy—enough to supply the world's current energy demands for another 30,000 years.

Astrophysicists and nuclear scientists are equally interested in the problem of extracting as much energy as possible, and have suggested further processes which may work. By pouring matter down a *black hole*, that is a region in space where the matter is so condensed that nothing, not even light, can escape from it, it may be possible to extract as much as 43% of the rest mass of a particle as energy—the particle gives out radiation as it accelerates. No black holes are so far definitely known to exist, though there is no theoretical objection to them. But the only way of converting 100% of the rest mass into energy appears to be complete annihilation of matter by allowing it to meet *antimatter*.

Small amounts of antimatter—positrons, or anti-electrons—have been created, and when these interact with ordinary matter, all their mass indeed appears as energy. But the antimatter had to be created in the first place, causing an original loss of the same amount of energy. No reserves of antimatter are known in the universe, and unless some are found, it appears that the dream of completely converting a small amount of matter into enough energy to meet all of mankind's needs must remain an impossible one.

MASS PRODUCTION (see assembly line)

MASS SPECTROSCOPY

The study of chemistry and physics in the early part of this century was rapidly accelerated by the invention of the mass spectrometer. The various chemical ELEMENTS of which the Earth is made had been theoretically placed in an orderly sequence known as the PERIODIC TABLE. Their weights increased stepwise in this same sequence, and the mass spectrometer allowed these so-called *atomic weights* to be accurately measured. This was very important for detecting and analyzing unknown chemicals, particularly ISOTOPES, and for furthering the study of the periodic table.

Mass spectrometers The principle of the mass spectrometer consists of firing a narrow beam of atoms or molecules into a force FIELD so that the light elements are deflected differently from the heavy ones. If the atoms or molecules are electrically charged, magnetic and electrical fields can be used to deflect the beam. Knowledge of the exact field strengths leads one to a very accurately known mass for each particle based on the path it takes. The first mass spectrometers had a photographic plate positioned so as to intercept the beam of charged particles after deflection. Particles of different mass strike the plate at different positions and the result, when the plate is developed, is a series of lines each corresponding to a

OSBORNE / MARKS

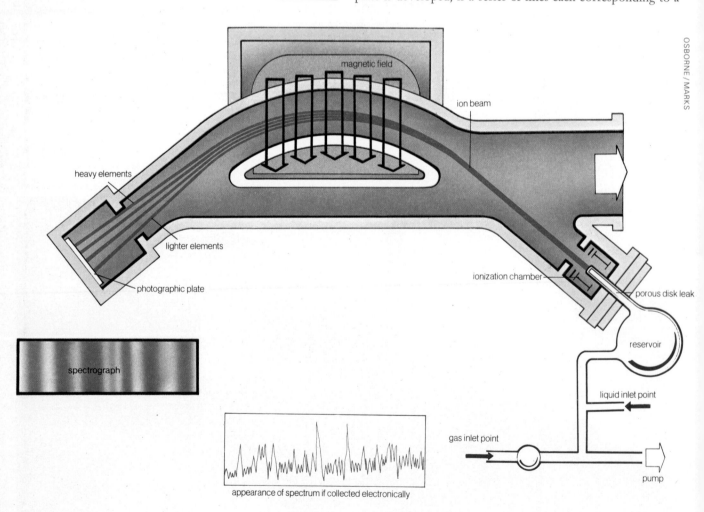

Above: the substance to be analyzed is ionized and the molecules, now with a net positive charge, accelerated through an electric field. The magnetic field deflects the individual molecules to different degrees

according to their molecular weight, and the resulting array then hits a photographic plate on a screen or enters an electronic analyzer to produce a mass spectrum.

different mass value. The darkness of the various lines indicates the relative amounts of the different particles in the beam. Machines which use a photographic plate to detect the deflected beam are called *mass spectrographs*.

The particles are usually charged by taking one electron out of the atom or molecule, leaving an ION with one positive charge. This can be done by subjecting the sample to be analyzed to an electric discharge such as a spark or an intense beam of electrons. There are also other methods of ionizing the sample, but these are the commonest in use at the present time. To allow the ionized particles to move freely, as many as possible of the unwanted air molecules are removed by enclosing the apparatus in a sealed chamber and reducing the pressure by means of a vacuum pump until it is less than about 100 millionths of atmospheric pressure. The average distance which one particle can travel in such a vacuum before colliding with another one is about 5 metres (16 ft), and this is much less than the distance between the ionizer and the photographic plate, which is usually less than 0.5 metre (20 inch).

Many modern mass spectrometers use the magnetic field from a powerful electromagnet (see ELECTROMAGNETISM) to deflect the ionized beams, and then detect the ions electrically using an *electron multiplier* instead of a photographic plate. An

Left: the output display of a mass spectrometer. The two peaks represent the isotopes rubidium-85 (left) and rubidium-87 (right). The peak heights give the relative proportions of the two isotopes in the sample.

Below: the ionizer filament of a mass spectrometer. The sample material can be seen on the middle of the filament.

electron multiplier can amplify the initial signal produced by the ions by as much as a million times. Electronic equipment displays the result of the analysis, and computers can be connected for automatic control and calibration of the data. The photographic plate is still used, however, in instruments which ionize the sample by means of a spark. Some materials, particularly metals and CERAMICS, can only be analyzed in this way. The spark does not produce a steady stream of ions, and the random variations are normally smoothed out by allowing a long time exposure on the plate.

Another type of analyzer uses a radio frequency signal to separate the various ions in the beam. Only the ions with a specific mass can get through to the detector by oscillating between electrodes in the analyzer at the same frequency as the applied signal. Heavier or lighter ions can only move slower or faster, and consequently collide with the walls and are absorbed. One analyzer of this type is called the *quadrupole* analyzer because the electrodes to which the radio frequency is applied are in the form of four rods. The particular mass which the analyzer will pass can be selected simply by selecting the appropriate frequency; the mass passed is inversely proportional to the frequency.

Uses One of the first uses of the instrument was to study the cause of deviation from the simple periodic table theory. Hydrogen, the lightest element, was arbitrarily taken as having a relative mass of 1.000. The same number of atoms of other elements should then have exactly a whole number relationship to hydrogen. Determination of atomic weights by traditional methods seemed to show that this was not true, for example chlorine was found to have an atomic weight of about 35.5. The mass spectrometer showed why this was so. Instead of a single line, two lines were observed on the mass spectrograph plate corresponding to whole number atomic weights of 35 and 37 respectively. Naturally occurring chlorine was thus shown to consist of two isotopes having exactly the same chemical properties but different masses. It is now known that chlorine contains 75.4% of the isotope whose atomic weight is 35 and 24.6% of the isotope whose atomic weight is 37; the traditionally determined value of 35.5 was simply an average value.

Isotopes of the other elements were detected in a similar way using mass spectrometers. Very accurate determination of the atomic weights of isotopes by this technique shows slight variations from the predicted values. This is due to the BINDING ENERGY involved in the formation of the atom. Many radioactive isotopes have a very short lifetime and have been proved to exist only by observation of mass spectrometer results. It is also possible to prepare very pure isotopes by collecting them at the exit position of the spectrometer. Although the amounts which can be prepared in this way are exceedingly small (less than a millionth of a gramme) this technique is invaluable when purification is impossible by any other means.

One of the chief advantages of the mass spectrometer is that it can analyze a very small sample, and present day applications range from using the extremely high sensitivity to detect and measure the residual molecules left in the most complete vacuum that man can make, to detecting and identifying complicated molecules coming from a *gas chromatograph* (see CHROMATOGRAPHY). The presence of a minute leak into a vacuum system can easily be detected if a fine jet of helium is directed at the suspected area. A mass spectrometer attached to the system and tuned to the helium mass will then give an extremely sensitive indication of the position and size of the leak as the helium flows through the hole and reaches the mass spectrometer. This technique can be applied to testing any sealed unit which it is possible to evacuate first, for instance a hydraulic system or a gas filled chamber. Manned spacecraft need such a check and the cabin atmosphere on recent flights was continuously monitored for impurities by a miniature mass spectrometer.

Hospital doctors can measure a patient's breathing efficiency by using the rapid response of a mass spectrometer to analyze the various components of the breath, and anaesthetists have used the technique to watch the progress of a patient during a long operation.

The organic chemist identifies complicated molecules by recognizing the breakdown pattern during ionization. The highest mass recorded gives the *molecular weight* and the major fragments suggest the main building blocks of the molecules. The extreme sensitivity and speed of response makes the technique suitable for detecting unknown compounds coming from a gas chromatograph. Chemists investigating flavours or perfumes which are extremely complicated mixtures of organic chemicals can now analyze many naturally occurring products this way. The chemist needs such a technique to be able to control and diagnose the effect on people and the environment of drugs or pesticides which are harmful in trace quantities. Another application is in dating and authenticating archaeological relics or works of art by taking minute samples and subjecting them to analysis by a mass spectrometer. The slight change in isotope ratios over the centuries, or the special materials used by different artists, give a very accurate means of classification.

Below: the output of a gas chromatograph (left) is analyzed by means of a mass spectrometer. The picture shows the ionizer (centre), the detector (right) and the cylindrical poles of the electromagnet.

MATCH manufacture

The invention of the friction match in the early 1800s was described by Herbert Spencer, the philosopher, as 'the greatest boon and blessing that had come to mankind in the nineteenth century'. Although methods of generating fire by spontaneous chemical reaction had been known since the isolation of *white* PHOSPHORUS in the second half of the seventeenth century, friction matches were not produced commercially until 1827, by John Walker in England. Walker's matches were of the 'strike anywhere' type being made from *potassium chlorate*, $KClO_3$, *antimony sulphide*, Sb_2S_3, and gum arabic. They were, however, somewhat unreliable and difficult to strike. Subsequently, and up to the end of the nineteenth century, strike anywhere matches almost invariably contained white phosphorus. The incidence of 'phossy jaw'—a particularly horrible industrial disease—among workers in match factories rendered it imperative to find a substitute for this material and, from the turn of the century, *phosphorus sesquisulphide*, P_4S_3, has replaced white phosphorus in strike anywhere matches.

The safety match The discovery in the 1840s of a much less reactive form, or *allotrope*, of phosphorus, called *red phosphorus*, provided a material which opened the way for the production of safety matches, which are struck only on a prepared surface. The striking surface of safety matches contains red phosphorus bound to the side of the box with gum arabic, urea formaldehyde or other powerful adhesives. The potassium chlorate contained in the match head is, on striking the match, brought into contact with the phosphorus on the box and the resultant chemical reaction generates sufficient localized heat to initiate the burning of the match. Safety matches, in addition to potassium chlorate, contain SULPHUR with which it reacts and diluents such as powdered glass and iron oxide, Fe_2O_3, which are inert and so control the burning rate. A binder is also required; this is normally animal glue,

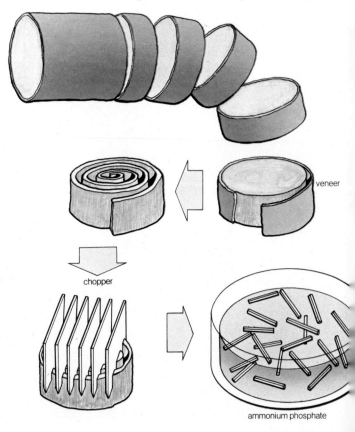

veneer

chopper

ammonium phosphate

which consolidates the constituents and binds them to the end of the match stick.

Strike anywhere matches contain phosphorus sesquisulphide, which is more reactive than sulphur and, in consequence, friction on a rough surface is sufficient to trigger off a reaction between this material and potassium chlorate, which causes the matches to ignite.

Colour matches of either the safety or strike anywhere variety are made by the addition of suitable dyes and, in these instances, highly coloured ingredients such as iron oxide and manganese dioxide, MnO_2, are omitted and replaced by a white material which is normally zinc oxide, ZnO.

The matchstick

After the various chemicals, wood is probably the most important material used in match making. Various other materials can, however, be used for the sticks of matches, including wax coated cotton, paper and cardboard. Timber for matchsticks should be white and odourless, straight grained, easy to work and sufficiently porous to absorb paraffin wax. It must neither be too hard nor too soft. If it is too hard it will not absorb paraffin wax, if too soft it will bend out of shape. The ends of the matchsticks which carry the heads are soaked in hot *paraffin wax* before the head is put on. This helps the match to burn by transferring the flame from the match head composition to the stick. Without the paraffin wax the match would go out as soon as the combustible matter in the match head was burnt. Matchsticks are also impregnated with *ammonium phosphate*, a fire retarding agent, so that they will not continue to glow or smoulder after being put out.

To make the matchsticks, logs weighing about 125 kg (276 lb) and about three metres (9.8 ft) long are first sawn into *billets* about $\frac{1}{2}$ metre (1.6 ft) long. These are cut into *veneers* on a *peeling machine*. The long strips of veneer, about 2.3 mm (0.09 inch) thick, then move on to the *choppers*. Every cut of the chopper through a stack of veneer produces about 1000 match-

Above: a nineteenth century match factory in England. Because white phosphorus was used in the match head composition, the disease 'phossy jaw' was a constant threat to workers in match factories.

Below: a schematic representation of match manufacture. To make the match sticks, logs are cut into billets, the bark is removed and the billets are cut into veneers on a peeling machine. The veneers are cut into splints which are then impregnated with ammonium phosphate, a fire retardant. The splints are dried, polished and cleaned in a rotating drum and then attached to a steel conveyer belt. The heads are dipped in paraffin wax and then the head composition. When the heads are dry the matches are boxed.

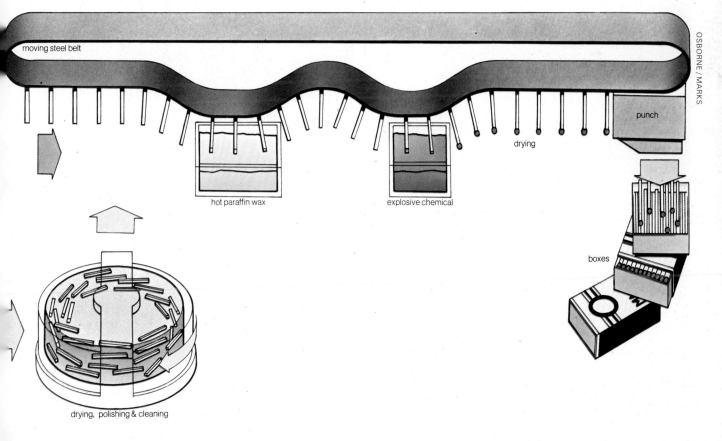

moving steel belt

hot paraffin wax

explosive chemical

drying

punch

boxes

drying, polishing & cleaning

Above: freshly cut matchsticks, or splints, are blown along steel tubes to a conveyer belt which carries them to the match machine.

Below: dipped matches pass slowly through the match machine on a perforated steel belt. The match heads must be dried slowly if the matches are to strike properly.

sticks, or over one million in less than five minutes. The sticks are then impregnated with ammonium phosphate, dried, polished and cleaned in rotating drums. Finally they are blown along steel pipes to the match machines.

The continuous match machine These machines can be operated by as few as eight people and can produce and box about 20 million matches per day. The sticks are fed automatically into suitably spaced holes in the machine's slowly moving steel belt. First they pass through a bath of hot paraffin wax. A little further on the steel belt stops over a table covered with the chemical composition for the match heads. The sticks, nearly 6000 at a time, are lowered into the liquid mixture and as they are raised each stick carries a drop of composition which forms the striking head. The next stage is to dry the head, and this must be done very slowly or the match will not strike properly. It takes 50 to 60 minutes of slow movement through the machine before the matches are ready for the boxes. At any time during the day there are about two million matches on the machine. When the drying process is finished the steel belt travels downwards to the inner boxes which are moving steadily across its path. The machine then punches the matches out of their holes in the belt so that they fall neatly and in the correct numbers into the inner boxes as these pass by. The filled inner boxes move on conveyers parallel to the outer boxes. Both conveyers stop momentarily and 16 inners are rapidly pushed into 16 outers, and the conveyers move on again. This operation is repeated 50 times every minute.

Book matches, which consist of a *comb* of wood or cardboard stapled into a cardboard cover, are made in very much the same way. The combs are first cut from a strip of wood or cardboard and then fed to the match machine. When the match heads are dry, the combs are passed to a booking machine where the covers are attached.

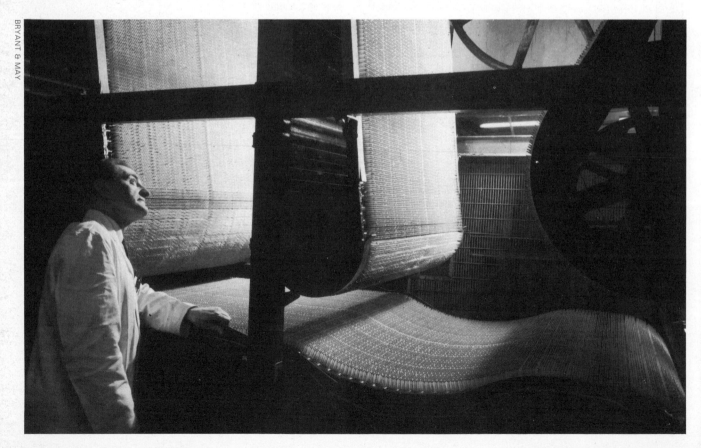

MATHEMATICS

Mathematics is often thought of as dealing with numbers, and associating numbers with quantities, but it is much more than that. It is a language in its own right, which has been evolved to define exactly the relationships between physical objects, and to simplify discussion of them, just as any other language is used to talk about humans' thoughts and feelings. It has many of the qualities of a natural language, and involves more than computing or arithmetic.

In branches such as geometry, numbers play no real part (although it is possible to re-express the results in terms of numbers); in others such as calculus and algebra the language deals with the most general case, and numbers do not occur until the final stage when they are substituted for letters to study special cases. Today, electronic COMPUTERS and calculators do all the manipulation of numbers, where this is needed at all.

It is tempting, but unwise, to classify branches of mathematics according to their practical value. The important application of mathematics over the last century have been of results found earlier, which seemed at the time quite useless.

Numbers
Arithmetic began with the natural numbers, 1, 2, 3 . . . (in mathematics, the symbol '. . .' means 'and so on', without specifying the actual numbers), and the operations of addition and multiplication. The natural numbers are inconvenient because subtraction is not always possible: we can take 3 from 5 but not 5 from 3. Accordingly the *integers* or whole numbers (positive and negative) are defined to always allow subtraction, by the rule that since 3 from 5 is 2, 5 from 3 is to be written −2. This can be shown as follows:

sequence of integer numbers

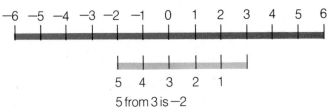

5 from 3 is −2

The same problem arises with division, and is again answered by inventing new numbers. 24 divided by 4 gives 6, but divided by 5 does not give a natural number. The *fractions*, or *rational* numbers, were invented with the result that dividing 24 by 5 is written 24/5. The rational numbers are *dense* in the sense that between any two there lies another (their average, for example), so there is no 'next' one.

The early Greek geometers thought that the rationals were all the numbers there were and set up their theory of *similar figures* on that basis. The idea was to represent numbers by suitable shapes, which is why we talk today of a number multiplied by itself as being its square, while a number multiplied by itself twice is the *cube* of the number:

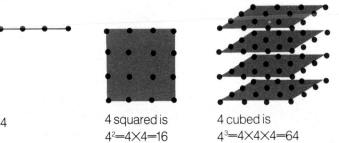

4 squared is
$4^2 = 4 \times 4 = 16$

4 cubed is
$4^3 = 4 \times 4 \times 4 = 64$

By this means Pythagoras, or maybe his collaborators, were able around 500 BC to prove the theorem that the square of the side opposite the right angle, the hypotenuse, in a right angled triangle, is the sum of the squares on the other two sides. (A theorem is any proposition which is not obvious, but which can nevertheless be proved).

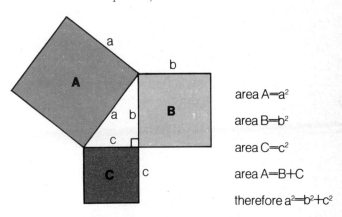

area A = a^2

area B = b^2

area C = c^2

area A = B + C

therefore $a^2 = b^2 + c^2$

Pythagoras' theorem gives a good insight into the way mathematics relates to the physical world: the relationship $a^2 = b^2 + c^2$, which holds true for any right angled triangle ever drawn, shows how to turn shapes into mathematics. It can be used to find unknown quantities—given any two sides, the third can be calculated—and so has immediate practical uses.

Applied to a square which has sides one unit long, the theorem says that the square of the diagonal must be 2 units; but no rational number can be squared to give the answer 2.

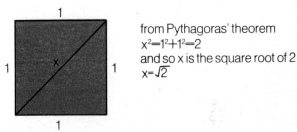

from Pythagoras' theorem
$x^2 = 1^2 + 1^2 = 2$
and so x is the square root of 2
$x = \sqrt{2}$

The proof that the square root of 2 ($\sqrt{2}$) cannot be represented by a rational number was discovered by Pythagoras. A rational number is a number that can be represented as a fraction—one integer (whole number) divided by another. In this way, the rational number 6.2 can be represented as $\frac{31}{5}$.

To prove the irrationality of $\sqrt{2}$, take two integers m and n such that $\frac{m}{n}$ cannot be reduced to a fraction containing smaller integers—unlike, for example, $\frac{62}{10}$, which can be reduced to $\frac{31}{5}$, leaving its value unchanged, by dividing the top and bottom by 2.

Therefore m and n cannot both be even numbers, or they would both be divisible by 2.

Now if $\frac{m}{n} = \sqrt{2}$, then $\frac{m^2}{n^2} = 2$, and $m^2 = 2n^2$. But twice any integer is an even number; therefore m^2 is even, which means that m is also even (an even number multiplied by an even number gives another even number).

Thus, there must be another integer which is half of m. Call it p. m = 2p, so $m^2 = 4p^2$. Substituting $4p^2$ for m^2 in the original statement $\frac{m^2}{n^2} = 2$ gives $\frac{4p^2}{n^2} = 2$. It therefore follows that $n = 2p^2$.

By the same argument, however, n^2 must therefore be even, and so must n. m has already been shown to be even.

But m and n cannot both be even (see above), so there can be no rational number of the form $\frac{m}{n}$ such that $\frac{m}{n} = \sqrt{2}$. Therefore $\sqrt{2}$ is irrational.

This result gave rise to the first of the great crises to the foundations of mathematics, which was solved by inventing yet more numbers—the *irrationals*. These and the rationals together form the *real* numbers—all numbers expressed by (finite and infinite) decimals. The number whose square is 2 (the *square root* of 2) is now 1.41421 . . . .

The square of 1.41421 differs from 2 by 0.0000100759; no matter how many more figures are taken the square cannot quite be 2. But it can approach 2 are nearly as desired. The real numbers are the final step in constructing bigger number systems so long as we restrict attention to numbers which are in some order (so that for any unequal pair we can determine which is the greater). But it became necessary from the sixteenth century onwards to extend the number system one stage further, by giving up the requirement of ordering.

This need arose in the solution of equations, and because of the 'double negative' situation. In mathematics, as in any language, two negatives multiplied together produce a positive (for example, 'to not not do something' means 'to do something'). If we ask what numbers when squared give the answer 1, the answer is two-fold: 1 and −1. If we ask what numbers when squared give zero, there is but one, zero. But if we ask what numbers when squared give −1, there are no such real numbers. It was possible to invent *complex numbers*, defined in terms of reals and one other unit, called i by mathematicians and now j by electrical engineers, whose square is −1.

Whereas real numbers can be represented on a straight line, complex numbers (which contain both real and imaginary numbers) are represented on a surface or plane, in what is called an Argand diagram.

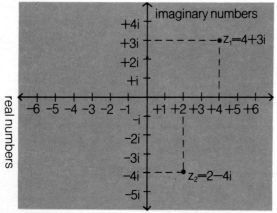

Argand diagram showing the complex numbers z_1 and z_2

Algebra General results about numbers are the domain of algebra, using symbols (usually letters) to represent quantities. An example of this has already occurred, for the statement $a^2 = b^2 + c^2$ is an algebraic one referring to the right angled triangle, in which numbers do not arise until we need a specific result.

Algebra depends on equalities, and interprets the relationships between quantities in terms of equations. By making a number of statements about a situation, each one an equation, it is then possible to draw inferences from the statements using simple rules, and arrive at an answer for an unknown quantity or quantities.

A simple algebraic equation is, for example, $y = \frac{9}{5}x + 32$. This is the conversion of a temperature of $x°$ Centigrade into its equivalent in Fahrenheit, $y°$F. A graph of y against x looks like:

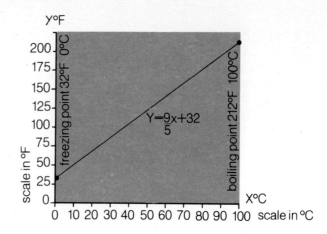

This gives a straight line graph, and the equation $y = \frac{9}{5}x + 32$ is therefore called a *linear* equation. It has the general form $y = ax + b$, where a and b are *constants*, which can be replaced by any numbers, depending on the application; x is called the *independent variable* and y the *dependent variable*, since it depends on x.

Many quantities, however, do not vary linearly but involve squares, cubes or higher *powers* of numbers. Power in this case means the number of times the number is multiplied by itself— 2 to the power 4, or '2 to the fourth', is $2^4 = 2 \times 2 \times 2 \times 2 = 16$.

An example of a non-linear equation is $y = 2x^2$, which looks like:

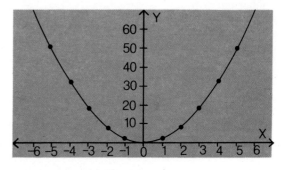

graph of the parabola $y = 2x^2$

Non-linear equations have a curved graph, this one being the curve called a *parabola*. Because the square of a negative number is positive, the values of y are always positive and the curve has two upward arms. This gives the result that when, say, y = 8, x has two values (called the *roots* of the equation): either +2 or −2. An equation of this form is called a *quadratic*, with the general form $y = ax^2 + bx + c$.

Real progress in algebra had to wait till the sixteenth century when the detailed solution of equations was attempted. For quadratic equations the rule had been known since Babylonian times; but if the cube of the unknown enters the problem (*cubic* equations), the solution (found about 1500) involves first solving a certain quadratic. Half a century later equations involving the fourth power of the unknown (biquadratics) could be solved, the process involving first solving a subsidiary cubic. But equations of fifth degree (quintics) when tackled similarly relied for their solution on an equation of sixth degree. It was not till the nineteenth century that Abel showed that no such method could be found for the quintic.

Geometry Geometry is the study of relationships in space and was the principal component of Greek mathematics. Among its most widely known results are the properties of the circle:

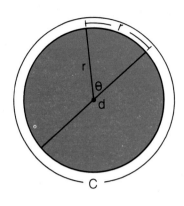

Basic properties of a circle: diameter d = 2r where r is the radius. An arc whose length is equal to the radius, r, always subtends the same angle, θ, at the centre of the circle. θ = 57.3° and this angle is called one radian. The ratio of the circumference, c, of a circle, to its diameter is a constant number given the Greek symbol π (pi). $\pi = \frac{c}{2r} = 3.1416. \ldots$ The circumference c is equal to $2\pi r$ because there are 2π radians around a circle (360° = 2π radians). Area of a circle = πr^2.

As well as straight lines and circles in the plane (that is, flat), the Greeks studied three dimensional geometry and the shapes made by cutting circular cones with planes. These shapes are called the *conic sections*—the ellipses, parabolas and hyperbolas.

Plane sections of the cone. Plane 1 cuts the cone twice, so producing the two branches of the hyperbola, plane 2 cuts in an ellipse, plane 3 is parallel to the generators and so produces the parabola.

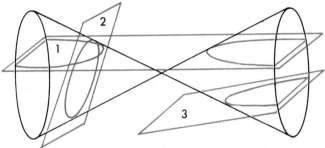

But for us the importance of these curves is in *celestial mechanics* —the motions of planets, satellites, and so on. Kepler found that the orbits of the planets round the Sun were ellipses; the orbit of an artificial satellite round the Earth is an ellipse; and the limiting case of this, when we throw a ball in the air, is a parabola.

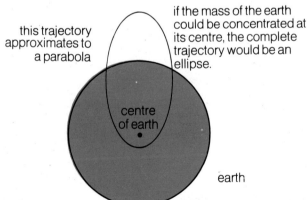

this trajectory approximates to a parabola

if the mass of the earth could be concentrated at its centre, the complete trajectory would be an ellipse.

centre of earth

earth

We do not now derive these properties by the methods of the Greeks, but two things from Greek geometry remain valuable to us. One is the *axiomatic* system—that everything is supposed to be derived from *axioms* or 'self-evident truths'. Greek or *Euclidean* geometry is confined to flat planes. But this is not the only sort possible, and it was by questioning the absolute truth of these axioms that Euclidean geometry was supplemented by non-Euclidean geometries. These were used by Einstein in 1915 to replace Newton's theory of GRAVITATION by General RELATIVITY.

The second important aspect of Greek geometry was the invention of trigonometry by Hipparchus (about 125 BC) and Ptolemy (about 150 AD).

Trigonometry

If two triangles have the same angles, but different sizes, their corresponding sides are proportional. Hipparchus realized that a table could be made relating the ratio of the sides to the angles in degrees. It proved sufficient to do this for right angled triangles: the ratio of the side opposite one of the smaller angles to the hypotenuse is called the *sine* (abbreviated to sin) of the angle.

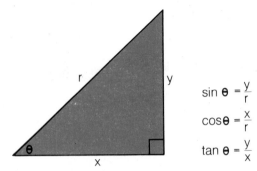

$$\sin \theta = \frac{y}{r}$$

$$\cos \theta = \frac{x}{r}$$

$$\tan \theta = \frac{y}{x}$$

Since any triangle can be divided into two right angled ones by forming a perpendicular from one corner to the opposite side, tables of sines of angles expressed in degrees suffice to calculate the ratios of sides for all triangles.

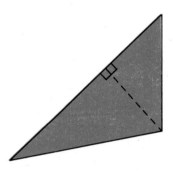

any triangle can be divided into two right angled triangles

The Greeks were originally interested in trigonometry for astronomy: it was only much later that it was used for surveying the Earth as in the triangulation method used in MAP-MAKING. But its importance is not in applications but in the introduction of the idea of a *function*.

Functions

A function is a rule that governs the way one value depends on another. It assigns to every number in a certain set (its *domain*) exactly one value, the value of the function. The sine function assigns a certain ratio to every angle. The *cosine* (cos) and *tangent* (tan) are other examples of functions based on the sides and angles of a right angled triangle. The sine and other trigonometric functions were for a long time the only examples, until the invention of the LOGARITHM and exponential functions; and they were the most important ones, because they are *periodic functions*.

If an arm rotates, so as to sweep out an ever increasing angle, it will have made a complete rotation at 360°; for larger angles than that, the sine repeats itself.

Mathematicians rarely describe angles in degrees, but instead use radians, where 360° = 2π radians. This arises because a *radian* is defined as the angle between the centre of a circle and an arc the length of the radius. Since the circumference is $2\pi r$, there are 2π radians around a circle, in 360°.

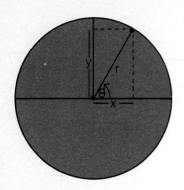

Equation of circle is $x^2+y^2 = r^2$ (from Pythagoras' theorem). As θ increases, the radial arm sweeps around the circle. When it has travelled 360° (2π radians) it has completed one circle. But $\sin\theta = \frac{y}{r}$ so adding 2π to θ does not change the value of $\sin\theta$. $\sin\theta = \sin(2\pi+\theta) = \sin(4\pi+\theta) \ldots \sin\theta$ is therefore a periodic function.

So for the sine function there is a certain number, the period, here 2π, which is such that adding it to any element of the domain leaves the value of the function unchanged. Periodic phenomena are very common in practice (see SINE WAVE). It was realized in the eighteenth century that the behaviour of almost anything which varies periodically can be reproduced by adding a sufficient number of sines or cosines of different sizes—called *Fourier analysis*.

The motion of a heavy stretched string or the oscillation of a particle along a line attracted to a fixed point on the line are examples of two problems in which sines enter although there is no connection with angles. In the same way, logarithms enter in problems of natural growth when the original use for multiplication does not come in at all.

Calculus

The later investigations of functions all hinge on the *calculus*, which arose in the seventeenth century in mechanics, the study of the forces on objects and the motion they produce (see DYNAMICS and STATICS). The key notation is the 'derivative function of a function'.

It is easy enough, for example, to calculate the distance, x, travelled by a particle moving with a steady velocity, v, in a time, t, using the formula $x = v \times t$. In reverse, we can calculate the average velocity by dividing the distance travelled by the time taken, in other words $v = \frac{x}{t}$. In many problems, however, the velocity itself will be changing, such as that of a stone accelerating towards the ground:

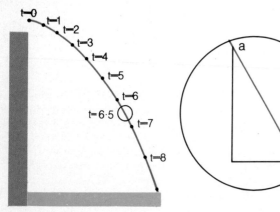

Trajectory of body thrown off cliff. Because of earth's gravity its vertical velocity increases (from zero), while its horizontal velocity remains unchanged. The body therefore falls in a curved path.

ab is a small part of the body's trajectory. When the distance ab is made small enough the trajectory can be considered a straight line. Around time t = 6.5 secs the instantaneous velocity is distance ab divided by time taken to travel ab—as ab approaches zero.

It is then important to know how the velocity changes with respect to time. This introduces the idea of *instantaneous velocity*, that is, velocity at an instant. This can be found by considering very small intervals of time, and the correspondingly short distances travelled. Over very short intervals, the velocity can be said to be practically constant. This can be done at each instant of the motion and so the velocity is, in turn, a function of time, the *derived function* or *derivative* of distance with respect to time. This process is called *differentiation*.

The mathematical process of differentiation, which can be applied to any desired function (not just velocity), is a matter of manipulation of the function according to standard rules.

During each minute time interval, the distance travelled by the falling stone is the instantaneous velocity multiplied by the time interval. Consequently, the total distance travelled by the stone will be the sum of all these small distances. This process is called *integration*, and is the reverse of differentiation.

The falling stone example is a simple case of the most important problems in calculus especially where applications are concerned, the solution of *differential equations*.

Infinite series

In many problems encountered in science and engineering an exact answer cannot be found. Instead an approximate answer is determined which contains a series of terms where each succeeding term is of less importance than the one before it. Only with an infinitely large number of such terms can the exact answer be found, but an engineer is not concerned with such accuracy—he only needs to know how many terms to include to give a sufficiently precise value for his purposes. Infinite series are, however, very important.

As already mentioned, Fourier analysis of a generally periodic function (of f periods per second, that is, a fundamental frequency f) indicates that it is composed of an infinite series of sine waveforms (*sinusoids*) of frequency f, 2f, 3f. . . . But if each of the terms (sinusoids) of this infinite series were of roughly the same magnitude, the combined effect would be an infinitely large function. Yet we know that this is not so—the original periodic function is finite and measurable. Fourier analysis also shows that each succeeding term is of less importance than the last—that is, the higher frequency components in the series are of diminishing magnitude.

The theory of convergence worked out in the nineteenth century, particularly by Cauchy, provided the criterion of whether an infinite series has a finite sum or not. For example, the series $1+\frac{1}{2}+\frac{1}{4}+\frac{1}{8}+\frac{1}{16}+\ldots$ is convergent and has a sum (in the limit, its sum is 2).

geometrical demonstration that the sum $1+\frac{1}{2}+\frac{1}{4}+\frac{1}{8}+\frac{1}{16}+\frac{1}{32}$ never exceeds 2

first term	½ ¼ ⅛
first 2 terms	
first 3 terms	
first 4 terms	
first 5 terms	
first 6 terms	

Not all decreasing series converge, however; the most famous one that does not is called the *harmonic series* $1+\frac{1}{2}+\frac{1}{3}+\frac{1}{4}+\frac{1}{5}+\ldots$. It is easy to see this, because $\frac{1}{3}+\frac{1}{4}$ is greater than $\frac{2}{4}=\frac{1}{2}$; $\frac{1}{5}+\frac{1}{6}+\frac{1}{7}+\frac{1}{8}$ is greater than $\frac{4}{8}=\frac{1}{2}$ and so on. So the sum, if the series were convergent, would be greater than $1+\frac{1}{2}+\frac{1}{2}+\frac{1}{2}+\ldots$. Actually the sum of n terms of the harmonic series differs by an almost constant amount from the natural logarithm (that is, to the base e) of the number n; this constant, whose value is roughly 0.577 . . ., is called Euler's constant. It is rather a mysterious number. No one knows yet whether it is the solution of an algebraic equation.

MATTER, properties of

In everyday experience matter occurs in one of three *states*; solid, liquid or gas. Roughly speaking, at a given temperature and pressure, a solid has a constant size and shape; a liquid will change its shape by flowing, but keeps its volume constant, while a gas expands indefinitely to fill its container. Sometimes the distinction between states may not be obvious. Pitch and glass, for example, are both liquids. They will both flow, although in the case of glass it takes centuries for the effect to become noticeable and normally before this the glass crystallizes into the solid, opaque, form. The *density* of a substance, or mass per unit volume (measured, for example, in grammes per cubic centimetre; it is known as *specific gravity* when measured relative to the density of water), is usually greatest when it is in the solid form, and least as a gas.

All matter at everyday temperatures and pressures is composed of MOLECULES (groups of atoms), and the differences in state are due to the difference in relations between these constituent molecules.

Solids
In the solid state the molecules are held in fixed positions relative to each other by chemical bonds. The directions and lengths of these bonds are fixed for any chemical compound, so a large number of molecules form a regular solid (a crystal), whose shape is characteristic of the compound. The CRYSTALS of common salt, for example, are cubic.

In some compounds the molecules can be packed together in more than one configuration, which gives rise to different crystalline forms, usually with different densities. The best known example of this *allotropy* is the element CARBON, which can occur either as graphite (pencil 'lead') or as diamond, depending on the arrangement of the carbon atoms. The term 'phase' is used to denote different allotropes as well as the different states of matter.

The crystals of all the METALS, and those of a few non-metals (such as graphite) can conduct electricity because the atoms easily 'lose' electrons which can then move freely through the crystal, and constitute an electric current when a voltage is applied. In an INSULATOR the electrons are too tightly bound to the molecules to be able to move in an external electric field. There are a few intermediate substances, the SEMICONDUCTORS, whose electric properties can be altered by the addition of minute quantities of impurities. They have made possible TRANSISTORS, INTEGRATED CIRCUITS and other compact electronic components.

The magnetic properties of a solid, on the other hand, depend on the bound electrons of the molecules (see MAGNETISM). Normally the electrons form pairs with their inherent magnetic components opposed, so as to cancel out the overall magnetic effect. A few elements (in particular, iron, cobalt and nickel) have unpaired electrons which can be lined up with the magnetic fields of their counterparts in neighbouring atoms to produce a relatively powerful overall field.

The BONDS in a solid are not completely rigid, and application of an external force will make the atoms move slightly closer. When the force is removed, the repulsion between the negatively charged electrons of adjacent atoms forces them back to their original positions, and the solid regains its shape. This is the phenomenon of ELASTICITY. There is also a continuous vibration of each atom about its average position, and the average energy of oscillation is a measure of the TEMPERATURE of the body (although even at the absolute zero of

Familiar materials can behave in unusual ways under extreme circumstances. During a volcanic eruption, rock in its liquid form at over 1000°C emerges from vents. This eruption, at Surtsey, Iceland, in 1964, is about to vaporize the sea water on contact.

temperature there is still some movement of the atoms). As the temperature of a solid is increased the oscillations increase in amplitude, and so the bond length becomes very slightly greater. The crystal therefore expands slightly with an increase in temperature (*thermal expansion*).

Liquids   In a liquid the attractive forces between the molecules (which give rise to bonds in solids) are not great enough to prevent them from moving about, and indeed the forces between the liquid and its container may be stronger than those between the liquid molecules themselves. For example, a drop of water placed on clean glass will spread out into a thin layer because of the strong force between the water molecules and the glass; but if the glass is slightly greasy the inter-molecular forces in the water are the stronger and the water forms into a small drop. This effect of SURFACE TENSION is also shown by the *meniscus:* a water surface will curve upwards slightly where it meets a vertical glass surface. The water inside a capillary tube (a very narrow tube) is pulled upwards by this force, against the force of gravity. It is this capillary effect in the very narrow gaps between the fibres of blotting paper which gives it the ability to soak up liquids.

Liquids generally expand with an increase in temperature, like solids, but water is an exception. Below 4°C it shows the opposite effect, expanding as the temperature is *decreased* owing to the formation of hydrogen bonds, and when it freezes (at 0°C) the ice occupies a *larger* volume than the original water. This is the reason why freezing water cracks pipes in the winter, and also why ice floats on water (since the ice occupies a larger volume, it is less dense than water and will float). In almost all other substances there is a shrinkage on freezing, and the solid sinks in the liquid.

Gases   The molecules of a gas are so far apart, and moving so fast, that they exert only very small forces on each other, and they can be thought of as completely independent particles (the *ideal gas* approximation). Their average speed is a measure of the temperature of the gas, while the force they exert on the walls of the container by bouncing off them is the *pressure* of the gas. The latter depends on both the speed of the molecules (that is, the temperature) and the frequency at which they strike the wall, and this in turn depends on the density of the gas. This relation between the temperature, pressure and density of an ideal gas is given mathematically by the GAS LAWS.

When the pressure is too high, or the temperature too low, the forces between the molecules become important and the behaviour deviates from that predicted by the gas laws. In extreme enough conditions the gas will liquefy.

Phase changes   A change of phase, from one state or allotrope to another, can be brought about by either tem-perature or pressure. The importance of both these conditions is shown by the fact that water boils at less than 100°C at the top of a mountain, where the pressure is less than that at sea level. At any particular pressure, however, the boiling point and melting point of pure substances are constant, and this provides a useful method for the identification of compounds, especially in organic chemistry. The boiling point or melting point of an unknown compound is often measured as a check, after an identification is deduced from the chemical ANALYSIS.

While a pan of water is boiling into steam, heat is being con-tinuously supplied without the temperature changing. This *latent heat of vaporization* is the energy needed to separate the

ICELAND TOURIST BUREAU

DEPT OF METEOROLOGY, EDINBURGH UNIV

Left: ice is unusual in that it is a solid which is less dense than the liquid form. Most solids sink in their liquids. Even ice only just manages to float: 90% of these ice floes off Iceland are under the water and only the tips show, making them a shipping hazard.

Above: plasma is a gas which is wholly or partly ionized, but which has no great overall charge because the electrons are still present. A thin plasma, the solar wind, constantly streams from the Sun; when gusts strike the upper atmosphere a glowing aurora is the result.

molecules against the attractive forces which hold them together in the liquid state. Latent heat is put to use in the STEAM ENGINE, where water is boiled under pressure and the energy of the steam as it expands back to atmospheric pressure is used to drive a piston. A scald from steam is more serious than one from hot water because the latent heat released as the steam condenses increases the skin damage.

The melting point of a substance is less dependent on pressure than is the boiling point. There is a *latent heat of fusion* required to melt a solid, although this is usually much less than the latent heat of vaporization.

Changes of phases can also be brought about by pressure, keeping the temperature constant. If steam at a temperature less than 374°C is compressed sufficiently it will liquefy, but above the *critical temperature* of 374°C no amount of pressure will liquefy it. The critical temperature depends on the gas, that of hydrogen, for example, being −240°C; so that hydrogen cannot be liquefied at room temperature, whatever pressure is applied. A gas above its critical temperature is known as a *permanent* gas; below, as a vapour.

Other states Recent research has shown that materials can exist in peculiar phases which can be regarded as separate states. Among these are LIQUID CRYSTALS, composed of long molecules which can move about (like those of a liquid), but all point in the same direction (like those of a solid crystal); and helium-II, a form of liquid helium which can exist only at temperatures less than −271°C (2 kelvins, or 2° above absolute zero) and is *superfluid*. It has zero viscosity (the tendency for a liquid or gas to slow down an object moving through it), and can escape from an open container by flowing up the inside walls and down the outside.

Most of the matter in the Universe is neither solid, liquid nor gas, however, but is in the form of *plasma*. This is material in which the temperature is so high that some of the electrons are separated from the atoms. All stars, and much of the material between the stars, is composed of this 'fourth state of matter', which for many purposes can be treated as an electrically conducting gas. Plasmas have been produced in the laboratory, although they are difficult to control because of their very high temperatures.

Astronomy has also produced evidence for the existence of 'superdense' matter, in which the pressure is so high that ordinary atoms cannot exist. The material behaves as a solid or liquid composed of elementary particles rather than atoms. In the case of *white dwarf* stars it is electrons which hold the star up against the force of gravity, and the density of the star is about ten million times that of water. The neutron star (known as a pulsar when it emits radio waves) is a million times denser still, and is held up by the pressure of neutrons. At even higher densities it is possible that matter may form a 'black hole' and disappear entirely from our Universe, as nothing, not even light, has enough energy to 'climb out' of it.

Below: phase diagram of water illustrating the temperatures and pressures at which the three possible states exist. At the triple point ice, water and steam all exist in equilibrium.
Below right: the three states of matter. In the gas the molecules are free and move randomly. In the liquid they are packed more closely but can still flow over one another, while in a solid they are restrained in regular arrays.

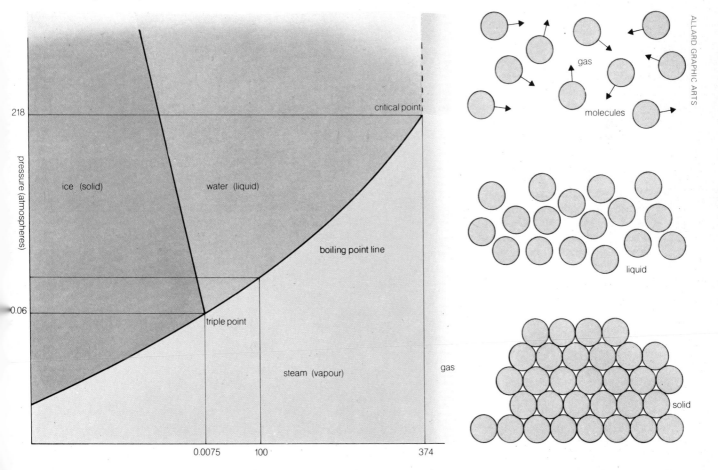

phase diagram of water (not to scale)

temperature°c

ALLARD GRAPHIC ARTS

MAUDSLAY, Henry (1771–1831)

Henry Maudslay was a pioneer of precision engineering, and one of the first to bring the standards of accuracy that previously had been limited to the making of clocks and scientific instruments to the manufacture of heavy duty machinery. He refined the screwcutting LATHE so as to be able to produce screws not only of high accuracy, but also of sufficient uniformity to be interchangeable. On this principle later mass production depends.

His father had served as a wheelwright in the Royal Engineers, but was wounded in action, and so given a post as a storekeeper, at Woolwich Arsenal where Henry Maudslay was born. At the age of 12 he began work there, filling cartridges. Soon he 'graduated' to the woodworking shop, and then to the smithy. By the age of 18 he had acquired such a reputation for his skill as a metalworker that he was called in by Joseph Bramah to construct machines to manufacture his patent LOCK. There is some dispute as to how much Maudslay contributed to the design of the machines he executed for Bramah; he seems to have been always best at putting other people's ideas into workable practice, rather than an original thinker, and only with Bramah could Maudslay have been trained in the ways of complex machinery.

In 1791, he married his master's housemaid Sarah Tindale. Six years later, the father of three children, and recognized as Bramah's right-hand man, he asked for a raise in wages but when this was refused, set up on his own as a maker of precise metal work. While he was still with Bramah, the latter had patented a new type of lathe with a slide rest to hold the cutting tool so that its advance could be mechanically controlled; this would be particularly valuable when cutting a screw on a large metal bar or cylinder, where imperfect control would lead to irregular pitch. Maudslay may have built this lathe; he certainly constructed a series of screw-cutting lathes of increasing accuracy not long after he left Bramah. Although the basic principles of slide rest and screw lathe were already known, Maudslay's (which still survive) were the most successful, and the techniques they embody were adopted, and adapted, by his successors.

A fine screw in his shop window led to a commission from Sir Marc Isambard Brunel to make models of a proposed series of machines for shaping blocks for the Navy. Maudslay then built the machinery itself between 1803–09. It applied the ideas of interchangeable parts and continuous flow treatment to the sequence of operations used in making these wooden blocks. On the profits of this, his greatest undertaking, Maudslay set up as a manufacturer of steam engines in Lambeth, in 1810. Marine engines became a speciality, but he also made sawmills, printing machines and machines for government mints. He was among the first to go over to belt transmission, and devised machinery to punch regular holes in the metal plates of boilers. But his main contribution was the introduction of surface plates to obtain a smooth plane surface and the improvement of screws by means of his lathes. The system of interchangeable bolts and nuts began in his workshop—formerly each screw would only fit its own nut. All this required measurement to new standards of accuracy, down to thousandths of an inch; Maudslay took over from the scientific instrument trade the MICROMETER, and turned it into an engine-maker's tool. He nicknamed his own micrometer 'Lord Chancellor', for from it there was no appeal.

Maudslay insisted that machines should be compact, firmly based and uncomplicated. Tidiness and order were his watch-

Top: Henry Maudslay, the English engineer and inventor. During the Industrial Revolution, his development of precision machine tools made possible the accurate construction of steam engines and machinery.

Above: a Maudslay lathe, built in 1810, now in London's Science Museum. Maudslay built the first lathes with automatic traverse of the carriage on precision-made slideways and provision for thread-cutting. In this photograph the feed screw can be seen.

words; he kept all his old models neatly arranged to guide him with future developments, and a collection of musical boxes to play while he was working. He had no great interest in ingenuity for its own sake, preferring to work out the simplest and shortest way to any particular mechanical objective. Many of the outstanding mechanical engineers of the next generation such as Clement, Roberts, NASMYTH, WHITWORTH worked under him. He patented little; but he virtually founded the British machine tool industry.

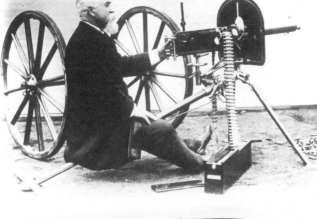

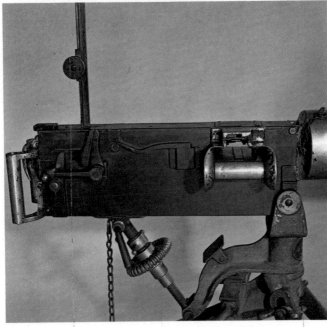

Top: Sir Hiram Maxim is depicted with his most famous invention, the fully automatic machine gun, or Maxim gun.

Middle: another invention of Maxim was this flying machine, which showed that the lift of an aircraft can be greater than its weight.

Bottom: is a close-up view of the Maxim gun's breech. The gun used the principle of a short recoil firing mechanism.

MAXIM, Sir Hiram (1840–1916)

Hiram Stevens Maxim was born on 5 February 1840 at Sangerville, Maine, in the USA where his father was a farmer. As a boy Hiram became acquainted with machinery when his father gave up farming to become a woodturner. Then at 14, young Hiram was apprenticed to a coachbuilder, but drifted into a wandering life trying his hand as a bartender, a machine tool operator and even a prizefighter.

At the age of 25 Maxim settled down with a company making gas machines and invented a new machine for making lighting gas. Other inventions followed, many of them for improvements to the steam engine, but again Maxim's career changed direction when at the age of 38 he became chief engineer to an electric lighting company. In 1881 he represented this company at the Paris Exhibition and while in Europe became interested in automatic guns. Maxim moved to London, where in 1884 he produced his most famous invention—a fully automatic MACHINE GUN appropriately named the MAXIM gun. This brought him fame and fortune. He became a British subject in 1900 and the following year was knighted.

Not content with his success, Hiram Maxim turned his attention to the problems of flight and set out 'to build a flying machine that would lift itself from the ground'. This was only a half-way stage to true flight, however, for Maxim realized that controlling an aircraft in free flight was yet another problem. He was perhaps more interested in finding out about flight than actually flying himself. Maxim knew that the wings of an aircraft had to produce an upward force or *lift* greater than the aircraft's overall weight (see AEROFOIL). The great difficulty was to find an engine which could develop enough power to overcome the *drag* or air resistance and propel the aircraft at a suitable speed.

At the time Maxim was starting his experiments, the petrol [gasoline] engine was still a new invention, unreliable and lacking power, so he turned to the well-tried STEAM ENGINE. Unfortunately steam engines were large and heavy, so consequently Maxim had to design a huge flying machine to lift the weight. The wing span was an incredible 104 ft (31.7 m) and the total weight was $3\frac{1}{2}$ tons (3560 kg). Maxim designed a lightweight steam engine which developed 180 hp, and fitted two of these to his machine, each driving a propeller almost 18 ft (5.50 m) in diameter.

In 1893 Maxim assembled his flying machine at Baldwyns Park in Kent. For a runway he built a railway track 1800 ft (550 m) long, but as he did not want to make free flight he built a second rail 2 ft (0.61 m) above the first to restrain the machine when it lifted off the main rails. The first trial was made in 1894 but the wheels did not leave the rails. The steam pressure to the engines was increased for the second trial to give more power, and the wheels just lifted. A third run at an even higher pressure was then prepared. On 31 July 1894, Maxim's flying machine reached 42 miles per hour (68 km/h) and lifted off the lower rails. Maxim had proved his point: the lift was greater than the weight, but it had been costly.

Maxim turned his attention to his other inventions which included mousetraps, fire extinguishers and even a merry-go-round (see FAIRGROUND MACHINES). He once described himself as a 'chronic inventor'. But he returned to the problems of flight in 1908, when he wrote a book, *Natural and Artificial Flight*, and even designed a petrol engine. He built another aircraft in 1910 but it never flew. Maxim died six years later at the age of 76. One of his steam engines and a petrol engine are preserved in the Science Museum, London.

MAXWELL, James Clerk (1831–1879)

James Clerk Maxwell was born in Edinburgh on 13 June 1831. He made many significant contributions as a scientist, perhaps the most celebrated of which was his prediction of the existence of ELECTROMAGNETIC RADIATION. He was the first to realize that LIGHT is electromagnetic and a form of WAVE MOTION.

Maxwell's scientific career started early, for at the age of 14, while still at school, he had a paper on geometry read at the Royal Society of Edinburgh. Two years later he started attending lectures at the University of Edinburgh and in his three years there he researched into polarized light and such engineering problems as the bending of beams and twisting of cylinders. He then went to the University of Cambridge as an undergraduate but did little original research until his graduation in 1854. The next year his output of original work began to increase again, especially with work on colour vision.

In 1855 he published his first paper on electricity and magnetism, a discourse on the idea of 'lines of force' put forward by Michael FARADAY. Maxwell's picture was of 'tubes' of force containing an incompressible fluid which transmitted electrical force through space. His theory of ELECTROMAGNETISM was there in essence, although the extension of the fluid concept to that of waves was yet to come.

Three years as professor of natural philosophy at Aberdeen (a post which he took to be nearer his father) were followed in 1860, when he was 29, by a most fruitful five years during which he was professor of physics at King's College, London. It was there that he did much of his great work on the theory of gases, which is thought to have been prompted by his earlier work on Saturn's rings which he showed must consist of clouds of tiny particles. He was the founder of what is now called statistical mechanics, with his realization that all molecules in a gas do not travel at the same speed, but rather that the speeds are shared out among the molecules in a random manner according to probability theory. While at King's College he was able to keep in touch with Faraday, who worked at the Royal Institution in London, and during this period proposed that electromagnetic energy travelled in waves and that light was simply a particular kind of electromagnetic energy. (In the early part of the twentieth century, Max PLANCK, who contributed much to modern physics, was to show that electromagnetic waves travel in discrete quanta according to QUANTUM THEORY.)

In 1865, upon the death of his father, Maxwell gave up his Chair to return to his small family estate in Scotland, because of ill health and because he enjoyed that kind of life and felt little compulsion to maintain a professional position. Six years later, at the age of 40, Maxwell was persuaded to come out of semi-retirement to become Cavendish Professor of Experimental Physics at Cambridge and to bring the idea of a physics laboratory there—the legendary Cavendish Laboratory—to fruition. It was opened in 1874 and his mark has been on it ever since. As Max Planck said, 'By his birth James Clerk Maxwell belongs to Edinburgh, by his personality he belongs to Cambridge, by his work he belongs to the whole world'.

MEASUREMENT SYSTEMS (see units, systems of)

MELTING (see matter, properties of)

RADIO TIMES HULTON PICTURE LIBRARY

RONAN PICTURE LIBRARY

Above right: is a portrait of the Scottish mathematical physicist, James Clerk Maxwell, which was painted on china from an earlier photograph. Renowned for his great achievements in electrical research, Maxwell was a born scientist who applied his powers of imagination to the development of electromagnetism.

Above: Maxwell was fascinated by the science of colour. This painting shows the patterns made by polarized light when passed through unannealed glass. He also made the first colour photograph, by taking the same picture three times through different filters, then projecting them through the same filters on to a screen.

MEMORY DEVICES

One of the most important parts of a COMPUTER is its *memory* or *main storage*, the area into which the program instructions are loaded and which retains the data while it is being processed. The information is stored in binary digit (*bit*) form ('0' or '1'), the bits being commonly organized into groups or *bytes* (typically of eight bits each). Store sizes are usually expressed in terms of the number of bits or bytes they can store. In this context the term 'K' is often used, 1-K bytes being 1024 bytes (2^{10}), and not 1000 bytes as is sometimes supposed. Similarly 1 megabyte is 1,048,576 bytes (2^{20}) and not 1,000,000 bytes. Main storage capacity on modern machines may be as high as 4 megabytes or more.

Early types of store included cathode ray tube storage, delay line storage, and diode-capacitor storage. The magnetic core store was introduced in the mid-1950s and is at present the most widely used form of store, together with thin film and solid state stores. Possible future stores may be based on HOLOGRAPHY, cryogenic (superconducting) circuits, or light-sensitive PIEZOELECTRIC MATERIALS.

Delay lines

The delay line store in its original form consisted of a tube about 5 feet (1.5 m) long, which was filled with mercury and had a quartz crystal at each end. The data to be stored, in the form of a 'train' of pulses, was fed to one of the crystals, which converted the electrical signal into mechanical vibrations that passed through the mercury in about 1 or 2 milliseconds, being converted back to electrical pulses by the quartz at the other end.

Below right: this integrated circuit is a 5000-bit CDI 'read-only' memory, that is, one that reads without destroying the information.

Below: schematic diagram of a magnetic core store used in a juke box. Record B3 has been selected, and pulses have been written in through switches B and 3 to switch the appropriate core.

The usual length of the pulse train was 1024 bits, a '1' being represented by the presence of a pulse and a '0' by the absence of a pulse. By the time the pulses had travelled through the delay the waveform shape had deteriorated from its clean square-wave form, and so some kind of regeneration was necessary.

The regeneration was achieved by a 'clock' circuit, which delivered a clean new pulse to the delay line when it was triggered by a degraded pulse from the end of the line. The data was 'read' by using the pulses to trigger an output amplifier.

Other forms of delay line used nickel wire, fused quartz, or alcohol in place of the mercury, and nickel or quartz delays are still used in some large electronic calculators.

Core storage

In the magnetic core store the binary digits are represented by the direction of magnetization of tiny rings of ferrite, one direction representing a '1' and the other a '0'. The basic storage plane has a set of parallel wires running from top to bottom, and a similar set running from left to right. A ferrite core is threaded on to the wires at each intersection, so that if there are 64 vertical and 64 horizontal wires the number of cores in the plane will be 4096 (64×64). The cores may be less than 0.02 inch (0.5 mm) in diameter.

The direction in which the cores are magnetized depends on the direction of the currents in the wires at the intersection. To magnetize a core in the '0' direction the currents in its co-ordinate wires are passed one way (negative), and to magnetize it in the '1' direction the currents are passed the other way (positive). The current in each wire is not, by itself, strong enough to magnetize the core; it needs the combined effect of the currents in both wires to do this, and so the other cores on the wire are unaffected by the current.

In order to read the information from the store, a *sense wire* is threaded through all the cores in turn. To read an individual core, currents are passed through its co-ordinate wires to switch it to the 0 state. If it is already a 0, it will not have to

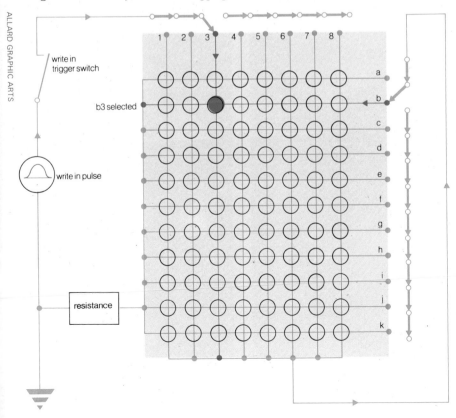

change its direction of magnetism and virtually no signal will be induced in the sense wire. If it is a 1, however, it will be switched to 0 and the change will induce a small signal in the sense wire. Thus during a read operation a signal induced in the sense wire shows that the core was a 1, and the absence of a signal shows that it was a 0.

This arrangement means that after a core has been read it will be in the 0 state regardless of its original value, and so the information in the store will have been effectively erased after being read. This *destructive reading* is unsuitable for most purposes, and so extra circuitry is provided to rewrite the data back into store after reading.

After every reading, the machine sends positive currents along the co-ordinate wires to reset the core to 1. If the core was originally at 0, a negative current is passed along another wire, the *inhibit wire*, which threads through all the cores. This current is not strong enough to change the state of any of the cores, but it is strong enough to cancel out some of the positive magnetic field from the rewrite currents and thus inhibit them from setting the core at 1 when it should be 0. This gives a *non-destructive* reading.

In some core storage assemblies the sense wire is arranged to perform the inhibit function as well. This means that each core has only three wires through its centre, and permits the use of smaller cores.

Thin film stores   A typical thin film store comprises a polished glass or non-magnetic metal (such as copper) sub-

strate with a thin layer of magnetizable alloy (for example 80% nickel, 17% iron and 3% cobalt) deposited on one surface. The film, between 750 and 1000 angstroms (0.000075 and 0.0001 mm) thick, is deposited on the substrate in the presence of a magnetic field. This makes it magnetically *anisotropic*, that is it is easily magnetized along one axis but hard to magnetize along the axis at 90° to the easy one.

Two sets of conducting strips, one parallel to the 'easy' direction and the other parallel to the 'hard' direction, are placed on top of the film insulated from it and each other by thin layers of silica. The bit elements are those areas of the film beneath the intersections of the conducting strips. The strips parallel to the hard direction are called the *word lines*, and those along the easy direction are called the *digit lines*.

To write a digit into one of the bit elements, a current is passed along its word line pulling its *magnetic vector* into the hard direction. With the current maintained in the word line, a current is passed along the digit line (from left to right for a 0 and from right to left for a 1) pulling the magnetic vector into an intermediate position between the easy and hard directions, the vector moving clockwise for a 0 and anticlockwise for a 1.

The word current is cut off, and the vector aligns with the nearest easy direction, pointing right for 0 and left for 1.

To read the bit, a current is passed along the word line, rotating the magnetic vector back into the hard direction. This rotation will induce a small current in the digit line and the direction of this current will depend on the direction in which

the vector has moved, so it is therefore easy for the machine to determine the value of the stored digit. As this is a destructive reading a rewrite arrangement is usually provided.

Magnetic core stores and thin film stores are two forms of *non-volatile* store, that is they retain the information if the power supply to the machine is removed. *Volatile* stores, such as delay lines, cathode ray tube stores and solid state stores, lose their stored information if the power supply is removed.

Solid state stores

The diode-capacitor store uses a CAPACITOR as the storage element, charged to $+2V$ for a 1 or $-2V$ for a 0. One end of the capacitor is connected to a pair of DIODES, the ends of which are held at -2 and $+2V$ respectively. The other end of the capacitor is connected to a resistor, the resistor being earthed [grounded]. A read amplifier is connected to the capacitor-resistor junction.

The store is read by reducing the terminal voltages of the diodes to 0, resulting in the discharge of the capacitor which produces a voltage across the resistor that is read by the amplifier. Storage can be regenerated after reading by feeding back the amplifier output to the resistor, and maintaining the diode clamp voltages at $+4V$ and $-4V$ until the write current is removed.

Readout and regeneration time is typically 10 microseconds, and the store will hold its charge for a couple of seconds without regeneration.

The fastest but most expensive form of store in current use is based on *bistable latches* (see LOGIC CIRCUITS), and by the use of monolithic INTEGRATED CIRCUITS extremely high storage capacities are possible; a single chip less than 4 mm (0.16 inch) square can store 1000 bits, and access times (the time taken to read any given data from the store) are in the order of several hundred nanoseconds (thousand millionths of a second).

The readout from monolithic memory devices is non-destructive, and this makes the very fast access times possible because the data does not have to be rewritten after it has been read.

Main memory stores, because of their cost and size, are not used for storing large files of information such as stock inventories or address lists. For this type of *backing store* other forms of DATA STORAGE, mainly magnetic tape, disks and drums, are used.

Below left: close-up of a single ferrite core, showing the two co-ordinate wires and a combined 'sense' and 'inhibit' wire threaded through the centre.

Below centre: part of a core store, but this time with separate wires for 'sense' and 'inhibit' functions.

Below: holographic techniques are also used to store a large amount of information on a single plate. The nature of laser light and the three-dimensional image produced make a satisfactory flat photograph impossible, but there is another view of a similar device in the 'holography' article on page 1211.

MENDELEEV, Dmitrii (1834–1907)

Dmitrii Ivanovich Mendeleev, the inventor of the modern PERIODIC TABLE of the chemical elements, was born on 8 February 1834, the seventeenth child of a schoolteacher in Tobolsk, Siberia.

Soon after Mendeleev's birth, his father was forced by blindness to retire on an inadequate pension, so his mother worked as manageress of a glass factory to support and educate her younger children. When Dmitrii was fourteen his father died, and his mother took him to St Petersburg (now Leningrad) to complete his schooling and to train as a teacher. She died very soon after their arrival, leaving Dmitrii alone and suffering from tuberculosis, but with the help of a scholarship he was able to complete his training.

After only one year of teaching chemistry in a school in Odessa (where his health recovered) he received a junior appointment at the University of St Petersburg in 1856, and after being sent by the Government to study in Germany for two years, he became Professor of Chemistry at the Technological Institute in 1861. Here he took a great interest in the new Russian petroleum industry. Throughout his life he worked to increase its efficiency, and it is for this, and for his work for Russian trade in general, that he is most honoured in Russia. Internationally, his reputation rests on his important textbook of chemistry, which went through many editions and translations, and his periodic table of the elements.

In the 1850s and 1860s several chemists in a number of countries put forward systems for classifying the elements which more or less resemble Mendeleev's; the most important of these were due to the English chemist William Odling (1865) and the German Lothar Meyer (1869). The idea of arranging the elements in increasing order of atomic weight, and determining how often properties recur, was a commonplace. So when Mendeleev put forward a new scheme in 1869, it was not thought remarkable or very useful.

What distinguished his system and ensured its ultimate adoption was his prediction in 1871 of new elements to fill the 'gaps' in his table; the discovery of *gallium* (1875), *scandium* (1879) and *germanium* (1886), whose physical and chemical properties had been predicted by Mendeleev, showed the power of his system: not only did it tie together an enormous amount of existing information about the nature of the chemical elements, but it pointed the way to further discovery. Once the system was adopted as the foundation of inorganic chemistry, rapid progress could be made.

Mendeleev's personal life was always stormy. Following his early difficulties, his first marriage in 1863 ended in divorce thirteen years later. He then married an art student before the statutory period of seven years had elapsed after his divorce, but no action was taken against this illegal marriage and he and his wife were very happy. In 1890 he resigned his professorship at St Petersburg for political reasons, but three years later he was appointed to be director of the bureau of weights and measures, a post which he held until his death from pneumonia on 20 January 1907.

In 1955 a new and very radioactive chemical element having the atomic number 101 was synthesized at the University of California. It was named Mendelevium (Md) in honour of Mendeleev.

Above: a portrait of Mendeleev by I J Repin.

Right: Mendeleev's first table of elements, drafted in March 1869.

MERCURY

The alchemists of the Middle Ages did not recognize mercury as a metal, but as the metallic essence of all metals which imparted to them their characteristic lustre, density, thermal conductivity and malleability. The other basic component was SULPHUR which accounted for the changes which metals underwent on heating. It was not until Braune succeeded in freezing mercury—it solidifies at $-39°C$ ($-38°F$)—one cold night in Leningrad in the winter of 1759 that mercury was generally accepted to be a metal in its own right. Chemically it is related to the metals cadmium and ZINC, which are members of the same group of the PERIODIC TABLE.

Occurrence
Mercury is sometimes found as native globules among outcrops of its ore, so its discovery must be credited to prehistoric man. It is mentioned by Aristotle (384 to 322 BC) who refers to its extraction from cinnabar, the only important ore. Cinnabar is red mercury sulphide HgS and has long been used to make the pigment vermilion.

Probably the most famous mercury mine is the Almadén mine in Spain, which has been worked continuously since before the time of Christ. The Idria mine has also been a large producer for several hundred years; originally in Austria, it was at times in both French and Italian hands and has been in Yugoslav territory since World War 2. The demand for mercury greatly increased on the introduction of the *patio* process for the extraction of SILVER in Mexico in 1557, and much of the supplies for this purpose were drawn from mines in Peru. Another increase in demand followed the California GOLD rush of 1849 and led to the development of the California mercury mines. The processes for extracting both gold and silver involved the use of mercury *amalgams* (see below).

Today the United States is still a major producer of mercury, with mines in Nevada, Idaho, Arizona, Oregon and Alaska as well as California.

Because mercury occurs in highly concentrated deposits it is not regarded as a rare metal, although it is less abundant in the Earth's crust than, for example, PLATINUM or URANIUM.

Extraction
Mercury is usually won from its ore by roasting in the presence of air and condensing the mercury vapour produced:

$$HgS + O_2 \rightarrow Hg + SO_2$$

cinnabar   oxygen   mercury   sulphur dioxide

It is possible to roast fairly coarse ore in a vertical shaft furnace. Finer ores, however, inhibit the air flow through the furnace and for this reason designs have been introduced in which the ore powder moves gradually down the shaft, falling progressively from one to another of a series of ledges inclined at 45° to each other. It is modern practice to crush all the ore to a fine powder and roast it either in a multi-hearth mechanical furnace where it is moved from one hearth to the next, lower one by rotating rakes, or in a rotary kiln, which is a long cylinder with its rotation axis inclined at a few degrees from the horizontal. When fine ores are roasted considerable dust is carried over into the flue by the furnace gases. The dust is removed before it reaches the mercury condensing tubes, which would

Below : a furnace for producing mercury which was installed at Idria towards the end of the 18th century. The ore A is heated by a furnace E, and mercury vapour passes into the chambers K where it is condensed and collected. Water flows down baffles in the final chamber to ensure complete condensation of the mercury vapour.

otherwise become clogged. The mercury collected from the condensers is separated from the soot by filtration, and the soot, which contains some mercury compounds, is treated with lime so as to recover metal. Finally the metal can be purified by vacuum DISTILLATION.

Uses of mercury

The mercury BAROMETER was invented by Torricelli in 1643 and the THERMOMETER by Fahrenheit in 1714. More recently mercury has found its place in many scientific and domestic devices such as *sphygmomanometers* (see MANOMETER) which doctors use to measure blood pressure and sealed SWITCHES in which a small amount of the metal is allowed to run on to a pair of contacts to make the electrical circuit. Another application is in mercury arc RECTIFIERS which are used to convert AC (alternating current) to DC (direct current) where heavy currents are involved, although semiconducting devices are steadily replacing such equipment. The brilliant blue-white light produced by an electrical discharge through mercury vapour is exploited in fluorescent strip lights (see DISCHARGE TUBE).

Alloys based on mercury are called *amalgams*. The most well known use of an amalgam is in dental fillings which are made by mixing mercury with fillings of an alloy composed of 69.4% silver, 3.6% copper, 0.8% zinc and 26.2% tin. The filling 'sets' as interdiffusion occurs between the liquid and solid phases. The ability of mercury to form amalgams is also made use of in the extraction of gold and silver. Mercury is used as the cathode in cells which produce CHLORINE by the ELECTROLYSIS of brine. The sodium liberated at the cathode immediately forms an amalgam and can subsequently be recovered as caustic soda. An amalgam of mercury with the metal thallium has a lower melting point, $-60°C$ $(-76°F)$, than mercury itself and is therefore used to make low temperature thermometers. Mercury BATTERIES have a higher power and a longer life than conventional batteries, and are used in applications where size must be kept to a minimum, for example in hearing aids and camera light meters. The anode in such batteries is an amalgam of mercury and zinc, and the cathode is formed of mercuric oxide HgO mixed with about 5% graphite.

Mercury compounds are used to a limited extent in industry and medicine. Mercuric sulphate, $HgSO_4$, is a *catalyst* in the production of acetaldehyde (see ALDEHYDE) from acetylene and water, and a complex salt of copper, mercury and iodine, $Cu_2(HgI_4)$, is a temperature indicator which changes colour on heating. Mercury fulminate, $Hg(CNO)_2$, is very sensitive to friction and shock, and is used in detonators for EXPLOSIVES. Some compounds such as *calomel*, Hg_2Cl_2, have been used as antiseptics, although their use is less common nowadays because of the toxicity of mercury and its compounds. Phenylmercuric acetate (PMA) is employed to control the growth of fungus on grain intended for planting. It has also been used to control slime in paper mills, to prevent the formation of fungus in wallpaper glue and to discourage the growth of coarse grass in lawns.

Toxicity

Mercury, particularly mercury vapour, and most of its compounds are poisonous, and it is now generally accepted that in environmental terms mercury is an appalling liability. Grain treated with PMA virtually wiped out Sweden's yellow bunting population, and was withdrawn in 1960. Treated grain has also accidentally been used as food on one or two occasions. In 1971 several hundred Iraqis died after eating PMA treated grain meant for sowing, and recently tens of thousands of head of livestock in Europe, had to be slaughtered because of a similar mistake.

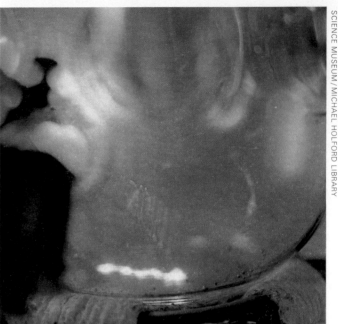

Top: a mercury arc rectifier. A pool of mercury metal (bottom) is contained in a glass bulb which has been pumped out to give a vacuum. The mercury acts as a cathode, and an auxiliary electrode strikes an arc on the surface of the mercury. The arc produces a 'cloud' of electrons which are attracted to an anode (not shown in this picture) when the latter is positively charged. Since electrons can only be produced at the cathode, they can only flow in one direction (from cathode to anode) through the rectifier.

Above: mercury discharge lamps. These are normally operated from an alternating current supply with an impedance in the external circuit which prevents dangerously high currents from building up.

Right: a diagram showing the internal structure of a metal. The metal ions (red) are regularly arranged in a 'cloud' of electrons which can move freely within the crystal lattice.

Far right: a section of a copper surface showing the crystal grains.

METAL

About 97% of the Universe (by mass) is composed of HYDRO-GEN and helium (see INERT GASES), the next most common elements being OXYGEN, IRON, NITROGEN and CARBON. As the Earth formed, the vast majority of hydrogen and helium, and a substantial proportion of carbon, nitrogen and oxygen were lost to space, as their atoms were not heavy enough to be retained by the Earth's gravitational field. The primaeval Earth was therefore mainly iron with other elements more or less present as impurities. During the gradual cooling which took place over many millions of years, the lighter and more reactive elements combined with oxygen and sulphur to form a 'slag' which floated on the surface of the molten iron core. In time the 'slag' solidified to form the Earth's crust on which we live. The most abundant metal in the Earth's crust is ALU-MINIUM followed by iron, calcium (see ALKALINE EARTH METAL), sodium (see ALKALI METAL), potassium and magnesium. Metals such as COPPER, SILVER, GOLD and URANIUM are much less common, but fortunately they are not evenly distributed. For example, workable deposits of copper represent a concentration of at least 200 times and gold at least 5000 times their abundance in the Earth's crust.

Discovery of metals

One would perhaps expect that the first metals to be exploited by man would be those which are most abundant, for example aluminium, iron and calcium. In fact this is far from the case, as the criterion determining the historical order in which metals were discovered and exploited has been the ease with which they can be separated from their ores. Gold must have been used before recorded times as its oxide and sulphide do not exist under normal conditions and it is always found in the *native* state, in other words as the metal itself rather than a compound. COPPER, SILVER and MERCURY can sometimes be found in the native state and their use is correspondingly ancient, but in any case their oxides are very easily reduced to the metal (see OXIDATION AND REDUCTION); a camp fire is all that is required. The discovery that copper and TIN could be extracted from their ores by heating with charcoal heralded the Bronze Age 5500 years ago (BRONZE is an ALLOY of tin and copper), and the acquisition of the more difficult skill of iron smelting 2000 years later marked the beginning of the Iron Age. LEAD was smelted in ancient Egypt and ZINC in the alloy BRASS was known in Roman times.

The extraction of the lighter and more abundant metals, aluminium, magnesium and calcium was not achieved until the nineteenth century, as the stability of their oxides is such that it is chemically impossible to reduce them with charcoal or coke. Their extraction on a commercial scale was made possible by the availability of electric power. About 1850, FARADAY and Bunsen developed the process for the smelting of magnesium by ELECTROLYSIS of its chloride. Aluminium had been discovered at about the same time as magnesium (1828) but its electrolytic extraction presented more problems as neither the aluminium oxide ore (*alumina*) nor any of its simple salts could be melted. In the 1850s aluminium was still a rare and precious metal, and it was not until 1886 that Hall and Héroult independently developed a viable electrolytic method for aluminium smelting, in which alumina is dissolved in sodium aluminium fluoride which has a melting point of 990°C. Today, in terms of the quantity produced annually, aluminium ranks second to iron.

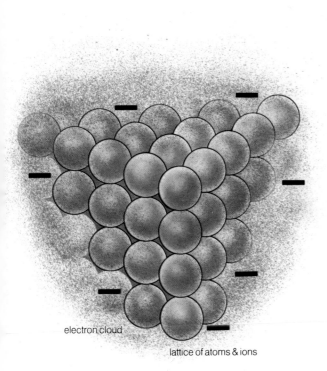

electron cloud

lattice of atoms & ions

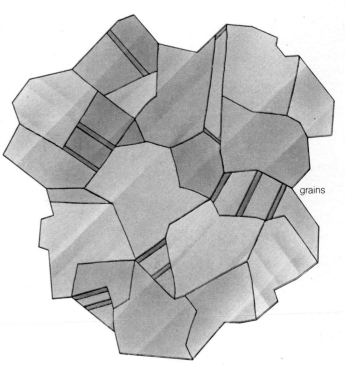

grains

microstructure of copper

Characteristics of a metal The *periodicity* (regular order) apparent in the properties of the elements when arranged in order of atomic number is the direct result of the order in which the various electron 'shells' are occupied by electrons. On moving across one row, or *period*, of the PERIODIC TABLE the properties of the elements change continuously as a particular electron shell is filled up. One such property is the first *ionization potential* which is a measure of the energy required to remove one outer electron from the ATOM; the higher the ionization potential the more tightly the electron is bound to the NUCLEUS. The ionization potential increases as a shell is progressively filled, because although the electrons in the outer shell all feel the attractive force of the positively charged nucleus equally, the number of protons in the nucleus, and hence the strength of its positive charge, increases linearly with atomic number.

Generally speaking elements will be metals if the outer electrons of their atoms are weakly bound, so that in the first periods of the periodic table the elements with lowest atomic weight are metals. The elements in the periods lower down the table have a lower average ionization potential and hence a greater proportion of them are metals. The TRANSITION ELEMENTS, the *rare earths* and the *transuranic elements* (see SYNTHETIC ELEMENT) are all metals.

Metals are recognized by their characteristic physical properties. They are good conductors of electricity and heat; they are opaque, they have a typical lustre and they are strong, ductile and often of high density. The most dense material known is the metal *osmium* which is twice as dense as lead. Metals have crystalline structures, the most common lattice types being *face-centred cubic*, *hexagonal close-packed* and *body-*

GOLD BULLETIN

centred cubic (see CRYSTALS).

The properties of metals stem from the fact that when metal atoms are brought together in the solid state, the outer weakly bound electrons break free from their atoms and form an 'electron gas' which permeates the atomic lattice. The very high mobility of the electrons in the 'gas' is responsible for the ease with which electricity and heat can be conducted. The free electrons also readily absorb and re-emit light, which explains the opacity and lustre. The 'gas', which is negatively charged, acts as a kind of 'glue' binding together the metal atoms, which are positively charged, having lost their outer electrons. This metallic bonding is comparatively strong. It is also non-directional, which means that atoms can slide past each other at stresses much lower than those required to actually break the metal. The result is high ductility. Metallic bonding enables

INSTITUTE OF GEOLOGICAL SCIENCES

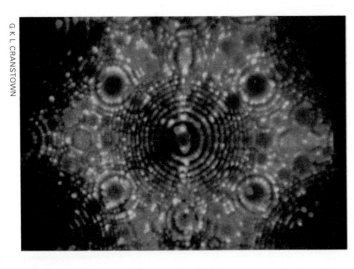

atoms to pack particularly closely together, in contrast to compounds and non-metallic elements, which tend to have more open structures.

Non-metallic atoms tend to form localized and specific bonds which 'tie up' the outer electrons so that they are not free to move as in metals. Non-metals are therefore bad conductors of heat and electricity. Some elements, SILICON and germanium for example, exhibit some characteristics of both metals and non-metals and are called SEMICONDUCTORS. When pure and held at very low temperatures, they behave as typical non-metals. At ambient temperatures, however, the electrons have enough thermal energy to form a 'thin' electron gas which is sufficient to give the material some metallic properties. Semiconductors are used in the manufacture of DIODES and TRANSISTORS.

Metal resources

The Earth's resources are finite and the rate at which metallic ores are mined increases every year. A recent report concluded that if ore MINING continues at its current rate then all known reserves of silver, gold, mercury, lead, platinum, tin and zinc will be exhausted by the year 2000, and that if the rate of usage increases as it has done over the last decade, copper, molybdenum and NICKEL must also be added to the list. This estimate is pessimistic in that it cannot take into account new mineral reserves yet to be discovered or possible improvements in metallurgical extraction techniques. The availability in the future of large amounts of cheap nuclear power is often viewed as the answer to diminishing metal resources, for it could enable exceptionally low grade ores to be economically processed. An extraction plant working on this basis, however, would generate enormous quantities of waste material which would have to be disposed of without undue disruption to the ecology of its environment.

Above left: a group of three standard kilogrammes made of an alloy of platinum and iridium.

Above) a field ion micrograph showing the body centred cubic structure of tungsten metal. The sample is in the form of a very fine point situated in a vacuum tube, and it is connected to a high tension positive supply. Ions leaving the surface of the point are attracted towards a cathode and they strike a fluorescent screen. This is a 'double exposure' showing the effects of corrosion.

Below left: an example of native silver. Many of the less reactive metals occur in the native state rather than as chemical compounds.

Below: a close up view of a gold foam structure. This experimental material is about 35 times less dense than solid gold.

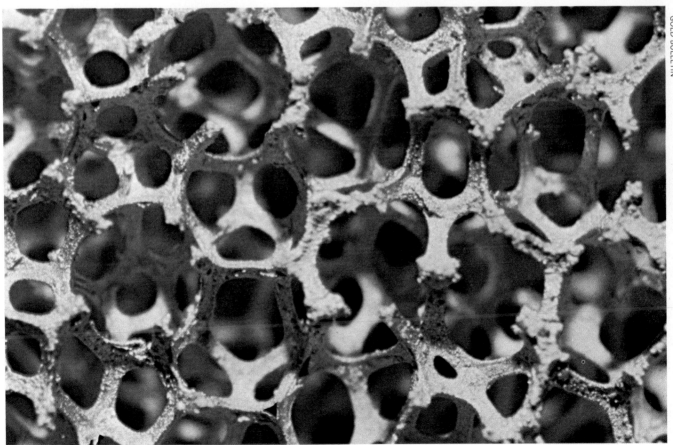

METAL DETECTORS

Metals have one important property possessed by no other elements that enables them to be readily distinguished with suitably sensitive apparatus—this property is their high electrical conductivity. By generating an alternating magnetic field in the vicinity of a metal object, electric currents are induced in the object (see INDUCTION) which in turn set up a magnetic field around the object which distorts the original field. By detecting this distortion, the metallic object can be located. Types of detector that employ this principle of *induced magnetism* include: *balanced search coil* units, *field search* units and *pulse magnetization* units.

One particular class of metals—the *ferromagnetic* materials—can also be detected using a different technique. Ferromagnetic materials have a high permeability, that is, they offer less 'resistance' to the flow of magnetic flux through them than any other material. A magnetic field, such as the Earth's magnetic field, generates lines of flux which will take the path of least resistance and therefore concentrate in the vicinity of any ferromagnetic material, causing a distortion of the general magnetic field which can be detected. Devices operating on this principle are known as *magnetic search units*.

Balanced coil   Balanced coil search units have two identical search coils, each with a primary and secondary winding. The primary windings are driven in series by an alternating current and so generate an alternating magnetic field. With the two coils placed over a non-metallic medium, the voltages induced in the secondary windings by this alternating field will be identical. In this situation, when the two secondaries are

connected in opposition, there is no signal. A metallic object, such as a coin, will, however, produce an induced magnetic field which interacts more strongly with the secondary to which it is closest. A nett signal (the difference between the signals in the two coils) is then produced which, when amplified and displayed, indicates the presence of a metallic object.

The problem with this type of unit and the others that operate on the principle of magnetic induction is that, when used over earth, variations in the earth's conductivity can affect the readings. Such detectors tend to be useful only over small distances of the order of six inches (15 cm).

Heterodyne unit   The heterodyne search unit also uses the principle of induced magnetism but consists of two coils with only one winding in each. They are separately connected to two OSCILLATOR circuits in which they form the inductive components. The two oscillators are initially adjusted to have the same frequency so that the two coils produce an alternating

Top left: a magnetic search unit is a sensitive device for detecting ferromagnetic materials. It works on the principle that such materials will distort the Earth's magnetic field, which can be measured.

Left: American archaeologist using metal detector in a systematic research of the original town of Petra in Jordan.

Centre: pulse magnetization unit—a magnetic 'radar'. Magnetic fields travel at the speed of light, inducing a field detected later.

Right: balanced coil type metal detector (right foreground).

magnetic field at that one frequency. A metal object placed close to one of the coils changes the inductance of that coil and therefore also the frequency of oscillation of that circuit. By mixing the signals from the two circuits, a beat frequency is generated (in the same way that two similar musical notes produce beats). This beat frequency can be reproduced through earphones thus enabling the operator to locate the object.

This type of detector can be very sensitive, but again, variations in the earth's conductivity can affect the results and it is difficult to obtain sufficiently stable oscillators.

Field search unit   The field search unit operates similarly to the balanced coil unit. It employs a loop of wire driven by a static high power oscillator which can generate an operating field over an area the size of a tennis court. Such a device, since it reacts to variations in the earth's conductivity as it does to the presence of metal, has an interesting archaeological use. If the detector readings of an archaeological site are plotted on a map, the outline of the buildings is often apparent from the variations in conductivity.

Pulse magnetization units   Pulse magnetization units rely on the fact that a magnetic field takes finite time to propagate through air or earth—in fact the speed of propagation is the same as for electromagnetic radiation, that is, the speed of light. Such units operate as magnetic 'radar' units. A short high power pulse is generated in a search coil, and after the pulse is cut off the unit goes from a transmit mode to a receive mode. If there is a metallic object within the field, this object generates its own magnetic field by the process of induced

magnetism, and this is detected a finite time after the transmitted pulse. Such units can be very effective, but again there are limitations due to the earth's conductivity.

Magnetic search units Iron, steel and other ferromagnetic materials are very much easier to detect using a magnetic search unit. This will find a one inch (2.54 cm) nail at a distance of about 24 inches (60 cm) or a car at 60 ft (18 m).

All objects on the Earth are in the Earth's magnetic field. Where there are not metallic objects this field can be considered as constant in strength and uniform—that is, in the same direction. Any metallic object will, however, distort the Earth's field because the lines of flux will tend to take the path of least 'resistance' (magnetic reluctance—see MAGNETISM) and be concentrated in the vicinity of the object. To detect this distortion in the Earth's field a magnetometer system is used. This is capable of detecting the difference in magnetic field strength at two points and is sensitive to field differences of the order of 1/100,000 part of the Earth's field.

In practice, two magnetometer probes are used. These are fixed in a tube about 12 inches (18 cm) apart and carefully aligned along the same axis. The tube is suspended by its own weight so that it measures the vertical component of the Earth's field. Being largely independent of the qualities of the earth over which it is used, such search units are extremely powerful even where non-magnetic coins and so on are sought because magnetic objects usually exist there as well. Having identified a site, the less powerful inductive units can be used.

METALWORKING TECHNIQUES (see individual techniques)

Below: diagram demonstrating the principle of a heterodyne type of metal detector. Two coils form the inductances in separate but similar oscillator circuits. A metal object brought close to the search coil influences the inductance in that coil, altering the oscillator frequency and generating a beat.

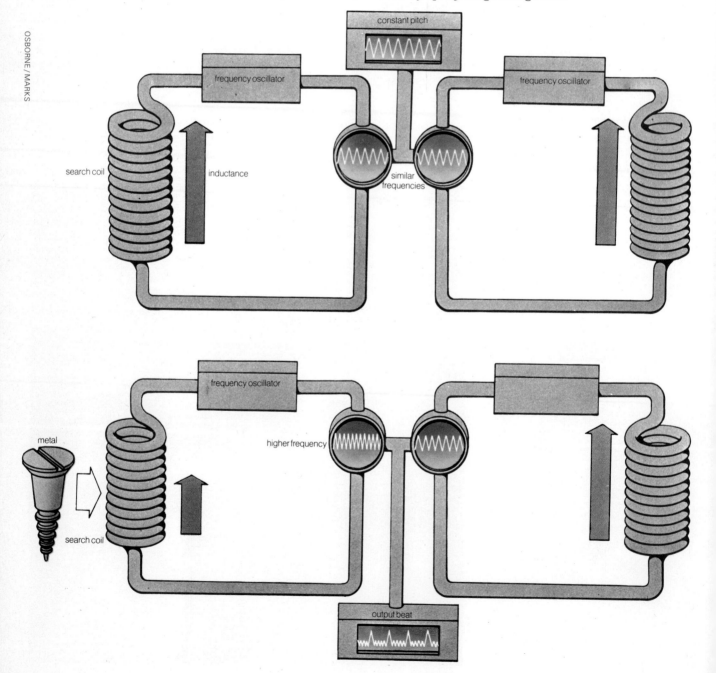

METEOROLOGY

Meteorology is the science of the atmosphere, which is an envelope of air some 200 miles deep surrounding the Earth. Weather as we know it is experienced in the eight miles or so of atmosphere nearest the Earth's surface. This is called the *troposphere*, its upper limit is the *tropopause*, and above it is the *stratosphere* which extends upwards for another 20 miles. One of the most complex and challenging problems in the whole of science, not only of meteorology is that of forecasting the weather (see WEATHER FORECASTING). Consequently it is the troposphere which receives most attention from the meteorologist.

Weather systems If the Earth is viewed from a SATELLITE, the clouds in the atmosphere appear white. They act like dye in the air, mapping out a wide variety of atmospheric motions. Some of the cloud shapes are in the form of a vortex spiralling inwards towards the centre. These are the *depressions* or areas of low pressure, which are characterized by rain and strong winds. The areas of high pressure or *anticyclones* also have a vortex type of circulation but a more gentle one, often with little or no cloud. Some atmospheric vortices are very large. The depressions and anticyclones of temperate latitudes may be over 1500 miles (2400 km) in diameter and extend upwards to 40,000 feet (which is 7.6 miles or 12.2 km)—about the top of the troposphere. Such very large vortices are almost stationary. The majority of moving vortices are relatively shallow (1 to 2 miles, 1.6 to 3.2 km, deep) and have diameters from about 1000 down to near 100 miles (1600 to 160 km). Hurricanes are about 500 miles (800 km) across. Waterspouts and tornadoes have diameters of some 200 to 500 yards (180 to 460 m).

Below: satellite view of the Earth shows clearly the cloud formations (white regions) on a grand scale. The vortices (spirals) are depressions and anticyclones centred mainly in temperate regions— their shape is caused by coriolis forces on polar-equatorial air currents.

NASA

Weather observation

Each day over 7000 land stations and some 1000 merchant ships make regular observations of the world's weather at internationally agreed times. Every observation comprises details of wind speed and direction, atmospheric pressure and the change of pressure over the previous three hours, TEMPERATURE and dew point, visibility, the type of cloud and the amount and height for each layer observed, and the weather itself, whether it is raining, snowing and so forth.

The upper air, that is the troposphere from just above the surface through to the lower stratosphere, is charted from nearly 800 stations which launch, either twice or four times daily, balloon-borne sounding instruments known as *radiosondes*. They transmit details of temperature, pressure and humidity to a ground station while radar tracking of the whole device enables the wind to be calculated.

A diagram showing warm and cold fronts near a depression centre. Where the warm and cold air masses are in contact, the warm, wet air is cooled causing clouds and rainfall.

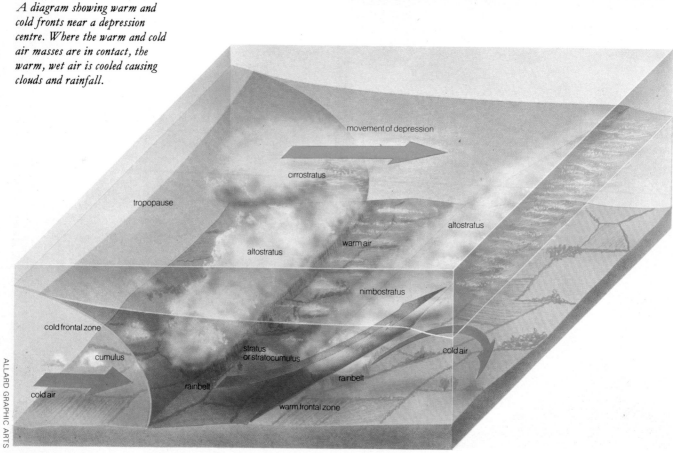

Left: this set of six photographs show the stages in development of an anvil-shaped cloud from cumulonimbus. Hot moist air rising from the surface of the Earth will condense when it reaches a certain height (called the condensation level). The cumulonimbus shape (low level, lumpy, rain cloud) then develops. Some of the water droplets grow in size and become too heavy to continue rising with the air stream and precipitate as rain. In the process, cold air is dragged down, which causes further precipitation. Lighter droplets, which are still rising in some regions of the cloud, reach the ice-crystal level, at which point the droplets freeze and the cloud flattens out into the recognizable anvil shape. The cloud texture now changes from its original lumpy appearance to one of 'satin' smoothness. The cloud levels off at a height of about 30,000 ft (which is just under 6 miles, approximately 9 km). Water vapour plays an important part in mechanics of the air, especially in heat transfer.

An anticyclone is a large mass of descending air. The air is compressed and warmed as it descends, and this gives rise to a temperature inversion zone in which any clouds present will evaporate. Anticyclones are associated with settled, dry weather. Long periods of dull weather in winter are often a result of anticyclones, the cloud being present beneath the inversion zone.

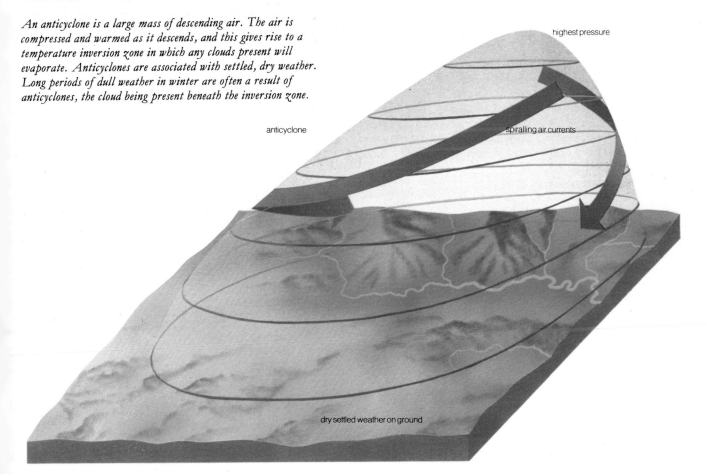

highest pressure

anticyclone

spiralling air currents

dry settled weather on ground

The world's weather observing network is nowhere near adequate to give a comprehensive picture of the weather. At any one time there are probably about 100,000 showers falling and as many as 2000 thunderstorms. Many of these are never recorded. In the southern hemisphere and parts of the tropics, observing stations are so sparse that not even the larger depressions and anticyclones can be properly charted.

Weather satellites are, however, now filling the gaps. The first one was launched in 1960 and today the whole Earth is scanned both day and night by satellites on polar orbits transmitting automatically in real time pictures recorded at both visible and infra-red wavelengths. These are available to any ground station equipped and tuned to receive them. Many forecasters today have the benefit of a series of satellite pictures covering the area within about 1000 miles (160 km) of their station at least once a day, and they are available within half an hour of being shot. These pictures do not identify individual clouds, but they do identify cloud systems larger than 2 or 3 miles (3 to 5 km) across.

The latest satellites supply data for direct input into computers and translation in terms of winds, temperatures and cloud throughout the troposphere. These methods are at an early stage of development but promise great improvements in the adequacy of the initial data on which more accurate forecasts must depend.

Charting the weather

In order to forecast the weather an initial picture is required of what is happening in the atmosphere, where the depressions and anticyclones are, their speed and direction of movement, the strength of the winds throughout the troposphere, the location of the main concentrations of water vapour, the variations in temperature of the air, and so on.

It is possible to construct a simple form of weather chart using only the observations of wind. This would identify the general layout of depressions and anticyclones. A much better chart, however, is obtained by using observations of wind and atmospheric pressure. The two are related, except near the Equator, by what is known as the geostrophic wind equation. Lines joining points having the same pressure give an immediate picture of the winds. These lines are called *isobars*. If the isobars are close together the winds are strong, if far apart they are light. The direction of the wind is related to the positions of high and low pressure. In the northern hemisphere winds blow clockwise around areas of high pressure and anticlockwise around areas of low pressure. This is most easily memorized in terms of Buys Ballot's Law, one of the oldest laws in meteorology, which says that in the northern hemisphere, if you stand with your back to the wind, low pressure will be on your left-hand side. The opposite applies in the southern hemisphere.

The isobaric chart may be compared with a contour map showing the topography of the land. Contours correspond to isobars, mountains to areas of high pressure and hollows to low pressure. Separating mountains and hollows are ridges and valleys (troughs), cols and so on. Similarly on isobaric charts ridges are extensions of areas of high pressure and troughs extensions of areas of low pressure. Cols appear where there is little or no pressure gradient.

Unfortunately the surface weather chart is only a two-dimensional representation. Yet the weather is essentially three-dimensional. For instance it is the up and down motion in the air which largely determines the distribution of cloud and rain. Depressions are generally areas of upward motion

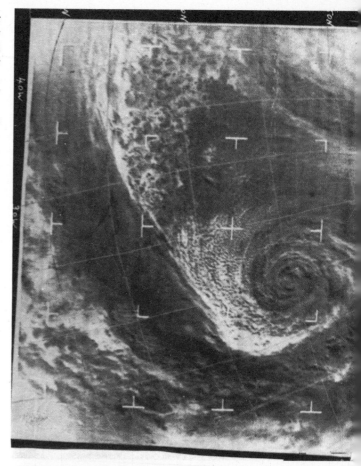

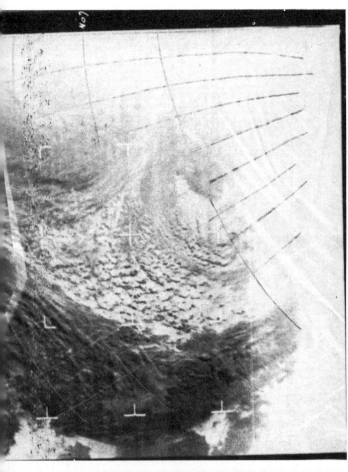

CROWN COPYRIGHT

NASA

and anticyclones of downward motion. This motion is relatively small and cannot normally be measured directly. The upward motion in middle and high latitude depressions is concentrated in troughs of low pressure.

A front is generally an area of upward motion and always lies in a trough, but a trough does not always contain a front.

Air masses *Isobars* were first introduced in the construction of weather maps in about 1860. The next great step forward did not come until about 1918 with the introduction of the front or boundary between different air masses.

If the air was everywhere stationary the air masses would be very easily definable. The air mass over the tropics would be tropical, and over the poles polar. Air masses over the sea would be maritime and those over the continents continental. All would have very distinct characteristics. Tropical maritime air would be warm and moist, polar maritime air cold and moist, tropical continental air warm and dry, and so on. In practice the winds are continually carrying the air from one part of the Earth to another, sometimes over continents and sometimes over oceans, and as far as possible air masses are defined according to where the air has come from.

The following are the characteristics of the four most distinctive air masses which may be observed over Britain. *Tropical maritime* air, because it has been cooled on its northward journey over cooler seas to a temperature below its dewpoint brings extensive low cloud and sea fog, and probably some drizzle and rain also. Lifting over the coasts and hills causes even thicker cloud and heavier drizzle and it feels warm and humid. *Polar maritime* air coming from northern seas has a relatively low dewpoint and is characteristically bright and fresh. Heating over the warmer seas around Britain causes mixing to a considerable height so that what little dust it picks up does not interfere with its very good visibility. For the same reason showers frequently develop. *Tropical continental* air from desert areas such as the Sahara is very warm and dry. Dust and smoke picked up on the way make it hazy, particularly as cooling of the air near the ground creates a temperature inversion and traps the dust and smoke picked up over Europe near the surface. *Polar continental* air is notable for its dryness, drying the skin and cracking the lips. Coming from over northern continental areas it has the lowest dewpoint of all. In summer it may be quite warm, but in winter it is usually very cold.

Only occasionally can these very distinctive air masses be experienced. Normally the air has taken a very roundabout route, partly over land and partly over sea and has modified characteristics depending on how long it has spent over the land or sea, over warm regions or cold regions.

Atmospheric energy Air, like all things which have mass, will not move without a driving force (see DYNAMICS). Even the small vortices which whirl leaves and dust around the corners of buildings need ENERGY to start them off and keep them going. They receive it from the overall energy of the

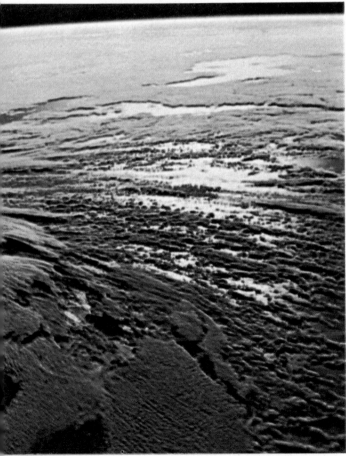

Above: hurricane Lois at 45 N 30 W photographed from space in 1966. In general, the smaller the vortex the more concentrated is its energy, wind speeds are higher and localized damage increased. Large vortices (about 1500 miles in diameter) are almost stationary and quite 'tame', hurricanes are typically about 500 miles in diameter and can cause considerable damage while tornadoes and waterspouts, no more than a few hundred yards in diameter, are most feared of all.

Left: hurricane Gladys photographed from space in October 1968.

wind which is blowing, just as depressions and anticyclones get at least some of their energy from the general motion of the atmosphere such as the belts of winds which circulate around the Earth. These belts are stronger in temperate latitudes and in the upper part of the troposphere. An impression of the energy 'stored' in these belts of wind can be obtained from the speeds in *jet streams*, the name given to the stronger belts of wind, which may reach 200 knots or more. The source of all this energy is the Sun. In the simplest model, solar energy drives the atmospheric circulation as a result of heated air rising in tropical regions and being replaced by colder air flowing in at the surface from polar regions. The balance is maintained aloft, where air which has risen in the tropics moves polewards to replace air subsiding in polar regions. In practice there are many modifying influences, particularly the rotation of the Earth and the distribution of land and sea. These result not in a simple circulation but in a very complex arrangement of winds, though with some features, such as the *Trade Winds*, which are persistent and recognizable from year to year.

The role of water vapour

One very important heat transfer agent is water vapour, and it is often responsible for determining the initial stages and the final intensity of an atmospheric vortex or depression. Water is continually evaporating from seas, lakes and moist ground. The large amount of heat needed for evaporation of water, called the *latent heat* of water (see MATTER), causes a drop in the temperature of the sea or moist ground unless the Sun makes good the difference. The vapour so produced rises into the air and is carried away on the wind until somewhere it forms cloud and falls out (condenses) as rain. During condensation the latent heat is released into the air. This extra source of energy sometimes tips the

Below: a radio sonde as currently in use at a number of upper air stations at home and abroad. The instruments, attached to the lower end of the suspension chain, transmit measurements of temperature, pressure and humidity. There is also a parachute and radar reflector.

G A ROBINSON

balance in favour of the development of a vortex. Tropical storms in particular develop where there is a large amount of warm and very moist air, yet where the general flow of air is weak. They receive almost all their energy from the release of latent heat by condensation.

A good deal of latent heat energy is made available where a warm moist mass of air meets a cold one. The cold air being relatively dense undercuts the warm air. The warm air, being relatively light, rises over the cold air. As it rises it cools, the water vapour condenses to form cloud, and latent heat is liberated. The boundary where two such differing air masses meet is known as a *front*, and it is because of the ready availability of latent heat energy that a front is a preferred area for the formations of depressions.

Clouds

All clouds comprise either condensed water droplets or ice crystals. A cloud on which the sun is shining will usually appear white, while if the sun is behind the cloud it may look dark and threatening. A cloud may also appear black if it contains a large amount of dirt in suspension, particularly over an industrial area.

Steam, fog and cloud are all the same. They are formed when air is cooled to a temperature below its *dewpoint*—this being defined as the temperature to which the air must be cooled for it to become *saturated* with water vapour. Air whose temperature is above its dewpoint is *unsaturated*.

One important requirement for condensation is the presence of the right sort of nuclei on which the tiny water droplets will grow. These are called *condensation nuclei* and comprise salt particles and certain types of dust. If they are absent, the air may become *supersaturated* (that is, with an excess of water vapour in it which is unable to condense into fog, cloud or rain).

Clouds exhibit a great variety in appearance but can be classified according to a few fairly distinct types. Today's International Classification of Clouds is based on a scheme originally proposed by Luke Howard in 1803 in which he distinguished three principal cloud forms: *stratus* (a layered cloud), *cumulus* (a heaped or lumpy cloud) and *cirrus* (a fibrous or feathery looking cloud). A further classification of clouds is based on their height and fall into three categories: *cirro-* (high cloud above 16,000 ft, 4.9 km), *alto-* (medium height cloud between 6,500 and 23,000 ft, approximately 2 to 7 km) and low cloud (below 6,500 ft, 2 km) which have no suffix and are just described by their appearance (for example, stratus, and cumulus). Rain clouds, which normally have their base in the low region, are given the prefix *nimbo-* or the suffix *nimbus* (for example, nimbostratus and cumulonimbus).

Cloud forming mechanisms

The most common cloud producing mechanism is the ascent of air, for as air rises it moves into an area of lower pressure. As this happens, the air mass expands, work is done on the air around and it cools. Ascent may be over mountains or in depressions, or in the case of cumulus clouds, bubbles of heated air rise from the surface (which may be a relatively warm sea or land which has been warmed by the Sun). Unsaturated air cools at a rate of 5.4°F for every 1000 ft (1°C for every 100 m). As soon as condensation starts, latent heat is liberated and the cooling rate drops to 3.5°F for every 1000 ft (1°C for every 150 m).

Fog is cloud on the ground. Fog which is formed over the land on a clear calm night is called *radiation fog*. The land cools quickly by radiation into space and then cools the air near it. Fog forming over the sea when warm moist air moves over colder water is *sea fog*. Fog which forms when warm moist air is lifted over a coast is *coastal fog*, and over hills is called *hill fog*.

METER, electricity

During the latter part of the nineteenth century most electricity supplies were direct current (DC), and so the majority of electricity meters were DC instruments. Ferranti pioneered a mercury motor ampere-hour meter, and a similar type developed by Hookham was a true watt-hour meter. Thompson's commutator motor meter, Wright's electrolytic meter and the Aron clock meter also enjoyed fairly widespread usage.

Ampere-hour meters depend only on the amount of current being consumed, and registration in watt-hours or kilowatt-hours (kWh or 'units') assumes a constant nominal value of supply voltage. Such meters are no longer used on public POWER SUPPLY systems, which are almost always alternating current (AC).

Single phase AC meters

The basic AC watt-hour meter consists of a horizontal aluminium disc with an electromagnetic coil mounted above and below it. The driving torque is derived from the interaction of EDDY CURRENTS induced in the disc and the flux from the two coils, which are arranged so that their fluxes are displaced relative to each other both in space and time. The speed of rotation of the disc is proportional to the amount of power passing through the meter, and a gear at the top of the disc spindle drives the counter dials.

In the simple single phase AC meter the flux in the upper electromagnet is proportional to the supply voltage, and that in the lower to the load current. The turning force or torque acting on the rotor disc is proportional to the product of the voltage and current and the *power factor* of the electrical load being metered. Power factor refers to the amount by which the load current waveform lags behind or leads the supply voltage waveform. It depends on the nature of the load, and can vary between 1 (zero lag or lead) and 0 (90° lag or lead).

Inductive loads have a *lagging* power factor, and capacitive loads a *leading* power factor.

To translate the torque acting on the rotor disc into proportional speed of rotation a permanent magnet brake is fitted which sets up eddy currents in the disc as it passes through an airgap in the magnet. These eddy currents are proportional to the speed of rotation of the rotor disc, and by Lenz's law link with the permanent magnet flux to oppose the rotation. The full load speed of the disc is adjusted by altering the position of the brake magnet. The meters also contain various devices which compensate for variations in operating conditions so as to maintain overall accuracy within about 2%.

Polyphase kWh meters

Industrial power networks, either 3 phase 3 wire or 3 phase 4 wire, are metered by *polyphase* meters having two driving elements (3 wire) or three driving elements (4 wire), each acting on a separate rotor disc mounted on a common spindle. Alternatively the drives can be concentrated on a single disc.

kVAh meters

Kilovoltampere-hour (kVAh) meters register independently of the nature of the load, that is, independently of the power factor. One method employs basically two polyphase kWh meters, one of which is cross-connected so as to cause it to meter the reactive or wattless component (kVArh) of the load. The two meters are mechanically coupled through a multiple DIFFERENTIAL mechanism which *summates* or computes the true kVAh. Another approach involves the conversion of the AC values of voltage and current to equiva-

Below : the upper pair of diagrams show cross-sections of a single phase meter, seen from the front and from the side. The lower two diagrams show the eddy currents induced by the permanent magnet brake, and a plan view of a polyphase meter for 3 phase 4 wire use.

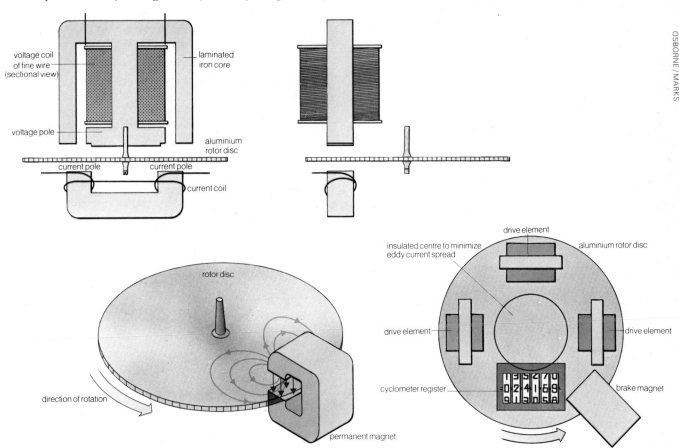

lent DC values. These are summated and reconverted to equivalent AC values which are independent of load power factor and can be metered as kVAh.

kVAh metering is important where large industrial consumers are concerned, because the reactive component which results from a power factor less than unity (1) will not be registered on an ordinary kWh meter, and so in effect energy would be consumed without being registered on the meter.

Maximum demand indicators

Another complication which arises in the supply of electricity to large consumers is that of maximum demand. Actual energy consumed over a period of time is indicated by the kWh metering, but there may be peak loads at various points during the day and the supply network must be capable of handling these peaks. This may involve the supply authority in extensive capital expenditure on plant and cabling to cope with the maximum demand, and so the consumer is billed for the actual power delivered plus a charge based on maximum demand during the billing period. This is to help offset the capital expenditure and to encourage the consumer to spread the demand more evenly.

The Merz pattern of maximum demand indicator (MDI), still widely used, embodies a pusher or drive arm which is continuously driven from the meter, except for a few seconds (usually at 30 minute intervals) when the arm is decoupled and returned to zero by a spring. The drive arm controls the angular movement of a slave pointer, manually reset at regular intervals (usually monthly), so that this pointer will indicate on a circular scale the maximum value of kW or kVA averaged over any single 30 minute interval during the billing period. The

coupling and decoupling of the drive from the meter is time-switch or relay operated.

When the MDI is separately housed it is actuated by electrical pulses from the master meter transmitted over 'pilot' wires from a device which produces a pulse for each revolution of the meter rotor. Summation of two or more circuit MDIs is possible, and the display can take the form of a digital printout.

Prepayment meters

The prepayment meter, an almost exclusively British development, followed the earlier widespread use of coin operated gas meters for domestic use.

Below left: two types of 'Trivector' meter which indicate kWh, kVAh and reactive kVAh, and incorporate maximum demand indicators. The upper meter has dial type counters, and the lower one (with its cover removed) has digital counters. When large loads are to be metered it is often impractical to connect the meters directly to the load current and voltage, so the meters are driven by current transformers and voltage transformers whose outputs are directly proportional to the load current and voltage.

Below: a mercury motor meter made by Chamberlain and Hookham in 1897, shown with a modern dual range domestic meter alongside. It was the first mercury meter to incorporate magnetic braking. The two smaller pictures at the bottom show two modern types of meter. The one on the left is a single phase domestic meter with the cover, register, and nameplate removed. The magnetic brake and its adjusting screw are at the left of the disc. The picture on the right is a kWh meter for 3 phase 4 wire operation, and has three rotor discs mounted on a common spindle.

The inserted coin is checked for size and weight, and if accepted it passes into the coin till, releasing the mechanism which is turned manually through a certain distance which is predetermined by a price setting device. This movement is stored as credit in a differential gear and causes the load current switch to close, if open, or to remain closed. The rotation of the meter rotor actuates the differential mechanism in the opposite sense, that is, by reducing the stored credit eventually to zero at which point a spring loaded mechanism will trip the switch and cut off the load current.

The more complex two part tariff prepayment meter incorporates a synchronous motor driving a timing mechanism which contributes to the total reduction of credit according to a pre-set fixed charge rate. When credit is exhausted the fixed charge device will build up a debit which must be cleared, by inserting sufficient coins, before the switch will close.

Testing Statutory regulations commonly require ordinary meters to be tested by one of three methods. In the first method, the registration of the meter is compared with that of a certified test meter, both meters being run on the same load for the same period of time. The second method involves the comparison of the rotor revolutions of the meter under test with those of a certified meter connected to the same load, with an additional comparison of the dial readings.

In the third method, the test load is measured by a precision indicating wattmeter and the rotor revolutions are timed with a stopwatch. A dial test is also carried out. Meters which are within the specified limits of accuracy are officially sealed and certified, usually for up to 15 or 20 years service.

METER, gas

Gas meters are instruments for measuring the volumetric flow rates of gases in the gas supply industry. Various types are available depending on the application. Where large flow rates need to be measured, for example, at the point of supply (the gas works) and by large industrial consumers, rotary (including turbine), orifice and heat capacity meters are employed. These last three types are mentioned in FLOWMETERS.

Small industrial and domestic consumers nowadays use *positive displacement meters*. These are robust and accurate meters which can be suitably adapted for use with prepayment and coin operated mechanisms.

History The first gas meters were invented by Clegg in about 1815 and were known as *wet meters* because they depended on a certain quantity of water or other liquid to ensure their working. Wet meters were used in the gas industry for over a hundred years but have now been superseded by dry meters.

Basically they consist of a measuring drum, casing and a counter mechanism. The measuring drum is mounted axially on bearings so that it can freely rotate and is divided into three or four radial compartments. This is positioned within the watertight casing and filled approximately half full with water. There is one inlet and one outlet aperture associated with each compartment so positioned that, at most, only one aperture of

Below: turbine gas meter showing internal components. The cone (in green) at left directs the gas in a chosen way over the turbine blades (white), causing them to turn. The turbine shaft can be linked to a rate counter or an integrator showing total volume passed.

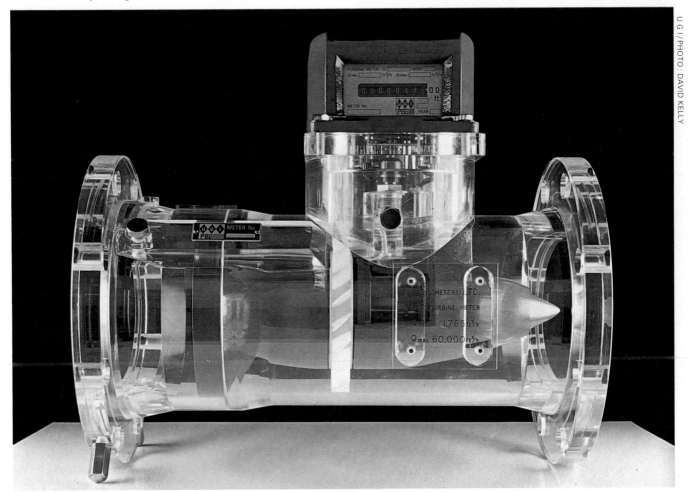

each compartment is above water. The compartment whose inlet aperture is above water receives gas from the common gas input supply to the meter, thus expelling any water in this chamber. This drives the drum round until the input aperture is immersed by which time the adjacent compartment is receiving gas—thus maintaining the rotary motion. Meanwhile, the gas in the first compartment is driven out through the outlet aperture by the water entering the submerged inlet. Knowing the volume of each chamber and counting the revolutions of the drum with the counter mechanism enables the quantity of exhausted gas leaving the meter to be measured.

The water acts as a perfect seal preventing unregistered gas flowing through the meter, although this is only true while the water level is maintained. Water evaporation is a major problem with this type of meter because this leads to a reduction in

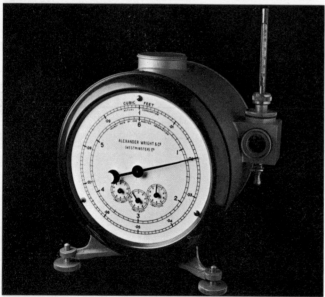

Top: this positive displacement meter is suitable for measuring small flow rates, such as those encountered in home installations.

Above: a modern laboratory water meter—their high accuracy ensures their use as standards for testing and calibrating other meters.

the water level. Also, condensation further along in the gas pipes can lead to partial blocking of the gas and a phenomenon known in the old days as 'jumpy lights'. In winter there was always the problems of freezing. They were, however, mechanically simple devices that maintained their accuracy over many years and are now used only as a standard to check other meters against.

Positive displacement meters

The modern positive displacement meter is based on a design originally developed between 1830 and 1850. Essentially they consist of two chambers which are alternately filled and emptied. Their reciprocal actions are connected via a linkage mechanism to the inlet and outlet valves associated with each chamber to control the gas flow, and also to a counter mechanism. Knowing the displacement volume of each chamber enables the flow rate to be measured.

In modern types, the chambers are separated by a leather (or synthetic material such as a high nitrile rubber) diaphragm which can be alternately stretched and relaxed. Also, to provide a more continuous flow of gas, two such double chambers are combined into one unit. These meters have good accuracy at low flow rates (hence their value in domestic installations), they are easy to install and service, and maintain their accuracy over many years.

Rotary meters

The main type of rotary meter—sometimes called a *lobed impeller meter*—consists of two or three precisely shaped and interlocking impellers (an impeller is *driven* by a fluid flow whereas a propeller drives). They are positioned inside a carefully shaped chamber such that at no time can the gas flow straight through the meter unregistered. The pressure of the gas entering the meter forces the impellers to rotate thus turning a counter mechanism. Each rotation of the impellers corresponds to a fixed volume of gas flowing through the meter.

There is very little pressure loss across this type of meter especially with high flow rates where frictional forces are less. They can be constructed from various materials but tend to be easily damaged by impurities in the gas (for example, water vapour). They are relatively costly to manufacture because of the precision engineering required.

The latest development is the turbine meter used for industrial applications. Basically it consists of a turbine blade which is operated by gas pressure. A mechanical or electronic sensing device monitors variations in temperature and pressure and a correction factor is then put into the reading on the meter. Such a meter, the size of two domestic meters, has replaced much larger installations the size of a small room.

Coin operated mechanisms

Prepayment mechanisms were first applied to wet meters in 1887. Here, an official of the gas company sets the meter to pass a fixed quantity of gas for which payment is made in advance. The quantity paid for is indicated on a dial, and when this has been used the counter mechanism shuts off the gas supply to the meter by closing a valve inside the meter which is operated by pressure in the mains. Coin operated mechanisms operate in a similar way, but the quantity of gas to be passed is set by the consumer. By entering a coin into the mechanism and turning a key the quantity of gas to be passed is registered.

Coin operated meters revolutionized the gas industry, putting the benefits of gas heating and lighting within the pockets of the poorer classes. Thereafter, the prohibitively high installation costs could be incorporated into the unit cost of the gas supplied.

METER, parking

The control of the movement and parking of vehicles in urban areas has been practised for at least 2000 years. In ancient Rome the authorities provided off-street parking areas for chariots, and traffic congestion became so bad that Julius Caesar banned vehicles from business areas of the city during certain hours of the day. This ban did not apply to vehicles on religious or State business.

The parking meter was invented by Carl Magee, and first used in 1935 in Oklahoma City. Meters were first installed in New York in 1951 and in London in 1957, and are now commonplace throughout the world.

Mechanisms

The basis of the parking meter is a clockwork mechanism, which is wound by an attendant about once a week in the case of the 'automatic' type, or by the user (by turning a knob after inserting a coin) in the case of the 'manual' type. In either case insertion of the coin begins the timing cycle, elapsed time being indicated by a pointer and scale arrangement. When the bought time period has expired a penalty 'flag' is displayed in the meter window.

Meters may be either *cumulative* or *non-cumulative*. The cumulative type add the bought time to any unexpired time left on the meter by the previous user, but the non-cumulative meters, on insertion of a coin, cancel any unexpired time and register only the amount of time bought by the coin.

Construction

The meters are usually mounted on steel posts at a height of from 3 to 5 feet (0.9 to 1.5 m) above the ground, or else on wall brackets where convenient. As the meters are exposed to a wide range of weather conditions, the bodies are made of non-corrodible alloy, usually diecast aluminium alloy, and the joints are sealed with waterproof gaskets.

The windows are of toughened glass or unbreakable acrylic material, and the clock mechanisms of brass, aluminium alloy, or stainless steel. A pair of adjacent parking spaces may be served by a pair of meters mounted on a single post, or a duplex meter which has two meters housed together in a single body, either back-to-back or side by side. Strengthened meter bodies are used in areas where there is a high risk of vandalism or attempted theft.

Coin collection

There are several types of coin receptacles in use, the simplest of which is merely a small metal box which is emptied periodically by an attendant. Where more security is required, the coins pass into a coinbox which locks automatically as it is withdrawn from the meter. Two keys are needed, one which the attendant uses to open the meter to remove the full coinbox and replace it with an empty one, and the other which is kept by the local authority treasury to open the coinbox. The clock mechanism is usually separated from the coin receptacle, and a separate key is used for access to the mechanism.

An alternative collecting method involves the use of a collecting trolley, the coins being jettisoned from the meter down a flexible metal tube and into a locked canister on the trolley. A variation of this method which provides greater security uses a locked coinbox, which is withdrawn from the meter and pushed into a receptacle on the canister. A key device in the receptacle unlocks the box and the coins are released into the canister. The box is automatically relocked as it is taken from the receptacle to be replaced in the meter.

Above: these Swedish meter mechanisms are of the manual type, being wound each time they are used by means of the knob below the coin slots on the front.

Left: the mechanism of an automatic type of parking meter, which only has to be wound about once a week. The coin gear, on the front, holds the last two coins that were inserted so that they can be seen through magnifying coin windows on the front of the case. This enables the attendant to check that the correct coins have been inserted. The case of the meter is weatherproof, all joints being sealed by neoprene gaskets, and the coin slot has a spring-loaded shutter to keep out dust and moisture. The entire mechanism can be removed for servicing or repair when necessary, and the meter head fitted with a new mechanism.

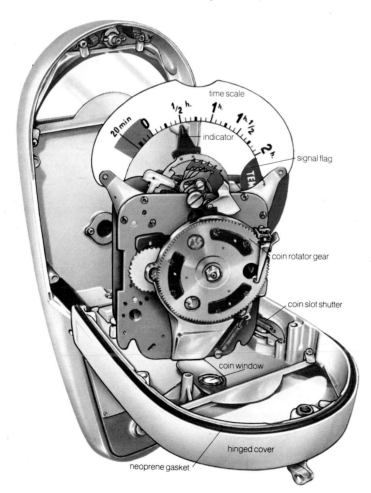

time scale

½ h. · 1 h. · 1 h ½

20 min · 0 · 2 h

indicator

signal flag

coin rotator gear

coin slot shutter

coin window

hinged cover

neoprene gasket

FRANK KENNARD

C A ANDERSSON & CO

METRONOME

The metronome is an instrument used for visually and audibly indicating the *tempo* or speed of music. In its simplest, clockwork, form it consists of a pivoted PENDULUM; below the pivot is a fixed weight, and above it a sliding weight. The beat is altered by sliding the weight up and down.

The history of the metronome goes back at least to the seventeenth century, when Etienne Loulié described in his *Eléments ou Principes de Musique...* (Paris, 1969) an instrument he called the *chronomètre*. This consisted of a metal bullet suspended on a cord so that it could swing from side to side. Provision was made to vary the length of swing to give 72 speeds. Other people, such as Joseph Sauveur, originator of the word acoustics, proposed similar instruments. Robert Bremner, the Scottish music publisher and instrument maker, wrote in 1756 that it was necessary to find a method whereby musical 'time in all churches may be equal', saying that a pendulum eight feet eight inches (2.67 m) long would by its double swing or *vibration* fix the length of the semibreve [whole note] (the longest note in common usage). He also suggested that such a pendulum be hung at the end of each school hall where church music was sung.

John Harrison, known for his invention of the perfect marine chronometer, noted the connection between time keeping and the tempi of music in 1775. In 1800, a German named Stöckel made a metronome which had a bell struck by a clock-type hammer.

Finally, in 1814, a German-born master organ builder living in Amsterdam, Dietrich Nikolaus Winkel, perfected the first reliable metronome having the double pendulum feature described above. This feature allowed a compact device to be built with then unrivalled accuracy. As a leading maker of clockwork BARREL ORGANS, Winkel was both musician and mechanic. His first instrument was a hinged box about 1 ft (30 cm) square containing a small infinitely adjustable double-weighted pendulum kept in motion by a clock-type escapement, powered by a small weight on the end of a cord wrapped around a drum.

Winkel demonstrated his instrument to Johann Nepomuk Maelzel, an unprincipled fellow who had a habit of capitalizing on the work of others. Maelzel for a time enjoyed the friendship of the great composer Beethoven, who was concerned that his music be played correctly. He was the first composer to include metronome markings in his scores, and one of the movements of his *Eighth Symphony* is said to have a beat inspired by the metronome.

Maelzel patented the metronome in his own name and set up a factory to produce it as the Maelzel Metronome, the name by which it is still known today. In spite of an investigation in Paris which upheld Winkel as the real inventor, and legal action over Maelzel's various misdemeanours, including stealing Beethoven's music and publishing it as his own.

Since then many kinds of metronomes have been built. One popular nineteenth century model was called Pinfold's Patent Metronome and was a pocket model with a pendulum which was reeled up like a tape measure; others can strike a bell at the first beat in a measure. Solid-state electronics have made possible small, extremely accurate metronomes; one model has a frequency generator which will emit a tunable A at the press of a button. Another model, which looks like a portable radio, can be set to beat any time signature, however complicated. An advantage of electronic metronomes is that, unlike the familiar pyramid-shaped Maelzel model, they do not have to stand on a level surface in order to work accurately.

MICHELSON—MORELEY EXPERIMENT (see ether)

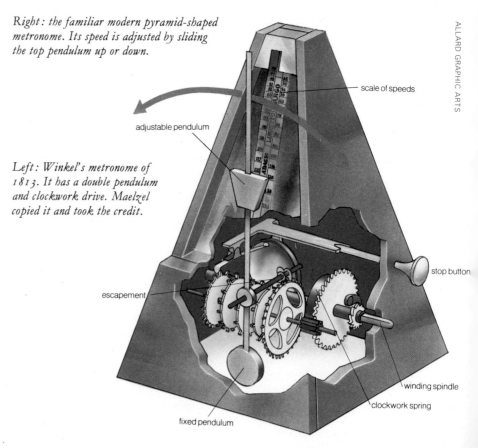

Right: the familiar modern pyramid-shaped metronome. Its speed is adjusted by sliding the top pendulum up or down.

Left: Winkel's metronome of 1813. It has a double pendulum and clockwork drive. Maelzel copied it and took the credit.

scale of speeds

adjustable pendulum

stop button

escapement

winding spindle

clockwork spring

fixed pendulum

MICROENCAPSULATION

Microencapsulation can best be described as a packaging technique which involves putting minute particles of a solid or droplets of a liquid into tiny capsules. A microencapsulated liquid behaves like a powdered solid, and the liquid is only released when the walls of the capsules are ruptured, for example by pressure or heating. The technique can be used to keep reactive materials apart until mixing is required, to prevent deterioration of unstable materials, to mask taste and odour, and to reduce volatility and flammability.

Mechanical encapsulation technology dates back to the late 1800s and the pharmaceutical industry in particular has pioneered in this field. They developed the familiar large gelatin capsule used by the medical profession to administer measured doses of drugs. In the 1930s two American chemists, H R Kruyt and H G Bungenberg de Jong, devised a technique which they called *coacervation*. They discovered that under certain conditions a *colloid* (a gluey substance such as gelatin) dispersed in a liquid to form two separate phases would form a thin wall around any third phase that was present. At that time, however, there was no practical application for this discovery.

The first significant application of microencapsulation technology was NCR (no carbon required) paper introduced in 1954. NCR paper uses two colourless chemicals which react to form a dye. One of the components is suspended in an oil and encapsulated into particles 14 microns in diameter (a micron is 1/1000 of a millimetre). These capsules are then coated on to the back of one sheet of paper, and the other component is coated on to the top of another sheet of paper. When the two sheets of paper are fed into a typewriter together, the local pressure of the type striking the top sheet ruptures the capsules and releases the first component of the dye. This then flows on to the top surface of the second sheet and reacts with the other dye component to produce the dye colour. A copy of the typed sheet is thus produced without the need for carbon paper. NCR paper allows duplicate copies to be made using continuous stationery on accounting machines and computer printouts without the wasteful use of rolls of carbon paper.

Manufacture

Microencapsulated products are made by a batch process consisting of three steps carried out under continuous agitation. The first step is the formation of three immiscible phases; a liquid carrier phase, a coating phase and a core material phase. The coating material is dissolved in the liquid carrier and the liquid or solid core material is dispersed in the resulting solution. Coacervation, the second step, is then induced by a change in temperature or pH value (a measure of the acidity of a solution) to form a three phase system. Once the coacervated coating phase is formed, it proceeds to concentrate and build up at the surface of the core material. *Adsorption* (the taking up of one substance on the surface of

Right: a series of photomicrographs showing the microencapsulation of an oil product. The top picture shows an oil droplet before the coacervated coating phase has begun to build up. In the second picture the coating material is beginning to accumulate around the oil droplets, and in third picture a thin coating can clearly be seen around each droplet. In the bottom picture coacervation is almost complete and a relatively thick oval shaped coating surrounds each droplet. After the coating has been hardened, the microencapsulated material can be dried to a free-flowing powder, and the oil will only be released when the capsules are ruptured either by pressure or heat. Capsule strength can be varied at will.

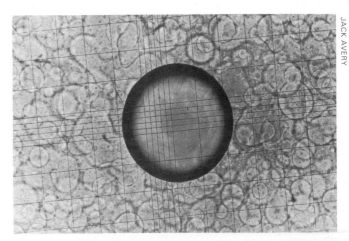

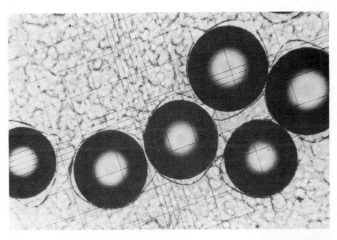

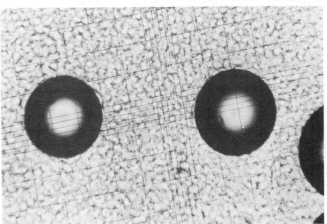

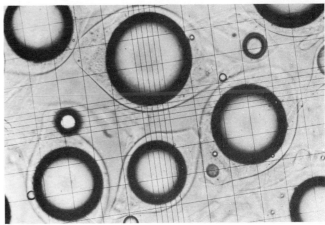

JACK AVERY

another, see SORPTION) continues until all the coating phase is wrapped around the core material particles. The final step involves the solidification of the coating material by chemical reaction. The capsules can now be dried to a free flowing powder or used directly as a slurry in the carrier liquid. Capsule properties, such as size, wall thickness and permeability, may be varied over a fairly wide range by careful control of the process and the choice of materials.

Uses

One of the most useful properties of microencapsulated products is the ability to provide sustained release of the capsule contents. Thus tablets containing a microencapsulated drug such as aspirin can give continuous benefit over a period of eight hours or so. Similarly, insecticides, herbicides and fungicides can be microencapsulated to provide sustained release over a predetermined period of time and to increase their storage life. Certain veterinary products are microencapsulated to overcome the animal's refusal to accept an unpleasant tasting drug. Adhesives and sealants which are activated by mixing two components can be packaged in a single container by microencapsulating one of the components; pressure or heat will rupture the capsules and activate the material. Rivets coated with microencapsulated anti-corrosion paint will remain dry to handle until the capsules break as they are driven home.

Perfume and fragrances can be applied in microencapsulated form to printed leaflets or labels, the odour only being released when the coated surface is scratched. This provides a very cheap way of distributing samples of a perfume for advertising purposes. Leaflets of this type informing customers of the smell of natural gas have been distributed in the United States by government order. A microencapsulated decongestant can be incorporated in paper handkerchiefs; the capsules break when the handkerchief is used, thus releasing the volatile decongestant.

Below: rivets are coated with a corrosion-resisting chromate paint which has been microencapsulated. When the rivets are driven home the capsules break and the paint is released.

MICROFILM

The term microfilm refers to the process of recording on film a unit of information such as an engineering drawing or the page of a book, photographically reducing it in size.

To many people the word microfilm has a rather ominous ring—secret plans reduced to a dot, secret files on a small roll of film concealed in a fountain pen, and so on. While these are particular aspects of MICROPHOTOGRAPHY, they have little to do with the part which microfilm plays in our personal and business lives.

Even a cheque you issue is probably stored in micro-image form, and a very high proportion of the statements and invoices you receive are duplicated on microfilm in the accounts offices of the issuing organization. Hospital records, personnel files, betting office forecast slips, records of births, deaths and marriages, and pension scheme records are just a few of the areas where microfilm is used for the communication and storage of information.

The first application of microphotography to commercial use was in 1925 when a New York bank clerk, G L McCarthy, filed a patent for a machine to photograph cheques—the 'Checkograph'. In May 1928, the Eastman Kodak Company produced the world's first commercial 16 mm microfilmers and the units were installed in two New York banks. Seven years later microfilm spread to Europe and microfilmers were operating in a number of banks and insurance companies in Britain.

During World War 2 microfilm played a very important part in the lives of hundreds of thousands of people in Britain and the United States and their Armed Forces overseas. Cargo space in all transport to and from the battle fronts was at a premium with very little available for personal correspondence. A system, called 'Airgraph' in Britain and 'V-mail' in the United States, provided a method whereby the letters, on special Post Office forms, were reduced to micro-images on 16 mm wide microfilm. 100 ft (30 m) rolls of processed microfilm, each about the size of a packet of 20 cigarettes and containing approximately 5000 letters, were shipped to special

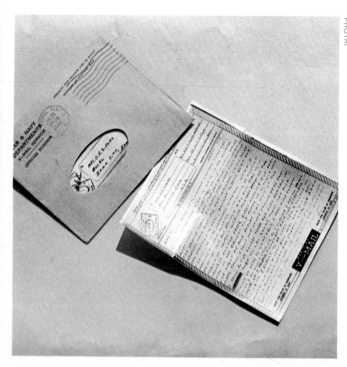

'Airgraph' stations where the 16 mm microfilm negatives were enlarged to readable size and forwarded to the addressees. It is estimated that approximately 1500 million Airgraph and V-mail letters were delivered between 1941 and August 1945.

Microfilm machines

The cameras that photograph documents, usually on to film either 16 mm, 35 mm or 105 mm wide, are collectively called *microfilmers*, and they fall broadly into three categories: *flatbed*, *flow type*, and *computer output*. The *flatbed microfilmer* is a conventional camera or 'film unit' containing lens, shutter and film drive mechanism, carried on a support column above the document table. It will expose either 16 mm or 35 mm microfilm and while this is the slowest of the three types, a very wide range of data can be accommodated. Documents, newspapers, bound volumes and engineering drawings up to a maximum size of 63×45 inches (160×114 cm) can be reduced to a single frame on 35 mm wide microfilm.

The most widely used microfilmers are flow type, which record micro-images on 16 mm wide microfilm at speeds up to 600 cheque-size documents per minute. They are designed for use in normal office environment and can be operated by non-photographic staff after a few minutes' training. The document is conveyed by a belt or drum system into the photographing area while the 16 mm microfilm is moving continuously in the opposite direction behind the lens in the film unit, so the image remains stationary on the moving film. The speed of the film movement past the lens is equivalent to the reduction factor of the lens employed—in a microfilmer producing a micro-image at a reduction ratio of 20:1 the film will be moving at 1/20th of the speed of the document. No shutter mechanism is employed, as exposures are controlled by switching on and off the lights. The leading edge of the document actuates the film movement and document illumination system, and as the trailing edge clears the photographic scanning area, film movement stops and the document illumination system returns to stand-by level.

Whereas the flatbed and flow type microfilmers produce micro-images from data recorded on paper, the computer

Left: millions of families received V-mail letters like this during World War 2. It was called 'Airgraph' in Britain.

Above: a microfiche reader with a simple pointer system for finding individual images. Below it, actual size images, usually on a postcard sized piece of film which can be easily stored in envelopes for quick reference.

Right: a high speed automatic flow type 16 mm microfilmer. A pile of the documents to be copied —cheques or invoice forms, for for example—is fed into the slot at the front. After automatic copying, the documents appear again at the top of the machine. The film is processed later, probably either daily or weekly.

output microfilmers convert data direct from magnetic tape into plain language micro-images without the need for paper intermediates. The computer data on magnetic tape is converted into images which are displayed on the face of a CATHODE RAY TUBE and photographed on to microfilm. The microfilmer can record the displayed information on 16 mm, 35 mm, 82.5 mm or 105 mm film widths at rates up to 120,000 characters per second, which is twenty times faster than the fastest 'hard copy' (paper) computer LINEPRINTER.

Microforms

Micro-images can be retained in various *microforms*. The most commonly used microform, especially in financial and business systems, 16 mm or 35 mm roll film, is retained in lengths up to 225 ft (69 m) on spools approximately 4 inches (10 cm) in diameter. Magazines or cassettes are mainly used in 16 mm systems requiring frequent high speed reference to information. The plastic magazine protects the microfilm and facilitates automatic loading of the viewing unit.

Where it is essential to maintain information in specific groups while retaining the ability to add or delete at any future date, *microfilm jackets* are used. These consist of two thin transparent sheets, sealed together to form channels accommodating either 16 mm or 35 mm film, or a combination.

Microfiches are used in 'micropublishing' systems where it is necessary to distribute a large number of microfilm copies, such as in the dissemination of information to libraries and the engineering parts and servicing industry. A sheet microform, usually 6×4 inch (15×10 cm) or 80 column punched card size, contains between 60 (20:1 reduction) to 200 (40:1 reduction) micro-images. The *ultrafiche* with micro-images at a reduction ratio of 150:1 will accommodate approximately 3000 micro-images on one A6 microfiche.

The *aperture card* is a data processing 80 column punched card containing one or more holes specially designed to accept 16 mm or 35 mm micro-images. Its main application area is in engineering drawing microfilm systems where one 35 mm micro-image occupies one frame in the aperture card.

Viewing microfilm

As the micro-images cannot be read with the unaided eye, a wide range of readers is available to enable fast, comfortable reference to be made to the microfilmed information. Some of these incorporate a unit to enable an enlarged paper copy to be produced from the image projected on to the reader screen. These are *reader printers*.

The ease and speed of retrieval of information on micro-images is directly related to the quality of the film, the microfilmer, the microfilm reader and the method of indexing.

One of the fastest micro-image retrieval systems is *image control blip indexing*. A 'blip' recorded beneath each image on the roll of microfilm provides image number location when used with photoelectric counters. By reference to an index the operator is able to key in the required image number on the reader keyboard and within seconds the image is displayed on the reader screen. In most instances these systems are fully integrated with a company's computer program.

An advanced system now in use is *optical code indexing*. Whereas other systems require the use of an external index to identify the document location on the microfilm, the optical code systems enable the operator to search by document 'content' search details—that is, to search for information without knowing the location of the document or even what document contains the information. For example, on the Kodak Miracode II system, each document is given a code when it is photographed, this code being formed by a pattern of clear and opaque rectangles on the film next to the document. To retrieve the image, the operator keys in the code, and the machine automatically searches for that particular image.

With the increase in population and standards of living, information of all types has to be stored in increasing amounts. As supplies of raw materials for paper production decline, and as more compact storage systems become necessary, microfilm plays an increasing part in information storage.

A variety of microforms—16 and 35 mm magazines, and microfiches.

MICROMETER

A micrometer caliper is a measuring device widely used in engineering to measure the diameter of round objects or the thickness of flat pieces. It consists of an accurately ground screw or *spindle* which is rotated in a fixed nut. The end of the spindle advances or retracts, opening or closing the distance to an *anvil*.

The thread grinding to the spindle is done with an almost DIAMOND-hard formed stone grinding wheel and the thread is inspected rigorously. The pitch diameter taper tolerance and the uniformity of thread and pitch must be held to within 0.00005 inch (1.20 micron). With the micrometer assembled, the anvil and spindle faces are ground parallel and then lapped. The tolerance to which lapping must be held is about three *lightbands* with flatness tied to within one lightband. (A lightband is a unit of measure used in INTERFEROMETRY, the measure of very small distances by the use of light. A lightband is the wavelength of *sodium*, a yellow colour: 0.000011 inch, or about $\frac{1}{4}$ micron.)

A micrometer spindle which measures in inches has a pitch of forty threads to the inch, so that one complete turn of the spindle advances the spindle face exactly one-fortieth or 0.025 inch. The spindle revolves inside a fixed nut covered by a sleeve which is marked with a longitudinal line having forty graduations. The outside shell of the micrometer spindle is called the *thimble* and has a bevelled edge which covers these graduations as it is turned; on the bevelled edge are 25 graduations which correspond to thousandths of an inch.

When the micrometer is closed, only the zero line can be seen on the sleeve next to the bevelled edge of the thimble. A measurement is taken by reading the number of longitudinal

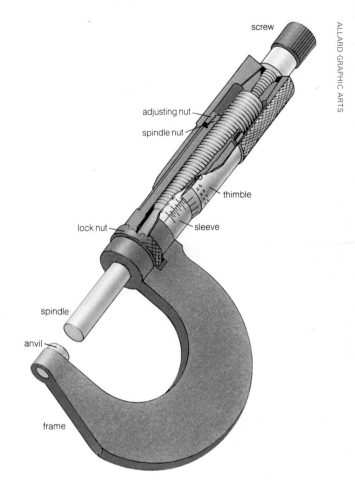

Below: a machinist's micrometer, measuring zero to one inch. The 'mike' in the photo is open to .335 inch. Inside micrometers are also available for measuring the size of holes; they comprise the thimble mechanism plus interchangeable rods of precise lengths.

Above: the micrometer, one of the most useful of all tools in the mechanical trades. In the manufacture of durable consumer goods, there may be hundreds of inspections along the way, and nearly all the inspectors use micrometers, as well as other precision tools.

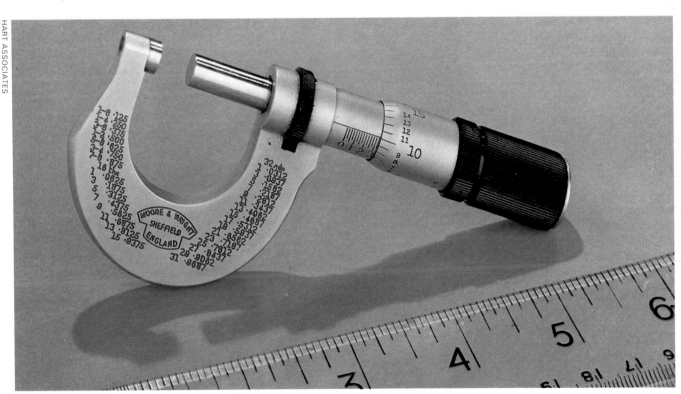

Above: an inspector using a three-to-four inch micrometer to measure the size of pistons for a diesel engine.

graduations uncovered and adding the number of thousandths above the zero mark on the thimble. Thus, for example, measuring the size of a piece of ground bar stock of 0.259 inch, ten longitudinal lines will be uncovered on the sleeve (10 × 0.025 = 0.250 or ¼ inch) plus nine lines on the bevelled edge of the thimble.

Metric micrometers are used the same way. The pitch of the spindle thread is 0.5 mm, one revolution of the thimble advancing or retracting the spindle ½ millimetre. The longitudinal line on the sleeve is graduated from zero to 25 millimetres and each millimetre is subdivided in half. The thimble is graduated in fifty divisions so that each graduation equals 1/50th of 0.5 mm or 0.01 mm.

At an extra cost, some micrometers have an additional VERNIER scale on the thimble so that they can be read, for example, to one ten-thousandth of an inch (0.0001 inch).

Micrometers are made in graduated sizes. The most common micrometre measures zero to one inch (or zero to 25 millimetres); the next size is for measuring one inch to two inches, (or 25 to 50 mm) and so forth. Thus the spindle, thimble and other parts are identical on all micrometers, and the size of the body of the instrument is the variant. When learning to use a micrometer, some practice is necessary to get the 'feel' of the device—for example, the thimble is never tightened as though it were a clamp. This would result in excess wear of the threads and inaccurate measurement. The object being measured should slip between the anvil and the spindle face without looseness but without excessive tightness.

Adjustment to the micrometer is seldom necessary, but with constant use play sometimes develops in the spindle due to wear of the spindle nut. By backing off the spindle an adjusting nut becomes accessible and ·by slightly tightening this nut, play is eliminated. Sleeve adjustment is possible by having spindle and anvil faces in contact and rotating the sleeve very slightly by means of a tiny spanner, supplied with the micrometer, until the line on the sleeve coincides perfectly with the zero line on the thimble.

Micrometers are used by motor mechanics, instrument technicians, toolmakers, inspectors and many others. An employee in a wire rope factory will carry a micrometer and use it often to check the size of wires to be used in the cable winding machinery.

MICROPHONE

A microphone is an electro-mechanical device for converting sound energy into electrical ENERGY. It usually has a flexible diaphragm which moves in response to minute changes in air pressure caused by sound waves. There are basically two ways of utilizing these pressure variations; *pressure operation* and *pressure gradient operation*.

Any microphone whose diaphragm is open to the air on one side only is said to be *pressure operated*. The magnitude of the force on the diaphragm depends on its area and the instantaneous PRESSURE in the sound wave (pressure is force per unit area). When both sides of the diaphragm are exposed to the air, the microphone is said to be pressure gradient operated. The diaphragm only moves when there is a *difference* in pressure between the back and the front, the pressure difference being due to a difference in *phase* (one wave has to travel further to reach the far side of the diaphragm and thus arrives later).

Types of microphone

There are various ways in which sound energy can be converted into electrical energy—the most important types being the carbon, moving coil, ribbon, electrostatic and crystal microphone.

In the *carbon microphone*, pressure variations in the sound waves cause the diaphragm to vibrate. The resultant alternating pressure on the carbon granules held behind the diaphragm causes a change in their electrical resistance about its mean value. This imposes an alternating current on the steady current drawn from a battery and, by means of a transformer, the alternating current can be 'tapped off' as output. Although such microphones do not provide 'high fidelity', they are cheap to produce and sturdy and are used extensively in TELEPHONES.

The *moving coil microphone* works on the electromagnetic principle (see ELECTROMAGNETISM). A coil attached to the vibrating diaphragm moves in the magnetic field of a strong permanent magnet and the relative motion induces a current in the coil (see INDUCTANCE), which is directly related to the incident sound wave.

The *ribbon microphone* also works on the electromagnetic principle. A corrugated metal ribbon suspended between the poles of a permanant magnet acts as the diaphragm and, like the moving coil, it receives an induced current which is related

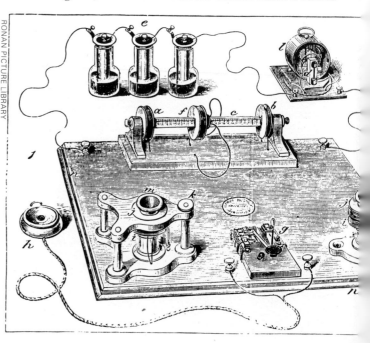

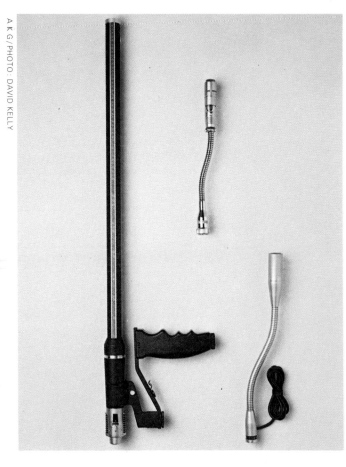

Above: a selection of modern microphones. Left is a dynamic 'gun' microphone—this has highly directional characteristics excellent for picking up distant and localized sounds. Top right is a dynamic noise cancelling microphone with 'hypercardioid' polar plot and below is a dynamic omnidirectional type with spherical polar plot.

Below: various views of an early Hughes' microphone—1879.

Right: a studio quality unidirectional (cardioid) microphone.

to the incident sound waves.

The *electrostatic microphone* is really a CAPACITOR with one plate fixed and the other acting as the flexible diaphragm. As the diaphragm vibrates, the capacitance varies about its mean value. With a constant voltage applied between the plates, the amount of stored charge will vary with changes in CAPACITANCE, causing an alternating current to flow related to the incident sound wave. With ELECTRET microphones the principle is the same, but the electret material contains its own 'in-built' voltage source and no external voltage is required.

The *crystal microphone* relies on the PIEZOELECTRIC effect—that is, when a piece of Rochelle salt is bent or twisted by the application of an alternating force an alternating current is produced. A 'sandwich' of Rochelle salt held within the microphone produces an alternating voltage when excited by an incident sound wave.

Frequency response The frequency response of a microphone is assessed by subjecting it to sounds of various pitch (frequencies) while monitoring its electrical output. The two resultant sets of figures; frequency, measured in *hertz* (the number of pressure variations, or cycles, per second) and the relative electrical outputs, measured in decibels, or dB (a unit used to compare sound intensities), are plotted graphically.

A horizontal line on a frequency response graph means that the microphone produces the same electrical power for all frequencies. In practice this is not achieved, but modern design techniques have enabled the production of microphones that come very close to this perfect situation within the audible frequency range (see HI-FI SYSTEMS).

Directional properties A *polar diagram* of a microphone is a graph of the relative voltage outputs for sounds arriving at different angles. Angles are measured from the microphone axis and separate polar diagrams are drawn for various frequencies and planes. In practice three different types of polar diagram are obtained—a circle, figure of eight and heart shape (*cardioid*).

A circle represents an *omni-directional* microphone, that is, one which is equally sensitive to sounds arriving from all angles. A figure of eight illustrates the characteristics of a *bi-directional* microphone which is sensitive to sounds arriving

J. T. BALCOMB. DEL.

electrostatic microphone

capacitor

back plate

diaphragm (front plate)

output

battery and resistance of high value to maintain a constant charge on the capacitor formed by the front and back plates

ribbon microphone

corrugated ribbon (diaphragm)

pole pieces

output

permanent magnet

moving coil microphone

diaphragm

coils

permanent magnet

output

carbon microphone

diaphragm

carbon granules

battery

transformer

output

multi-tube line microphone

sound from front reaches rear of diaphragm later, producing a phase difference and so moving it, sound from side strikes front and rear of diaphragm at same time, so it does not move.

side

front

parallel tubes

microphone

front

side

derivation of cardioid diagram by addition of circle and figure of eight

0°

270°

90°

180°

omnidirectional
bi-directional
cardioid

The diagrams show the basic configurations of an electrostatic and ribbon microphone (top), moving coil and carbon types (next to top) and how directional properties are achieved with polar plots (above).

at the front and the back of its diaphragm but not to those arriving from either side. A heart shape illustrates the characteristics of a microphone which is most sensitive to sounds arriving from the front.

A circle (really a sphere when three dimensions are considered) is usually associated with a *pressure operated* system. All pressure operated microphones have a similar set of polar diagrams. They are omni-directional at low frequencies, tending to a more one sided response at higher frequencies. This change in response is due to the *obstacle effect*. This effect is caused by the fact that objects tend to reflect sounds whose wavelengths are smaller than the dimensions of the object. Thus an object the size of a microphone only starts to reflect when the frequency exceeds about one kHz (1000 cycles per second).

A figure of eight usually illustrates the characteristics of a *pressure gradient* operated system. As mentioned earlier, a pressure gradient operated microphone has both sides of its diaphragm exposed to the air, the diaphragm only moving when there is a difference in air pressure between the two sides. This only occurs when there is a difference in 'phase' between the sound arriving at the front and the sound arriving at the back of the diaphragm, this in turn being dependent on the angle of incidence of the sound wave (see WAVE MOTION). If the sound originates from a point directly in front or directly behind the microphone a maximum pressure difference is obtained. If the sound, however, approaches the microphone from either side, there is no difference in phase as the sound

Below and right: cutaway views of various types of microphone. Below is a desk type and on right (top) a dynamic cardioid microphone and two double system dynamic cardioid microphones.

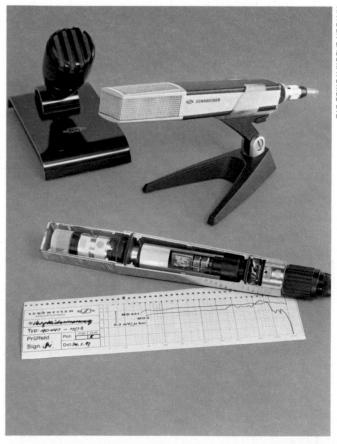

waves have travelled equal distances in order to reach the two sides of the diaphragm. This means that there is no pressure difference and no movement of the diaphragm. Sounds approaching from other angles produce pressure differences between the maximum and minimum values.

The cardioid polar diagram indicates that a microphone is uni-directional. This type of response is particularly useful for discussions, where extraneous noises, like those produced by an audience, are to be minimized. It is obtained by combining the characteristics of pressure operation and pressure gradient operation. At the front of a cardioid microphone the two elements operate in phase so that their electrical outputs add thus producing an electrical signal, whereas at the back of the microphone the elements operate out of phase, resulting in the complete cancellation of the electrical outputs.

It is possible to obtain a cardioid response by using a single element which combines both the characteristics of pressure operations and pressure gradient operation. This technique has been evolved in *electrostatic microphones* which have holes bored in their rear plate. The discovery of the cardioid electrostatic microphone then led to the development of an extremely versatile microphone, which possessed two diaphragms and behaved like two cardioid microphones placed back to back. The resulting microphone could be switched to give either a uni-directional, a bi-directional or cardioid response.

Highly directional microphones There are circumstances when sound must be picked up from a distance. To achieve this, a system which will boost the required sound and

reject unwanted, ambient, sounds is required. Two systems in use today are the *parabolic reflector* and the *line (rifle) microphone*.

Parabolic reflectors, like those used in RADAR, concentrate the required information at their focal point. A microphone, normally pressure operated, positioned at the focus then converts the concentrated sound energy into an electrical signal. Because of the obstacle effect, only very large reflectors are capable of reflecting the whole audible frequency range, but as a compromise between efficiency and portability, reflectors are usually about three feet (1 m) in diameter. They are built of aluminium backed with thick sponge rubber to reduce the noise produced by rain when they are used for outdoor work.

The line or rifle device consists of a large number of narrow parallel tubes terminated by a microphone. Sounds approaching the microphone along its axis (that is, parallel to the tubes) effectively have the same distance to travel in order to reach the diaphragm and thus arrive in phase, but sounds approaching from any other angle travel different distances, thus arriving at the diaphragm out of phase. This results in the effective cancellation of the sound wave. It is also possible to achieve highly directional results with a single tube which has a large number of holes (sound entrances) evenly distributed along its length. Like the multi-tube microphone it utilizes the fact that sounds approaching the microphone from any direction other than that from the front arrive at the diaphragm out of phase. Only a single row of holes is needed to cancel sounds from any unwanted direction.

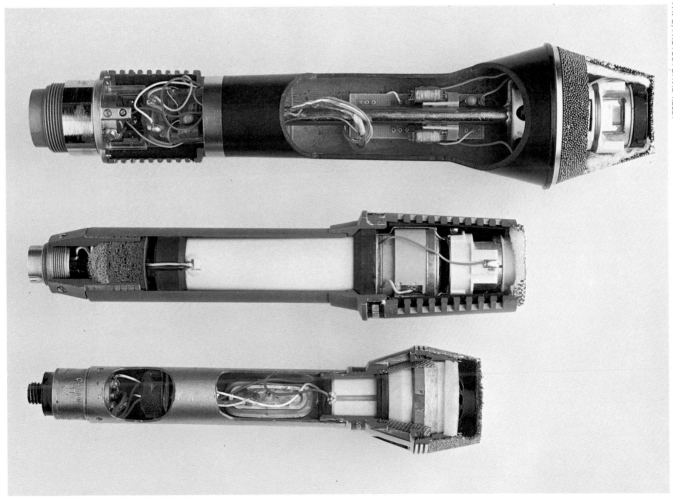

A K G / PHOTOS : DAVID KELLY

MICROPHOTOGRAPHY

Microphotography is the photographic production of minute pictures, usually of such subjects as a page of text or a drawing. (It should not be confused with *photomicrography*, which is the production of normal sized photographs of small objects with the aid of a microscope). Using microphotography, the height of a book page can be reduced a hundredfold or more to the size of a pinhead or a dot on the page without loss of legibility.

Microphotography began soon after the invention of photography itself, when J B Dancer successfully produced legible micro-images of several pages of text in Manchester about 1839. The first record we have of its practical use, however, is during the Franco-Prussian war of 1870–71, when Paris was besieged for several months. Dagron, a French photographer, used carrier pigeons to fly 115,000 important messages on microfilm between Tours and Paris.

This use, as an information storage system, is now represented by the MICROFILM industry, in which vast numbers of documents and books are daily reduced on to compact rolls or sheets of film. But microphotography has found another important use in the production of microelectronic devices, as well as in the rather more dramatic fields of espionage where information is reduced to a readily-concealed microdot.

Materials and equipment

The first requirement is a photographic emulsion capable of recording fine details. The *grains* (light-sensitive particles) of a normal FILM are too large for this work. Ultra-fine grains are needed not only to give the required fine structure, but also to prevent the sharpness of the picture being spoiled by scatter (the spread of light in the emulsion). Very high resolution emulsions are therefore virtually transparent. They are, however, very insensitive and

'contrasty' compared with ordinary film. Photographic plates of this sort, with silver halide grains as in normal film, have been commercially available since the 1940s, and are processed by conventional methods. A more recent alternative, however, is the PCMI or photochromic micro-image process. This uses light sensitive organic dyes of molecular size, so that the images are completely grain-free with the added advantage of being less contrasty than halide emulsions. Furthermore, they need no processing, though they need intense ultra-violet light for exposure. The life of the images is only a few hours at room temperature, but can be increased to months or years by cold storage.

The images can be erased by exposure to infra-red light, so the chief advantage of this material is in the production of master sheets of, say, a parts list for a car, which may have a

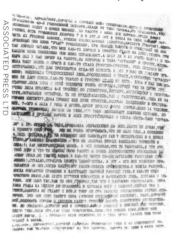

Left: a rare published spy microdot. This is apparently a private letter in Russian, found in the handbag of Helen Kroger in the form of a microdot the size of a match head. The Krogers were convicted in London in 1961.

Below: in the 1871 pigeon post, messages reduced on to emulsion were attached to a pigeon's tail feathers, some 50,000 at a time. On receipt, they were projected and hand copied.

huge number of separate images. Using PCMI, it is possible to make sure that each image is perfect before duplicates are made on ordinary halide emulsion.

To produce an image with the necessary detail demands a lens performance much better than that required for an ordinary camera. Fairly good results can be obtained by using only the middle of the image of a high quality camera lens, but the best results require the use of a 'perfect' lens such as a MICROSCOPE *objective*. The microphotographic camera has to focus the lens image with extreme accuracy on the plate surface.

Because the plates used are relatively insensitive, the image must be illuminated intensely to avoid inconveniently long exposure times. This requirement may be met by making an intermediate negative with a conventional camera, through which a great deal of light can be passed.

Applications An early use of microphotography was in the production of graticules or reticles—the scales seen in the field of view of optical instruments—telescopes, binoculars, machine tools and scientific instruments, for example. This use is still important. A more dramatic use is the microdot—the value of these for furtive communications became known during World War 2.

The most recent use of microphotography is in the production of INTEGRATED CIRCUITS, in which the pattern which is to eventually become a semiconductor layer is prepared on a large scale, then photographed down using microphotographic techniques. These techniques have made possible a vast reduction in the size of electronic devices from pocket calculators to spacecraft components.

MICROSCOPE, ELECTRON (see electron microscope)

MICROSCOPE

The use of two lenses gives the light microscope its alternative name of *compound* microscope. It is based on the principle that the image formed by one LENS (the *objective*, next to the specimen) is further magnified by a second lens (the *eyepiece*), to give much higher powers than could be obtained by a simple magnifying glass alone. The microscope, which has uses in all branches of science and technology, is one of the most valuable instruments ever invented.

The compound microscope was probably invented by Hans and Zacharias Janssen in Holland about 1600. It became well known through the work of Robert Hooke in England, especially through publication of his book *Micrographia* in 1665. During the eighteenth century the instrument was largely a plaything, but by 1830 the objective had been improved from a simple lens to a high-quality *achromatic* and *aplanatic* system (where the image is free from false colours round the image parts and from other defects which obscure detail), largely through the work of J J Lister. Many other people contributed to the perfection of the instrument in the next 50 years, until by 1880 Ernst Abbe had established and applied the theoretical framework which enabled the microscope to give a usable range of magnification from about $\times 30$ to $\times 2000$.

This maximum useful magnification cannot be exceeded because of the nature of light itself—a form of ELECTRO-MAGNETIC RADIATION. Because of its WAVE MOTION it simply

Below : this Nikon microscope has a device like a shadowgraph attached so that what the technician sees can be projected on to a screen. The projection can be overlaid with original working drawings and comparisons made for quality control.

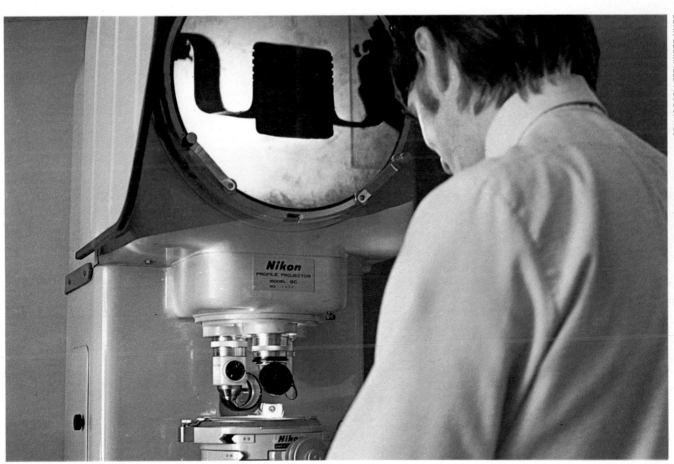

bends round very small objects without itself being affected: this makes very small objects invisible. Therefore, although it would be possible to make a microscope which would magnify more than ×2000 (for example, just by using a stronger eyepiece), because the *resolution* (ability to separate fine detail) is fixed not by the instrument but by the nature of light itself, further magnification would give no better resolution. Thus to resolve details closer together than 2500 angstrom units, or 0.000025 cm, an ELECTRON MICROSCOPE must be used, as electron waves have a shorter wavelength than light waves.

Illumination

In use, the microscope is arranged for either transmitted illumination, where the light goes through the specimen, or for reflected illumination, where the light bounces back from the specimen. Transmitted lighting is more usual nowadays. The light source for most work is some kind of electric lamp, as daylight is not reliable in quality or intensity. In some instruments the light is built into the *stand* itself, which is very convenient in use. If a separate lamp is used, the light has to be carefully directed up through the specimen by means of a mirror. On advanced instruments the lamp is complicated, with a lamp condenser and lamp iris controlling the light from a compact-filament bulb, usually operated at low voltage. A wide variety of lamps is available, to give selected wavelengths of illumination, some at very high intensity.

For the best results, a *substage condenser* is used to focus a corrected beam of light accurately on the specimen on the *stage*. Although for low power work this is not vital, for other requirements the illumination is not sufficiently intense nor sufficiently controlled without this condenser, which also has an iris diaphragm used to control the angle of the light reaching the specimen. After passing through the specimen slide, the light reaches the *objective*. This may be a very complicated and expensive lens system, containing as many as 14 separate lenses, some as small as 1 mm in diameter, and very carefully arranged relative to each other. The higher the magnification of the objective, the more complicated it becomes; in addition there are special types such as *flatfield* objectives for PHOTO-MICROGRAPHY, and *apochromatic* (having both spherical and chromatic aberrations corrected to a high degree) objectives. Each type makes further demands on the designer and is more complicated. For convenience, several objectives are usually carried on a revolving *nosepiece*, which allows different magnifications to be chosen simply by turning to a different position.

On a modern research microscope the range of powers of the objectives might be ×3, ×6, ×10, ×20, ×40 and ×100. The highest power would be of the kind called *oil-immersion*,

Right: A Wild M20 laboratory microscope. Over the years, designs have changed to make life easier: built in illumination and substage condensers are now standard features. The binocular head does not give a stereo view, since it simply splits a single beam, but it makes viewing less tiring as both eyes are used equally. Until recently, microscopes had to be tilted back to give a good viewing angle; now, a prism does this while keeping the specimen table level.

Far right: a selection of diatoms (unicellular algae) photographed through a microscope using three different methods of light transmission. Top: normal or transmitted light, directed through the specimen. Centre: darkground illumination, in which only oblique rays of light are transmitted through the specimen. Below: polarized lighting, which uses filters cutting off most light. Each method reveals different aspects of the specimen.

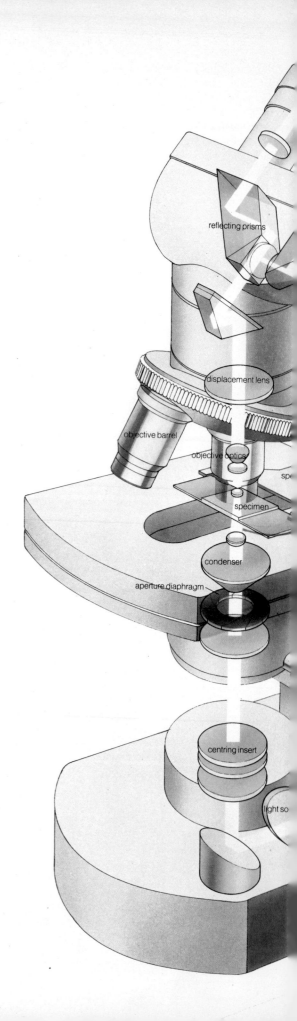

reflecting prisms

displacement lens

objective barrel

objective optics

sp

specimen

condenser

aperture diaphragm

centring insert

light so

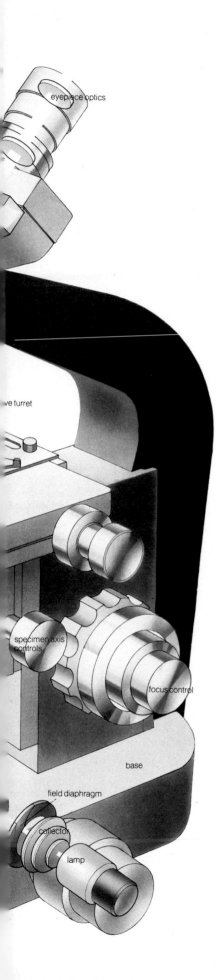

eyepiece optics

ve turret

specimen axis controls

focus control

base

field diaphragm

collector

lamp

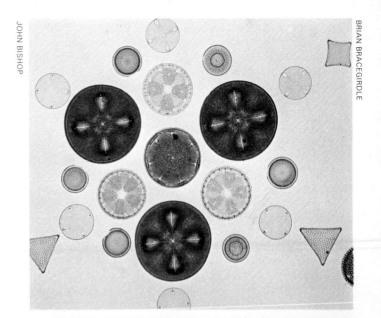

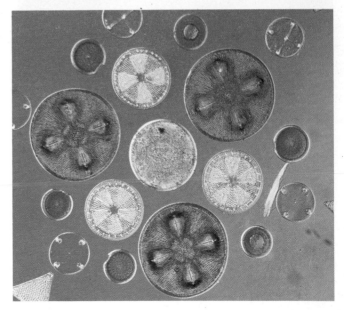

because it has to be used with a drop of oil between the front of the objective and the slide being viewed. At the top end of the *body-tube* is the eyepiece, and these also are available in various powers. A usual range nowadays would be $\times 6$, $\times 10$ and $\times 15$. The total magnification is given simply by multiplying the power of the objective by that of the eyepiece, so the range of magnifications available, with the six objectives and three eyepieces mentioned above, would be from $\times 18$ to $\times 1500$.

When setting up a microscope, the correct alignment of all the optical components, from the lamp to the eyepiece, is of the greatest importance; modern microscopes have the most useful arrangement built-in.

Similar principles apply if the instrument is used with reflected light, for example, when studying metal surfaces. Here, intense lighting is required because so much is lost during reflection. Special accessories are required if higher powers are to be used with reflected light, and some instruments are designed solely for this purpose.

Other methods   In addition to the straightforward types of illumination mentioned above, which have not changed in essence since the instrument was first invented, the twentieth century has seen the addition of three new techniques. *Phase-contrast* illumination allows specimens which appear almost invisible by normal illumination to be seen clearly, and is thus of major importance for direct investigation of living cells. The system was invented by Zernicke in the 1930s, and relies on condenser and objective pairs arranged in such a manner that light going through part of the condenser is slowed down relative to the rest, and is thus put out of *phase*, causing dif-

ferences in refractive power to show up as differences in light and shade.

Interference microscopy also relies on the interference of light beams with each other, and was developed after the phase-contrast microscope had shown the advantages of the method. The beam of light is split into two, one of which goes through the specimen and is modified by it before being recombined with the first beam. Differences in the light-retarding properties of the specimen show up as different colours. The advantage of the method is that actual precise measurements of the thickness of objects and other dimensions can be made.

Fluorescence microscopy requires the minimum of specialized equipment, but does need staining techniques, developed for this method. The principle is that blue or ultraviolet illumination is used to make parts of a specially-treated specimen emit light of various colours. Barrier *filters* absorb the light used to illuminate the specimen, which shows up only in the colours generated by the technique. This technique is of great use in *histochemistry*, which is the chemistry of living tissues.

Mounting specimens   The modern microscope is versatile and relatively simple to use, many of the accessories thought essential in the last century are now being superseded. By itself, though, the instrument may be of little use: preparation of specimens for viewing through it is also most important, for most things are far too large to be viewed directly. The most usual technique is to make a slice of a specimen (see MICROTOME), so that it is thin enough to be transparent. It will then need staining with coloured dyes to make the structure

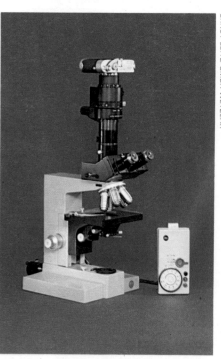

Above: a Dialux binocular microscope, of German manufacture, with 35 mm camera attached. A mirror allows the viewer to see exactly what will be in the photograph. The light is variable in intensity.

Left: a revolving nosepiece.

clear, and it will need mounting on a protective *slide* surrounded by a resin such as Canada balsam to give it the correct characteristics for viewing. The standard size of slide is 3 × 1 inches, and all kinds of specimens are mounted on these.

Other means of illuminating specimens show to advantage with some older slides. Two techniques have come down from Victorian times, *darkground* illumination and *polarized* illumination, and these can still give useful results after more than a century of application. In darkground work all direct light is cut off by a disc under the substage condenser, so that only very oblique rays are bent upwards by the specimen to enter the objective. This gives the effect of the specimen showing up brilliant white on a black background, and is especially useful for small living things. Polarized lighting requires polarizing filters, one below the specimen and one somewhere above, and relies on one of the properties of light as a wave motion. This is that the waves occur at all angles to the line of direction of the beam, and a polarizing filter cuts off all angles except a very few. If two such filters are used at right angles to each other no direct light can pass, but if the specimen is a crystal it may be able to alter some of the waves to enable them to pass the second filter, causing brilliant colours to be generated.

All these techniques are formidable tools for the scientist in his exploration of our Universe, in an instrument which is relatively inexpensive and easy to use. The microscope has developed from a curiosity to become a symbol of scientific research. As Louis Pasteur once remarked, 'the part played by the infinitely small seems to be infinitely great'.

MICROTOME

A microtome is an instrument used to cut very thin *sections* (slices) of specimens for examination under a light MICROSCOPE. Even thinner sections are needed when using an ELECTRON MICROSCOPE, which has led to the development of the *ultramicrotome*.

The optical resolution of the light microscope is such that specimens are often best examined as thin sections, rather than whole. Nowadays medical and biological techniques require specimens of the order of 1 to 50 μm, the usual thickness being 4 to 5 μm (1μm, micrometre or micron is one-thousandth of a millimetre). Specimens are usually chemically preserved in a solution such as formalin (formaldehyde in water), dehydrated and embedded in wax. The wax block is firmly clamped on to a microtome—originally known as a 'cutting engine'—and sections cut with a specially prepared very sharp steel knife.

Types of microtome   There are three main types of microtome: the *rocking*, the *rotary* and the *sliding* microtome.

On the rocking design, the knife is clamped in a fixed horizontal position with the edge uppermost. The wax block is attached to the end of an arm pivoted near the knife and is moved or rocked in an arc past the knife edge. On the downward

Below: an ultramicrotome has three main parts: the optical system, the main cutting unit and the electronic controls. The specimen, mounted in plastic, is inserted into the specimen holder, which falls electrodynamically past the glass knife, thereby shaving off sections which are collected in a line on a liquid in the collecting trough. The microscope is used for adjusting the angle of the knife edge.

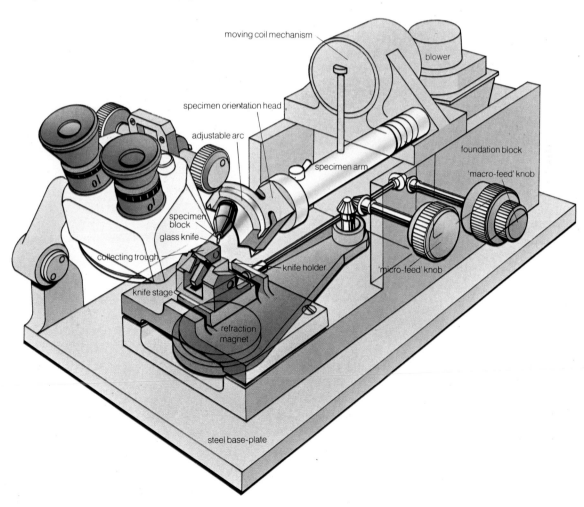

moving coil mechanism

blower

specimen orientation head

adjustable arc

specimen arm

foundation block

'macro-feed' knob

specimen block

glass knife

collecting trough

knife holder

'micro-feed' knob

knife stage

refraction magnet

steel base-plate

stroke the knife removes a thin section of the specimen. The block is advanced towards the knife by a ratchet mechanism with a MICROMETER thread for adjusting section thickness.

On a rotary microtome, the specimen block moves up and down in a vertical plane and the feed mechanism is actuated by a large hand wheel of which one rotation produces a complete cutting cycle. Larger and harder specimens can be sectioned on these machines and their rotary action is adapted easily to automatic power drive.

Sliding microtomes are the heaviest of all, enabling small and large sections to be cut of whole human lung and brain. One type of sliding microtome has a moving knife, drawn horizontally across the block, and is particularly useful for specimens which have been embedded in cellulose nitrate. The other most common and versatile type is the base sledge, where the specimen is mounted on a moving carriage or sledge and the knife is fixed. The micrometer feed mechanism is operated after each cutting stroke, either manually or by a trip device.

Ultramicrotomes

The greater resolution of the electron microscope over the light microscope requires even thinner sections. To obtain these, small 0.5 to 1.0 cubic millimetre biological specimens are embedded in very hard synthetic resins, for example methacrylate ('Perspex' or 'Plexiglas'), epoxy and polyester. Microtomes capable of cutting ultra-thin sections of these hard embedments—ultramicrotomes—have developed rapidly since 1950, allowing reliable and reproducible sections of even thickness to be obtained. A range of thickness for most machines is 5 to 150 nm (1 nm = one thousand millionth of a metre) with biological specimens being sectioned between 20 and 100 nm.

The embedded specimen is attached to a metal arm or tube which moves in a vertical plane past the knife edge. The knives are usually small pieces of plate glass broken in a controlled way to produce a fine edge 6 mm (0.24 inch) long and much sharper than any steel knife. Alternatively, expensive diamond

knives are used with a long-lasting edge only 1.5 mm (0.06 inch) in length. As sections are cut they float out on to water contained in a trough, attached to the knife, and are often so small (0.1 mm square or less) that a stereoscopic binocular microscope is needed to see them. They are then collected on to small metal grids for insertion into the electron microscope.

The fine precision of the feed mechanism on these machines can be obtained either mechanically by a micrometer thread, reduced 250 times by a lever and leaf-spring system, or more often by electrically controlled thermal expansion of the rod or tube carrying the specimen. The rate of expansion and therefore section thickness will depend not only on the current applied but also on cutting speed.

During the cutting cycle the specimen block must not damage the knife edge on the return stroke, and this may be achieved by the specimen arm being displaced sideways on a D-ring movement after the section is cut. A less common but more advanced method is to retract the knife about 25 μm from its cutting position. This is done by means of a large electromagnet in the base of the machine, which is energized momentarily after a section is cut, while the specimen arm returns ready for another cutting stroke. Most ultramicrotomes can be automatically operated, the automatic models having complicated electrical circuitry.

Freezing microtomes

Both the microtomes and ultra-microtomes described above have attachments capable of allowing sections to be cut of frozen unembedded specimens, thus avoiding damage to cells and tissue structures from chemical reagents and resins. Some microtomes are made specifically for this purpose, together with the Cryostat—a refrigerated cabinet at −20°C in which the microtome is placed. With this machine, rapid frozen sections are produced of material removed from a patient during an operation allowing a diagnosis to be made within a few minutes and acted upon immediately.

Right: the earliest microtomes were little more than holders for, say, a botanical specimen, which was positioned in the central hole and thinly sliced with a sharp knife.

Centre: a modern base sledge type of microtome. The specimen, usually embedded in wax, is mounted on a moving carriage or sledge which slides beneath the fixed knife edge above. There is a micrometer feed mechanism which is operated after each cut. The thin sections are collected on a paper ribbon.

Top: even thinner sections are needed for electron microscopy. These are taken by an ultramicrotome. The specimen is embedded in a very hard resin attached to a metal arm which moves vertically past the knife edge. Specimens are taken from the trough by a collector device.

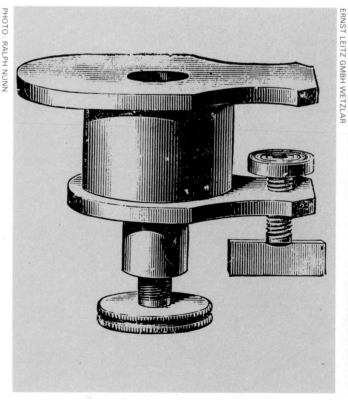

PHOTO: RALPH NUNN

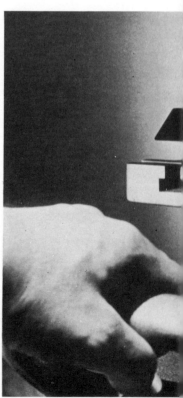

ERNST LEITZ GMBH WETZLAR

MICROWAVES

Microwaves are a form of ELECTROMAGNETIC RADIATION—
they are a part of the whole spectrum which includes LIGHT and
RADIO waves, but have wavelengths approximately midway
between the two: longer than INFRA-RED but shorter than radio.
They share some of the properties of both, and like radio waves
are used for communications, while like infra-red they can be
used for cooking.

Microwaves have wavelengths between 30 cm and 1 mm,
that is, frequencies between 1 GHz (1000 MHz) and 300 GHz.
These divisions are rather arbitrary, and have no physical
significance. Infra-red radiation, however, is normally produced by heat, while microwaves are produced electronically.

Generation and amplification The actual generation and amplification of microwaves is achieved by a variety of
devices, each designed for a specific purpose. As with radio
waves, the devices produce rapidly oscillating electron currents, the frequency of the oscillation being the same as that of
the frequency of radiation desired. The high power microwave
sources have been developed from the thermionic VALVE
[vacuum tube]. These developments took place in the early
1920s to overcome the deficiencies of the more conventional
radio valve in its various forms when used to produce high
powers at the higher frequencies demanded by the rapidly
expanding communications industry, and resulted in the
magnetron, klystron and *travelling wave tube*. While the magnetron
is a self sustaining oscillator tube capable of producing pulses
of power well in excess of a megawatt, both the klystron and
travelling wave tube are essentially amplifying devices capable
of producing output powers of several kilowatts. Very low
power microwave sources may be derived from either low

*Below: microwaves are used extensively in communications and
broadcasting. This outside television unit has a parabolic microwave
aerial for transmitting broadcasts to the broadcasting centre.*

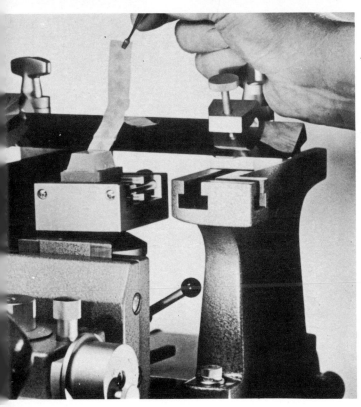

PHOTO: JOHN GOLDBLATT

power versions of the klystron or *reflex klystron*, or the *maser* (see LASER). In addition there are many forms of solid state microwave sources, which are very compact and which exploit the *Gunn effect* for their operation (see OSCILLATOR).

Propagation of microwaves

Microwaves can be modulated, just like longer radio waves (see, for example, FREQUENCY MODULATION and PULSE CODE MODULATION), and are therefore used for communications. Since light, radio and microwaves all obey the laws of OPTIC covering absorption, reflection, refraction, and diffraction, many of which depend upon the wavelength being used, microwaves have characteristics which make them useful in particular situations. For example, they can be beamed rather more easily than longer wavelengths—the AERIALS [antennas] are of less cumbersome size—and are thus useful for setting up a communications network, rather than for general broadcasting.

The most common medium through which microwaves are passed (the *propagation medium*) is the *troposphere*, the lowest region of the Earth's atmosphere. For most of the time this is an extremely complex and uneven region to microwaves because of the widely differing meteorological structures, such as fronts and temperature inversions, within the region. By virtue of its constituent gas and water vapour content, each part of the troposphere may have a different *radio refractive index* from its neighbour. As a result, the phenomena of reflection, refraction and so on, become extremely complex. Indeed certain microwave transmissions may be subject to various forms of 'scattering' due to either these meteorological

structures or rain, snow and so on. It is, however, the gas and water vapour components present in the region which influence the choice of suitable wavelengths to be used for transmission within this medium. At certain wavelengths the absorption of the medium is high.

While microwaves will generally pass through considerable distances of the troposphere, they cannot be reflected by the ionosphere, like longer radio waves. Consequently, microwave communications are restricted to comparatively short distances, of the order of 500 km, since they can only pass beyond the horizon by scattering and diffraction effects.

Microwave circuits

All sources of microwave energy require the use, in their design and construction, of very special electric circuit techniques which exploit both the electric and magnetic field properties of the wave. These techniques are necessary since both the physical dimensions and the electrical properties of the materials used in the construction of the more conventional electric circuit CONDUCTORS (wires and cables), INDUCTORS, CAPACITORS and RESISTORS are such that these components do not retain their basic electrical properties when carrying alternating currents at microwave frequencies.

Perhaps the most distinctive feature of any microwave 'circuit' is the array of 'conductors' which carry or *guide* the signal between components. These 'conductors' take the form of WAVEGUIDES, which are pipe-like structures having either rectangular or circular cross sections, usually constructed of material of high electrical conductivity and to a very high degree of precision. The effects of capacitance and inductance

CABLE & WIRELESS LTD

are introduced into waveguide 'circuits' by siting posts, stubs, annuli and so on, in the waveguide. The physical dimensions of these devices and their positions in relation to the guided field structure determine the type of effect that they are to produce. Microwave aerials are usually also quite different from the more conventional types in that, although they may have many different forms, most employ parabolic reflecting surfaces which are irradiated from waveguide *feeds* at their foci to produce highly directional beams.

Microwaves in radar It was the development of RADAR which initiated the application of microwaves in a variety of widely differing areas. Since World War 2, even the original simple radar principle of detecting and ranging a reflecting target has been developed to the point that the

Left and below: two different types of tropospheric scatter stations. Long distance microwave transmissions must rely on tropospheric scatter to reach receivers over the horizon. Atmospheric conditions in the troposphere (the first 13 km, 8 miles, of the atmosphere) have a considerable effect on the scattering of microwaves and transmissions are usually restricted to distances less than 500 km (about 300 miles). The curved tubular structure shown in the foreground of the left hand photograph is a large waveguide terminating at the focus.

Right: this photograph of a parabolic microwave aerial shows clearly the waveguide feed-receptor with its opening positioned at the focal point of the reflector. With such a system a highly directional beam can be transmitted. They are mainly used in communications relay.

GEC-MARCONI ELECTRONICS LTD

positions, speeds and courses of targets, moving at very high speeds at considerable distances from a radar installation, may now be continually recorded to accuracies of a few metres. In contrast, it is now possible to determine the position of a housefly at a range of about 2 km with microwave radar. There is, therefore, the capability of using modern radar for all types of target observation. As a result, most major air and sea ports throughout the world are equipped to operate full traffic control, both local and distant, on all types of vehicles or vessels using the ports (see AIR TRAFFIC CONTROL). Similarly, most of the world's aircraft and ships carry microwave radar as a navigational aid and also as a bad weather or storm detector. The ability to detect the positions of intense meteorological activities in the atmosphere has also contributed in recent years to the formation of the new science of radio METEOROLOGY where microwave radar has proved to be a valuable aid in the study of meteorology of our atmosphere.

Communications

As the demand for communication systems has increased throughout the world, there have been very rapid developments in the use of microwave radio relay systems to relieve some of the traffic load from existing cable and radio communication systems. More recently SATELLITE relay systems have become operational for international traffic, while long waveguides are being considered for local trunk traffic. Both employ microwave transmissions. Microwave equipment, which can be readily designed for mobile work, is also used extensively for both minor local communication systems, of the type frequently used by broadcasting companies for outside broadcast activities, and in space exploration projects.

Other applications

In addition to these rather more obvious uses of microwaves there are of course applications where, by combinations of both communications and radar techniques, vehicles, aircraft and so on are operated completely by automatic control.

The radio ALTIMETER relies on microwave transmissions being reflected from the ground to provide a method of measuring altitude. Similarly, the *tellurometer* is employed for the accurate measurement of distances in land SURVEYING. In the laboratory, microwave techniques are frequently employed in the study and measurement of both the physical and electrical properties of organic and inorganic substances.

For the home or hotel the modern microwave oven or cooker has been possible because of the high energy absorption by organic matter at these frequencies. Cooking times in these ovens are expressed in seconds or minutes and are in sharp contrast to the very much slower conventional cooker. A typical microwave oven uses a magnetron to produce power of the order of a kilowatt at a frequency of 2.5 GHz. The radiation is beamed by wave guides into a cavity designed to resonate at that frequency, so producing an even energy distribution.

MILEOMETER (see distance recorder)

Below left: microwaves are 'scattered' (reflected and refracted) by the troposphere (lower atmosphere). Clouds, air turbulence, water vapour and constituent gases affect this scattering.
Below: a double cavity klystron is used to amplify the microwave signals—this replaces the valve at these high frequencies.

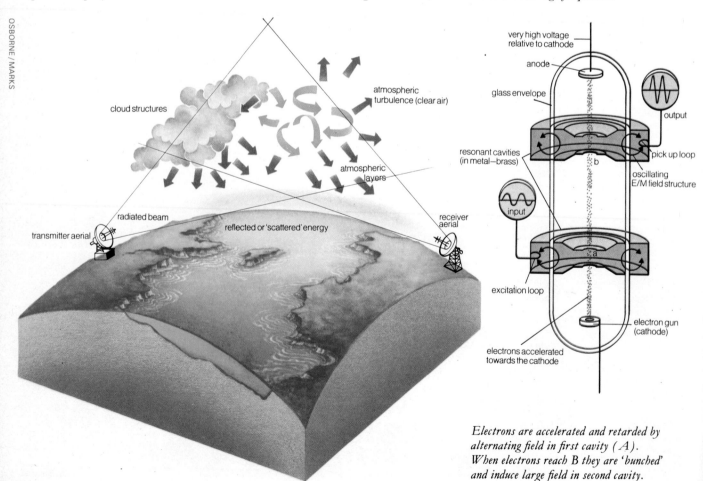

Electrons are accelerated and retarded by alternating field in first cavity (A).
When electrons reach B they are 'bunched' and induce large field in second cavity.

MILKING MACHINE

It is over 100 years since the first vacuum operated milking machine was developed, and few new principles have been added in the past 50 years. The first reference to the use of wheat straws as milk tubes, inserted into the cow's teat, appeared in Egypt in about 380 BC, and the idea reappeared in Britain in 1831 in a more advanced form. The susceptibility, however, of teats and udders to disease stopped the development of such devices. From 1870 onwards, attempts were made to milk cows with pressure devices which, on the whole, failed because of their complexity and the fact that they did not milk any faster than a good hand milker.

In 1879 the Royal Agricultural Society of England offered a £50 prize for a milking machine, the first to show promise being that of Murchland in Kilmarnock, Scotland, which was patented in 1889. This machine used continuous suction (vacuum) and required a great deal of labour, and for that reason was not a success. The second major development was that of Dr Shiels of Glasgow who, between 1895 and 1903, attempted to overcome swollen teats caused by continuous suction by using a 'pulsator', which alternated the suction level between 4 inch Hg and 15 inch Hg (100 mm and 380 mm Hg).

In 1913 the Royal Agricultural Society again offered prizes and this time there were 11 entries from countries including Australia, New Zealand, USA, Sweden and Britain. During World War 1 machine milking in Britain became established with moderate success, but several companies failed to survive the economic depression of the 1920s. Nowadays every advanced dairy farmer milks by machine, saving time and reducing the incidence of disease.

Above: an illustration from a late 19th century book, showing the Colvin vacuum operated milking machine.

Below left: an outdoor vacuum milking system in use in Germany.

Below: Holstein cows being milked in a herringbone type milking parlour. The milk is piped into calibrated recording jars so that the yield from each cow may be measured.

Machine milking

All milking machines follow similar principles in the extraction of milk from the cow: a stainless steel cup, lined with natural or synthetic rubber, fits around the cow's teat and a continuous vacuum of about 380 mm Hg (15 inch Hg) is applied to the teat from the bottom of the cup. An alternating vacuum is applied between the cup and the lining, causing it to collapse round the teat intermittently, thus providing a massaging action and making and breaking the constant vacuum applied to the teat.

The vacuum to operate both the milk removal and the pulsator action is provided by a vacuum pump situated remotely from the cow and providing vacuum sufficient for one or more units. The vacuum level within the milking system is regulated by a vacuum controller—a simple VALVE of varying design, but normally weight-loaded, which is preset to maintain a constant vacuum within the system. A vacuum gauge provides the operator with a visual check that the system is operating within the limits prescribed by the manufacturer.

The alternating vacuum applied to the teat cup liner is provided by a pulsator; several systems are used throughout the world. In general, the pulsator operates between 45 and 70 pulsations per minute, but should be preset for each installation so that cows are milked at a constant rate each day. The ratio of the vacuum phase to the atmospheric phase is termed the *pulsation ratio*. The vacuum phase of the system should not be less than 50% (1:1) and no more than 75% (3:1) of the pulsation time cycle, otherwise the interruption to the blood supply, caused by excessive squeezing within the teat, could prove harmful.

Milking plant

The first milking machines were for use in the traditional tied cowshed and were of a simple bucket design where the milk from one or two cows was collected in a container close to the animal. The milk was then carried to the reception area to be filtered into a churn and await collection by the dairy. The machine operator handled up to three such units, milking at the rate of up to 10 cows per unit per hour.

The continued expansion of dairy herds and the development of outwintering in the south of England led to the design of an *abreast parlour and bail*, which was in effect a portable milking machine. The bail was a shed on wheels, built to form six cow stalls, together with a portable hut for the engine. The milk was conveyed by vacuum via a recording jar (calibrated to show the yield of each cow) to a field milk can, which was changed by hand when full. The cows were let into the system three at a time, fed, and milked and then turned into the field or bedded area.

In 1916 there appeared in the *Australian Farm Implement and Machinery Review* a sketch of a *herringbone parlour*. The head of the dairying branch of the Department of Agriculture stated that this was the best way to handle cows because of the saving in labour and the ease of shed cleaning. The herringbone parlour, now rapidly gaining acceptance in Europe as an advanced milking system, holds the cows at an angle of 30° to and on both sides of the milker's work area—hence the name. The cows overlap each other and milking units are only 3 ft apart. Most such parlours are equipped with individual feeders which allow the rationing of feeding stuff and fully automated in-place cleaning systems, maintaining the extremely hygienic conditions required by dairy and health authorities.

The rapidly increasing herd sizes and escalating labour costs led to the development of probably the most effectively automated system—a *rotary parlour* in which the stalls rotate around the milker's work area. This permits the mechanization of any operation at one position. One of the most potentially successful designs is the *rotary herringbone* type, designed in Australia and developed in New Zealand.

The procedures adopted during machine milking should be designed to take advantage of the physiological mechanism which is responsible for milk ejection from the cow, and be completed as quickly as possible without causing damage or injury to the animal. In future it should be possible to eliminate all jobs other than putting the teat cups on and since this operation only takes about 15 seconds per cow, the final milking performance could be in the order of 240 cows per man per hour. To achieve this 20 or more units would be required. Recent developments, including programmed feeding (during milking) linked with cow identification, automatic teat cup removal, and automatic cow washing devices, have brought this situation somewhat nearer.

Ultimately total mechanization of feeding, watering, manure removal and milking can be achieved and current work in Germany indicates savings in labour and feeding costs by moving the cow in a portable compartment from function to function. The system which links the compartments moves a herd of cows in ventilated conditions, rather like a train, from the feeding station to the watering station and on to the milking station. The practical limit, however, to mechanization is the cost of equipment per cow. In many warm countries with ample natural feeding and a favourable climate, investment in milking equipment and subsequent low cost production will continue to provide surplus quantities of milk, required to fulfil the growing world demand for milk and milk products (see DAIRY INDUSTRY).

Below: this automated rotary milking parlour was opened in 1969 at the Dedelow agricultural co-operative in Neubrandenburg, East Germany, which has a herd of 2000 cows. The cows are fed while they are being milked.

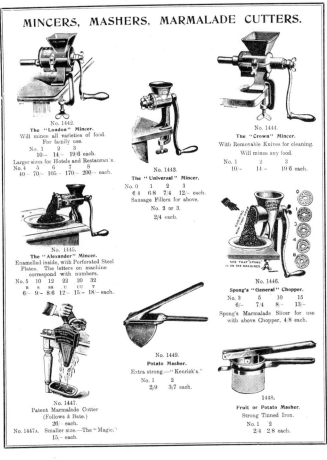

MINCER [meat grinder]

A mincing machine is used for grinding up meat to make mincemeat [hamburger] and sausage stuffing, and to enable housewives and food processing companies to make use of leftovers, poor cuts of meat, and so forth.

The most familiar type of mincer is the domestic type, which has been in use for well over a century. It is made of metal and designed to be clamped to the edge of a table or counter-top, facing inwards so that a bowl on the table catches the minced meat as it comes out and there is room for the swing of the crank handle. The body of the machine is a simple housing with a funnel on top and the clamp on the bottom. A worm with helical threads, based on the ARCHIMEDEAN SCREW principle, is inserted in the housing; it has a crank handle on one end and a thread projection on the other. A plate with holes or slots in it is placed over the threaded projection and a wing nut or a knurled nut is tightened on it to hold the assembly together. The food to be minced is pushed into the funnel; the crank handle is turned and the worm pushes the food through the holes or slots in the plate. Some mincers also have cutter knives fitted on the end of the worm as well as the plate.

A variety of plates are available for fine or coarse mincing, for chopping suet, cutting marmalade, mashing potatoes and so forth. For example, a plate with small holes is best for mincing cooked meat. Nowadays many kitchen machines consist of plastic housings with electric motors and a variety of attachments for blending, grinding coffee beans, shredding vegetables and other functions as well as mincing. If a mincer is electrically driven, it must be designed with care so that meat and other juices do not get into the motor or the gearbox.

Above: an illustration from a catalogue of 1900 showing various types of mincers and mashers. At centre right can be seen a selection of plates for the various functions. These devices were sturdy and lasted for many years.

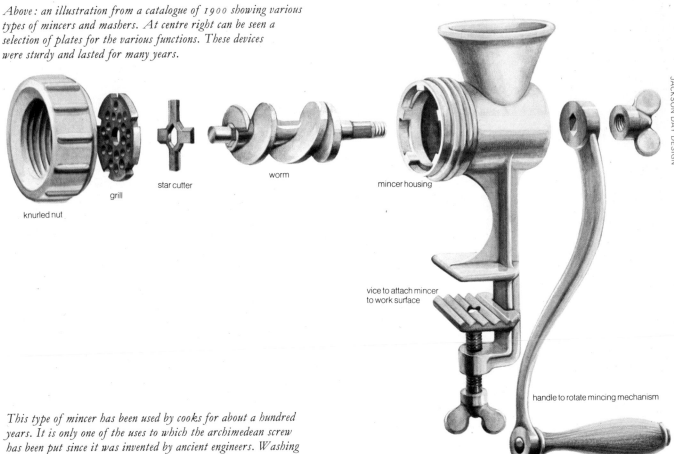

knurled nut

grill

star cutter

worm

mincer housing

vice to attach mincer to work surface

handle to rotate mincing mechanism

This type of mincer has been used by cooks for about a hundred years. It is only one of the uses to which the archimedean screw has been put since it was invented by ancient engineers. Washing up is easy since the mincer comes completely apart.

A gearbox is often necessary in such a machine to gear down the speed of the motor to a useful speed for the other moving parts. Some low-priced machines are designed without gearboxes, but these usually can only be run for a few minutes and then must be allowed to cool off. One such machine is made of polypropylene plastic and has a suction cup on the bottom for fastening it to a kitchen work-surface; another has the worm itself made of nylon.

Industrial heavy-duty mincers used by food processing firms and caterers have large stainless steel trays on top for loading on the meat. One such machine has the body made of aluminium, the plate stud and the drive stud of the worm made of case-hardened steel, and a replaceable whalebone washer to take up end thrust on the worm. It has a labyrinth seal on the drive shaft to keep out juices; a $\frac{1}{2}$ horsepower motor with sealed grease-packed bearings has a speed of 1425 rpm which is geared down to 145 rpm by double reduction helical gears running in an oil bath. It is supplied with three four-bladed knives, three plates and a feed stick for pushing down the meat on to the worm.

Below : a modern kitchen machine in use with mincing attachment. Such devices are electrically driven and can often be used with various attachments to grind coffee, squeeze fruit and so on. They must be designed to keep juices out of the motor.

MINE, explosive

Mines can be used at sea or on land, and differ from most other weapons in that they are not directed against specific targets. Once laid they can remain active for years, and modern types are difficult to detect and destroy.

Mines were first developed for naval use. In 1585 the Dutch succeeded in using a clockwork device to set off explosive charges placed in small boats and rowed out to the enemy Spanish ships. Although mines were used to a limited extent in both the American War of Independence and the American Civil War, it was not until World War 1 that their use became widespread; a total of about 240,000 mines were laid between 1914 and 1918. During World War 1 the Germans used mines to considerable advantage against both merchant ships and warships; Field Marshal Lord Kitchener was killed when the cruiser HMS Hampshire struck a mine off the Orkney Islands in 1916. In World War 2 techniques of laying mines from the air were developed, and this allowed internal waterways such as the River Danube to be mined.

The first land mines, used by the Germans in World War 1, consisted of artillery shells buried, fuze uppermost, in the ground so that they would be initiated by the weight of a TANK. Anti-personnel mines and mines specially designed for use against tanks were not introduced until World War 2 when they were widely used in North Africa and on the Russian front.

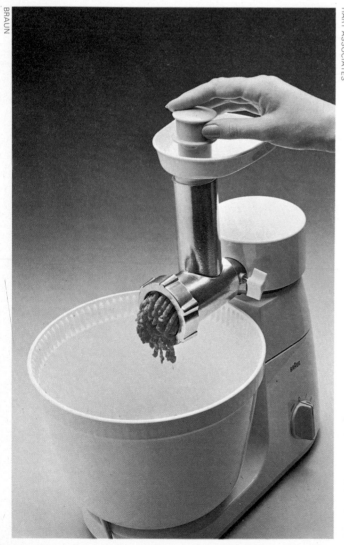

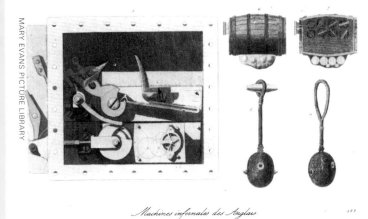

Machines infernales des Anglais

Above: early British naval mines (right) and a flintlock firing mechanism controlled by a preset clockwork timing device.

Below left: a naval mine and its mounting. This mine is attached to the mounting by a cable which is paid out when the mine is actuated.

Below: in a naval mine the detonator is triggered by a battery when one of the contact horns is struck by a ship. The land mine is triggered by foot pressure and has two explosive charges; one throws the mine into the air and the other propels the projectiles.

Naval mines

Mines represent a cheap and effective means of preventing the movement of shipping, and demand from the enemy a considerable effort in clearing lanes and keeping them clear. They have the advantage of attacking a ship in its weakest area under the water line and are rendered particularly effective by the non-compressibility of water, which transmits the blast extremely effectively to the target.

There are basically two types of mine: *controlled* and *independent*. Controlled mines are connected by cable to an observation and control station from which they are armed or made safe. They are used exclusively for harbour defence. Independent mines, which are either moored or grounded on the sea bed, are normally actuated by contact, magnetic, pressure or acoustic devices. In addition it is to be expected that other techniques may be used in the future, such as low yield atomic mines actuated by DOPPLER EFFECT devices or INFRA-RED sensors.

Contact mines are laid in a 'safe' condition, and when they sink to a pre-set depth the water pressure operates a hydrostatic device (see STATICS) which arms the firing circuit. The mine is equipped with contact *horns* (projections) which, when struck by a ship, pass an electric current to the DETONATOR which sets off the high explosive filling. *Magnetic mines* make use of the permanent and induced magnetic fields of a ship to trigger the firing mechanism, and the sensitivity of the device is set to

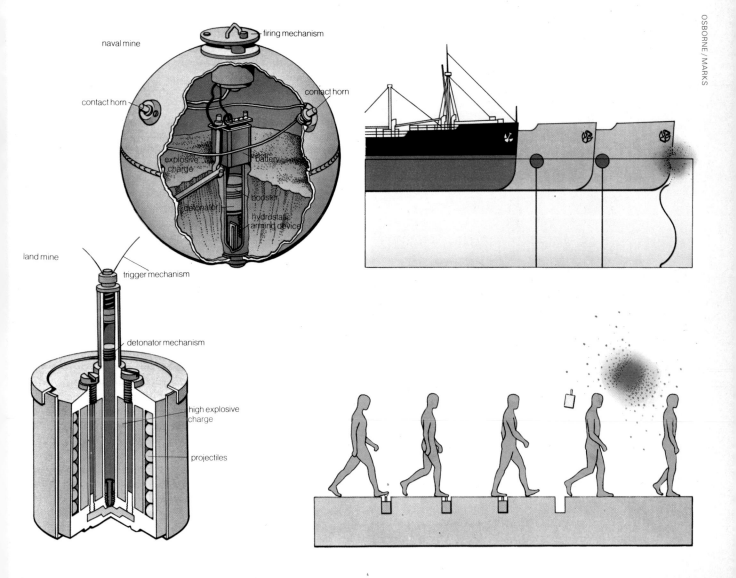